BESIDE THE MEON:

A Journey Through Time

by

JOAN HAINES

MEON VALLEY BOOKS

1996

Published by Meon Valley Books,
Meonside, East Meon, Hants GU32 1PD

Illustrations by   Shirley Whiting

Maps by   Vic Harley

Cover photograph by   Glynn Williams, M.B.E.

ISBN 0 9527687 0 4

Printed in England by
St. Richard's Press Ltd
Leigh Road, Chichester, West Sussex PO19 2TU

Contents

Introduction

THE MEON is a small river that rises in East Hampshire, runs through one of the most beautiful valleys in the country, and joins the Solent near Titchfield.

I am lucky enough to live in East Meon, a very attractive village lying not far from the river's source, and it is on this village that I have focused my book. Basically, this is a series of historical stories about the area, all based on fact and careful research, and all designed to illuminate the periods in which they are set. The main characters of each chapter are very varied – a female slave, a priest, a shepherd, a parish constable, a young boy, a dying woman, and so on – some of whom are rich and successful, while others endure hardship or tragedy. I have tried throughout to illuminate each century by connecting the local stories to national events, hoping that in this way the wider history of Southern England may be more easily understood.

Many of the people and incidents mentioned are historical, while others are purely fictional and these have been omitted from the Index. For the reader's convenience I have used modern spelling of place names, for otherwise they would be difficult to locate. ('Meon', for instance, was spelt in at least six different ways.)

Each chapter has a map and, at its conclusion, a list of the primary sources used, although many books, articles and documents have had to be omitted as they are too numerous to specify.

A great number of people are owed my thanks for their help and encouragement. The first is Mr F G Standfield, who not only lives in the village but is the author of the invaluable "A History of East Meon", and who advised, corrected and made suggestions which were immensely helpful. He also undertook the arduous task of proof-reading. When he was Vicar here, the Reverend P R Wadsworth allowed me access to various papers relating to the parish and gave me much help. Mr Edward Roberts, of whose work I made considerable use, very kindly read the episode set in the thirteenth century and solved many of my other problems.

I owe special thanks to the librarians of Petersfield and Winchester and the staff of the Hampshire County Records Office for their patience in finding books and references for me, but especially to Mrs P Stevens, the Local Studies Librarian at the Jewry Street Library, Winchester. It was she who first suggested I should write a locally-based social history that also referred to national events.

To the people of East Meon itself I owe particular thanks for not only alerting me to many items of local history but also for their interest and encouragement. I am also grateful to many people beyond the village who have let me use their own research or have suggested source documents. Finally, I owe special thanks to those at Tempo in Petersfield, who have changed my hand-written scrawls into meticulous typescript.

Without all their help this book could never have been written.

East Meon, 1996

Chapter One

The Story-teller, 400 B.C.

THE Story-teller waited until the clan was seated on the floor of the great roundhouse. Although the beaten earth was dry – the autumn rains were late that year - he had been given the seat of honour. His upturned log was well padded with sheep's fleece, so he was comfortable enough and warmed enough against the cool of dusk by the fire on the central hearth. He was treated well. He was the Honoured One.

"I have come today", he began, "across the land the Giants trod. They were the Giants that lived hereabouts long, long ago. But before they lived even greater Giants were here - and they were fearsome indeed for they were taller than two trees on end and fiercer than the wild boar, and they fought among themselves for mastery of the sky.

"Now, it so happens that in their time this land was flat and much under water and when a Great Giant stormed across it, roaring like a stag in rut and brandishing a forest tree for a club as if it was no more than a hazel twig, he splashed into this water, for to him it was no more than a puddle."

The Story-teller paused and stared into the fire. "I can see it now," he declared, "for I have the magic eye. I can look into the past as easily as I can into the future." Suddenly he raised his head and his gaze swept over his silent audience. "I can see things as they are," he said. "I can see the workings of the Underworld and of the Overworld and into all your minds. I am the Story-teller and I know all."

Nobody in the hut moved for they were deep afraid and had no wish to be singled out by the terror of his eye.

"Into the puddle the Great Giant trod, travelling from the point of the rising sun at the turn of the year towards the setting of the sun at the time of lambing, and where he trod his foot sank into the mud, setting up waves and ripples as he passed. And these waves washed the mud out of the water and piled it up into those hills that are all about us now.

"And when he had passed and the water had drained back off the slopes it was seen that the hills were no longer chalk-white, but green, for grass and a myriad of trees had sprouted on their tops. Then the water of the puddle disappeared, for it had followed the Great Giant and was seen no more. All that was left was the mark of his footprint, deep at the heel where the mud had been softest. Out of this heelmark now came a magical river called Meon. Then this river, too, hurried after the Great Giant and the waters that had been there before, and followed them for half a day's walk. Then it despaired of catching them up, turning instead towards the mid-day sun and, because it no longer hurried, grew fat and lazy and bred fish in its hair."

The Story-teller pointed out of the hut opening. "But the footprint is still there, and out of the spring-hole made by the heel, the slow snake of the Meon still comes. It comes from the Underworld, the magic River Snake of the gods, and it needs many gifts and many sacrifices, especially after hay-cutting when water is scarce. All snakes have tails, and if this snake came to the end of its coil then the footprint would lose its water and the river bed would dry. If you fail the River Snake it will fail you. Then the fish will flounder in the muddy throes of death and the cattle pastures will dry out and your women will exhaust themselves in seeking water for their pots."

At this point he cleared his throat and the headman's wife hurried over to give him a beaker of barley ale. "Master," her husband began humbly, "the Gods will be served. We already do honour to the Goddess of the Springhead."

"That is good," the Story-teller nodded. There was a pause while he drank and no-one spoke. When the wife proffered a strip of sun-dried sheep's meat he waved it away.

"I shall tell you now about the other Giants who came after the fearsome Great Giant who made the hills and caused the River Meon to appear. These lesser Giants, both male and female, were of a stature beyond that of any man now living. They did not favour the valley bottoms, for the land was still marshy and the trees thick-grown together, but lived on the hill tops. Their burial places are still there, built of chalk and flints, with turf laid over, and you can see for yourselves the size of those men. The Giant on the top of that hill yonder was taller than ten men and a child laid end to end – and they buried him on his back with his feet towards the rising of the mid-summer's sun, for you'll see that one end is higher than the other to allow for his upturned toes."

He took another long drink of the ale and wiped his drooping moustaches on the back of his hand. "These Giants were the ones who crafted in flint. But here is a thing very strange, for the tools they made were of a size good for our own use – they were not giant sized at all. So these Giants were great of body but had our sized hands. Why this should be no one can tell, for none can know the reason why Giants were as they were. They must have been very strange."

He shook his head in puzzlement and several of his audience did likewise, unable to imagine a hugely tall body with a great head and massive legs but hands no more than a span's width.

"Now at that time the Great Sky Father was angry with the Giants for they gave more worship to the Earth Mother, the Great Goddess of All Life, so he sent down a storm of hailstones, hoping to hurt the Giants. But the hailstones melted in the sun, so in the next shower he turned them into flints to hurt the more. So many did he send that the hills were covered white. But the Giants just laughed and gathered together the biggest of them and hid them in deep holes in the ground, for they thought the Sky God would one day descend from his thunder clouds to do battle with them and they wished to have their missiles ready. So they hid them in deep, deep shafts but, as son succeeded father many times, they came to forget where the big flints were hidden and so had only the small ones to hand."

A young boy of the clan, forgetting to be fearful, held out a roughly shaped stone. "Like this?" he asked.

"Like that," came the answer. "But, as over the years the Sky God did not challenge them to battle, they learnt to chip away at the smaller flints that lay about and made tools and weapons for themselves. Then the Earth Mother sent a dream to a man of a distant tribe who lived over towards the rising sun, but still on this ridge of hills, and he saw in his dream that she was tired of harbouring the biggest flints that had been buried in her body so long ago and wished to be rid of them. So she told the man where to dig. And he dug. And after many days' digging he had made a deep hole and found a band of fine flints which he brought to the surface in a leather bag. Then the other men of the clan came to join him down the shaft and the deeper they went the larger and better were the flints. So other men came. And others. And in this way many, many shafts were dug."

"But," said the headman, "why have we no deep shafts here? I have lived on this land all my life and my father before me and his father before that and never have I heard of these shafts".

"That is because the Giants buried no flints here. But it did not matter, for the hill track carried traders who brought great flint-cores, and bartered them with your ancestors for wheat and sheep and cheese. And your people learnt to chip away at the flints until they had made tools and weapons and axes. By this means they were able to cut down even more trees and scratch up even more soil and sow even more seed on the cleared land. They put sheep and cattle on the hills, too, and killed them with their flint knives, cutting up the flesh for the cooking pots and scraping the skins for leather. Thus many flint-shaping sites were set up on your land and skilled workmen knapped the stones into whatever was required."

A man near the hut opening nodded. "I've seen those piles of old flakes often enough."

The Story-teller drank deeply of his ale and the headman's wife refilled the beaker.

"And the Giants, Master?" the headman asked tentatively. "Do you know more of them?"

"I know all things of all things," the Story-teller replied. "Do not suspect otherwise." Again he drank. Finally he said, "The Giants all died. The Sky Father was still angry with them for their worship of the Earth Mother, so he stirred himself again and not liking the idea of being attacked with those large flints he had once sent down himself, he saw a better way. He made it happen that all the women of the Giants became barren and, as the old ones died and were buried, no new Giants were born. They were buried, as you know, beside the tracks and walkways on the hills so that all who passed by were reminded never to ignore the power of the Sky God, for he can send barrenness to women."

Again he turned to the headman. "Never neglect the Gods. Woe betide a clan that does, for it, too, shall be no more."

His audience then remembered the great long mounds of the Giants that they had passed so many times and became fearful that they had not shown a proper reverence. They had always respected them as sacred places, of course, and treated them as hallowed ground, but not until now did they understand why. The Sky Father was powerful indeed. Barrenness was something to be deeply feared. Tomorrow, when they passed, they would pay due homage (although, at the same time, seeking the blessing of the Earth Mother for the continuing fertility of their crops, animals, and not least, themselves. One had to be careful not to offend any of the Gods who, like humans, quarrelled among themselves and were jealous of each other's power).

The headman's wife now came with the delicacy of sheep's cheese and the Story-teller took several small pieces, washing them down with long draughts of ale.

"Now I'll tell you about the metal-workers who came later and filled the land to overflowing with their tribes and animals and new-ploughed fields." He reached out for another handful of cheese morsels and continued: "A chieftain called Redbeard lived hereabouts and powerful he was and rich he was, and his finery was finer than that of anyone else. He had a bronze ceremonial shield that dazzled more brightly than the sun on ice, and his breast and leg armours were marked with patterns more beautiful than those on a butterfly's wing. He had a wondrous crescent collar of beaten gold that even a hundred sheep could not have bought, and on this collar were engraved signs of great sacredness to protect him in time of war. His helmet was shaped to a point so fine that it could only have been made by a bronze-worker with magic in his tools, and his throwing-spear was so finely balanced that it sought its prey by guidance of the Gods alone.

"Redbeard was indeed a mighty man and favoured were his kinsmen. His warriors were strong of arm and fierce in defence of the tribal lands; his followers were many and thrived and bred until all the countryside was filled. But his enemy was Crookback - and crooked he was, for at his birth his mother had died and the old hag attending the birthing had thought he was dead too, and had placed him headfirst in a wooden bucket. When he cried out, he was seen to be alive, but from that day on his back was curved and he saw himself as cursed by all the Gods.

"Now Redbeard, from his camp on the hill near where we are now, looked across the river to the hills beyond and saw the land was rich. And he desired it – but knew it was the tribal land of Crookback, who also held dominion over the Long Hill and the Small Hill, and was not likely to yield his tribal property without a fight. Despite his fine warriors, Redbeard had no wish for deaths and thought that trickery might be a better way to gain possession. To this end, therefore, he sent Grog, his younger brother, to Crookback to solicit him for his sister in marriage.

"Crookback received him honourably and feasted him on wild boar and plovers' eggs, with the great patterned beaker filled many times with barley-beer well sweetened with honey. The welcome was all that could be desired and after the feasting the two men talked.

"'Your sister is as yet unmarried,' began Grog, 'and my brother, Redbeard, has a desire to do your tribe great honour by taking her to be his wife. She is some seasons older than is normal for a bride, so although the honour will be great, the bride-price will not.'

"Crookback looked sideways at Grog, dubious as to the honour intended, and then asked, 'What bride-price has your brother in mind? My sister may now be old, having reached child-bearing age three summers ago, but she is of high blood and still capable of children.'

"'This my brother Redbeard understands and looks forward to the mating. As to the bride-price, he thought twenty cattle sufficient.' Then feigning anxiety, he asked, 'Or would you need more?'.

"Seeing the subject was open to negotiation, Crookback became sly. 'Of course I need more!' he declared. 'A hundred and twenty at least.'

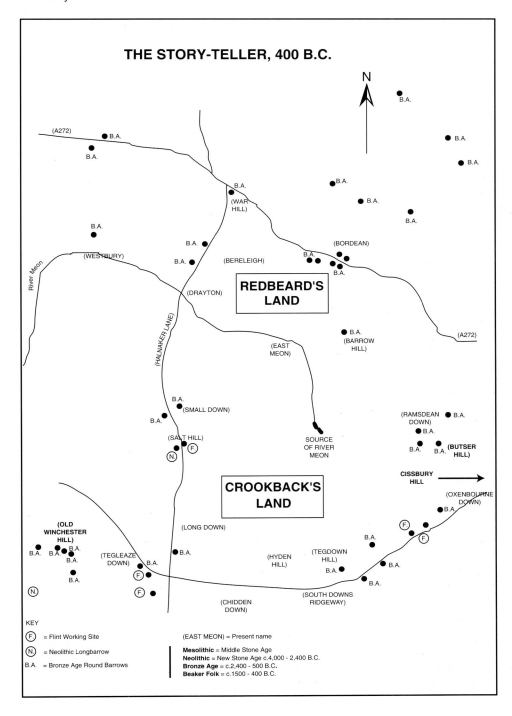

THE STORY-TELLER, 400 B.C.

N

(A272)
● B.A.
● B.A.

● B.A.
● B.A.

● B.A.
B.A. ●
(WAR HILL)

● B.A.

● B.A.

● B.A.

● B.A.

● B.A.
(WESTBURY)
B.A. ●
(BERELEIGH)
(BORDEAN)
● B.A.
● ● ● B.A.

REDBEARD'S LAND

(DRAYTON)

(HALNAKER LANE)

(EAST MEON)

● B.A.
(BARROW HILL)

(A272)

● B.A.
(SMALL DOWN)
B.A. ●

(RAMSDEAN DOWN) ● B.A.
● B.A.

(SALT HILL)
B.A. ●
Ⓕ
Ⓝ

SOURCE OF RIVER MEON

B.A. ●
● B.A. (BUTSER HILL)

CROOKBACK'S LAND

CISSBURY HILL →

(OXENBOURNE DOWN)

● B.A.

Ⓕ
(OLD WINCHESTER HILL)
B.A. ●
B.A. ●
● B.A.
● B.A.
(LONG DOWN)

● B.A.
(TEGLEAZE DOWN)
● B.A.

(HYDEN HILL)

(TEGDOWN HILL)
● B.A.

B.A. ●

Ⓕ

B.A. ●
● B.A.

B.A. ●
Ⓝ
Ⓕ ●
(SOUTH DOWNS RIDGEWAY)

(CHIDDEN DOWN)

River Meon

KEY

Ⓕ = Flint Working Site

Ⓝ = Neolithic Longbarrow

B.A. = Bronze Age Round Barrows

(EAST MEON) = Present name

Mesolithic = Middle Stone Age
Neolithic = New Stone Age c.4,000 - 2,400 B.C.
Bronze Age = c.2,400 - 500 B.C.
Beaker Folk = c.1500 - 400 B.C.

"Grog recoiled in mock horror. 'Too much! Too much!' he cried. 'Oh, what will my brother say? But your sister – I hope she is not beautiful?'

"'Very beautiful. And her beauty adds twenty sheep to the price.'

"'Oh, no!' cried Grog in apparent distress. 'And I suppose there are many supplicants for her hand?'

"'Of course! And the supplicants add another fifty sheep.'

"Grog cried out again: 'You're taking all the animals we have!'

"'Not so! There are still another forty cattle and sixty sheep that I have counted on your hill. If they are all handed over to me then your brother shall have his bride.'

"Now this was what crafty Redbeard had hoped for and on the return of Grog he laughed heartily, drank too much beer and fell off his stool. But the next day, being fully recovered, he bade his men round up every animal belonging to his tribe and had them driven off their own lands, across the river and up the hills to the South and so to Crookback's settlement. Amazed, Crookback and his people watched them come. Then in haste his sister was made ready for the exchange of vows. That night, after the carousing was finished, she returned to the camp of Redbeard as his wife.

"It so happened that Crookback's land was already somewhat overstocked with sheep and cattle and it came to pass within the few months of that very dry summer that there was no grazing left, for now Redbeard's animals made too many mouths for the grass to feed, and so there was famine. Thus the udders of the cattle withered and the calves went hungry for their milk; the sheep tottered on failing legs and the lambs did not thrive. Redbeard drank in glee, for his own people were well fed on deer from the woods and stored barley from the last year's seeding and they knew no hunger. He blessed, then, the foresight of the Old People of his land in not cutting down all the trees to make way for more pasture and yet more pasture, as had the ancestors of Crookback on his hilltop.

"And so it fell out that in Crookback's farmsteads death began to come and the people felt smitten by the Gods. The chiefest of their dead they therefore buried in bowl-shaped mounds with excessive and unusual honour. Grave gifts of beaten gold were given, fine bronze axes, golden rings for neck, arm and finger, belt-buckles, knives, hammers, spearheads – everything they could find. They were desperate in their attempts to placate the Gods and bring the rain, for the drought was long and the Sky God angry, and they had little to eat.

"Crookback was one that did not die. Not then. Instead, at his people's urging he sent an elder to Redbeard to ask him to take back his bride-gift of animals so that with fewer grazing, grass on the high hills could grow again and the famine be lifted. But Redbeard refused. 'My wife is now pregnant,' he declared, 'and with this blessing of the Gods why should I be so ungrateful as to take back her bride-price?' On a later day the elder returned with a new offer from Crookback. Not only would the animals be returned as a free gift to do honour to the fertility of Redbeard's wife but a stretch of land along the riverside would be given, too. Again Redbeard refused, and again messengers came offering more and yet more land, but it was not until all the land was offered with all the animals of Crookback's people did Redbeard relent.

"Then his own tribe crossed the river to drive the starving animals across to the lusher pastures and the cooling shade of his woodlands. He brought the hungry people from their scattered homesteads and gave them succulent deermeat and the richness of wild boars. Then, at the evening gathering, Redbeard made a great speech, declaring that both peoples were now one people, and both lands one land and that he, Redbeard, was their leader.

"And so it was," the Story-teller finished, "that he moved both tribes to the valley edges and divided the upper fields and pastures between them, marking out the whole of his territory with sarsen stones, or with great banks and ditches, or with the rounded graves of the important dead. He placed these graves on the top of Crookback's hills and along the trackways that formed the boundaries between his new lands and those of other tribes. But especially he took care not to trespass on that great hilltop estate that overlooks the lower valley of the Meon to the west and that other great property that lies towards the rising sun.

"Crookback died mysteriously and Redbeard had him buried in the cemetery in the centre of his lands, doing him just enough honour but not granting him the death-gifts of gold or bronze that a chieftain had a right to expect. So Crookback went to the Other World and to the meeting with the Gods and his ancestors unadorned and unprepared, and it is said that some have seen his shade hovering over the upturned bowl of his grave seeking his just due. And that, my friends, is how the people before you came to own such a vast tract of land and how your own settlements came to be along the valley sides and not only on the hill tops. The river still runs through your pastures and beside your ploughed fields but it is no longer a boundary between two tribes. Now there is peace."

When he had finished speaking the Story-teller drained his beaker, lay down on the floor and, pulling the sheepskin up to his chin, fell asleep. The telling of stories was hard work.

NOTES ON PREHISTORIC SITES.

(1) Cissbury Hill Flint Mines, West Sussex (TQ 137 079). The site is now owned by the National Trust and open to the public. The 150 or so shafts are thought to have been dug about 3,600 B.C.

(2) Other Neolithic flint mines on the South Downs:
West Stoke, West Sussex (SU 832 096) About twenty mines.
Long Down, West Sussex (SU 932 093) About twenty mines.
Hallow Hill, West Sussex (TQ 082 100) About one hundred mines.
Church Hill, Findon, West Sussex (TQ 114 083) About thirty mines.
Windover Hill, East Sussex (TQ 543 033) About nine mines.

(3) Local flint-working sites:
Teglease Copse (SU 650193) Mesolithic.
Teglease Down (SU 657 198) Mesolithic and Neolithic.
Salt Hill (SU 673 202) Mesolithic and Neolithic.
Hyden Hill (SU 687 192) Mesolithic.
Small Down (SU 675 205) Neolithic.
Chidden Down (SU 669 191) Mesolithic.
Tegdown Hill (SU 695 192) Mesolithic.
Oxenbourne Down (SU 715 185) Neolithic.

(4) Many Neolithic long barrows lie on either side of the South Downs Ridgeway between Butser Hill and Warnford, especially in the area near Old Winchester Hill. Most are badly damaged by ploughing and are almost obliterated but the most noteable is on Salt Hill (SU 672 201), having once had the North East end higher than the others in a style known as "Wessex". All are on private land and not accessible to the public.

(5) Local Bronze Age round barrows include:
Long Down, SU 669 197
Drayton, SU 673 239
Bereleigh, SU 676 243
War Down (2) SU 682 257
Barrow Hill, SU 700 223
Ramsdean Down, (3) SU 713 208
Various bowl barrows at Hyden Wood, Hyden Cross and Hyden Hill,
(SU 689 192)
Old Winchester Hill, SU 641 205 (several)
Butser Hill SU 714 209 (several)
Between Bordean House and Lower Bordean Farm, on either side of the present A272 there are many round barrows. (SU 693 247; SU 698 245; SU 691 247; SU 694 248; SU 694 245; SU 694 246)

Based on:
National Monuments Record, Swindon, Wiltshire.
Maps, documents and notes held in 'Sites and Monuments Records' in County
Planning Department, Winchester, Hampshire.
Hampshire Treasures, Hampshire County Council. 1982.
The Social Foundation of Prehistoric Britain by Richard Bradley. Longmans 1984.
A History of East Meon by F. G. Standfield. Phillimore, 1984.
Prehistoric Flint Mines by Robin Holgate. Shire Archaeology, 1991.
Bronze Age Metalwork in Southern Britain by Susan M. Pearce. Shire Archaeology, 1984.
Food and Cooking in Prehistoric Britain by Jane Renfrew. English Heritage, 1985.
Prehistoric and Roman Britain by Richard Muir & Humphrey Welfare. National Trust Guide, 1984.
A Guide to the Prehistoric Remains in Britain, Volume One by Richard Wainwright. Constable, 1978.

Chapter Two

The Celtic Warrior, 55 B.C.

THE day began normally enough. Lir had left the roundhouse in the early light to feed the animals while his wife, Usna, was blowing up the embers of last night's fire. Fionnuala, their daughter, was yawning loudly as she fetched the pitcher for milking the goats.

A normal day, like any other. How were they to know the Gods would send such trouble?

By true sun-up Lir had begun weeding the field of emmer wheat where the charlock was in danger of throttling the ripening crop. His land lay on the western slopes of a low hill, north of the river Meon, and facing another gentle slope which belonged to his kinsman, Bov. Both men were pleased with their lands, for each had a pond for watering animals and each was within reach of the huge tribal fort on top of the hill to the south, which was a refuge both for people and stock in dangerous times. Lir was not a great man of his tribe, being but a farmer. Nevertheless, he was proud of his increasing prosperity for he was able to exchange surplus grain and wool for other items at the great annual market, held at the festival of Lugnasadh after harvest. In previous years he had acquired in this way a few pieces of fine pottery, which pleased Usna, and for himself a new iron dagger with a decorated hilt. Most of his other ironwork was similarly acquired by exchange, often from traders living in forests further east where smelting was carried out in charcoal furnaces. Charcoal was a wonderful thing, he thought, for it could heat a furnace beyond anything that plain wood could do. It was only in such a heat that the iron was driven from the stone. Before the use of charcoal there had been but bronze and copper metals. His new tools were of much greater strength and sophistication than previously, the wooden point of his ploughing ard now having an iron tip while Usna's cooking-cauldron was of iron instead of earthenware. Most of his neighbours had used iron for many years, even generations, but his was a small farm and only recently had he been able to afford such modern luxuries.

When he had weeded several times back and forth across the small square field, he sat down to rest beneath an overhanging oak tree, glad of its shade. An oak seemed to Lir to be the very personification of the spirit of vegetation and even of life itself. After all, the fires at the Midsummer festival of Beltane were lit with heart-wood from oaks, thus ensuring that the sun at its zenith would be renewed and strengthened for its return in other years. Oaks had a life-force held by no other tree.

Lir now lay on his back and stared up at the leaf-laden branches. These were harbouring the young acorns which, later, would feed his pigs. The Gods were indeed bountiful. In gratitude he laid his hands reverently on the soil beside him and humbly thanked the Sky God that sent both sun and rain, and blessed the triple Earth Mothers for their benediction. He even sought forgiveness from the weeds he had just pulled up and left to die. All was life and all was entwined and all was holy.

While he was thus musing, he heard the voices of a band of horsemen riding down the track. He stood up and hurried to greet them. "Welcome!" he cried. "Be welcome to my land! Would you wish to take refreshment in my house? The day is yet early but we will soon have food and drink for you."

The young man who led the group accepted the invitation, thanking Lir for his hospitality.

Together they went the short distance to the homestead and entered the enclosure. After much cackling from the scattered hens and squawking from greylag geese, the horsemen dismounted, dusted the horsehairs from their trousers and laid aside both shields and heavy swords. Clearly they were great warriors and Lir felt honoured by their presence.

Usna greeted them warmly. Leading them into the cool of the roundhouse, she hurried to find drinking-horns and barley-ale, then loaves of unleavened bread, still hot from the clay oven. Neither she nor Lir joined in the repast but stood respectfully by while their guests ate and drank. Only when the small meal was over did Lir ask to where the visitors were travelling.

"Towards the rising of the winter sun," the young man answered. "We hear that great battles are to be fought, for men from across the sea have planned to land on our soil under a leader known as Caesar. We have come from our tribal centre half a day's ride from here, to seek glory and many battle honours."

Lir was bewildered. Battle with men from overseas was beyond his comprehension, for he could only envisage the normal aggression of local tribe against local tribe. He had known the wild shouting and reckless valour of his own clan in battle and had, indeed, fought for his chieftain when a neighbouring tribe launched a cattle-raid, but never had he heard of a battle against men from far away. It was then that his daughter came hurrying into the house, stopping abruptly when she saw the visitors.

"May the Gods be with you", she said formally, her breathing uneven from having hurried. "I did not hear your coming or else I would have joined the welcome".

"Lady," the young man said, rising to his feet, "your presence is welcome enough," and he gazed at her in open admiration. "My name is Phelim and these warriors are my companions."

Fionnuala gazed back at him and then turned to her father. "What hero is this who honours our homestead? Surely the Gods have sent this lord? The crows of good-omen have surely flown over us."

Despite Lir's explanation for the presence of the travellers, the two young people looked only at each other. At last the young man's companions urged him away. "We must go, Phelim", they declared. "The Gods of battle will not be delayed. We must go - our honour demands it."

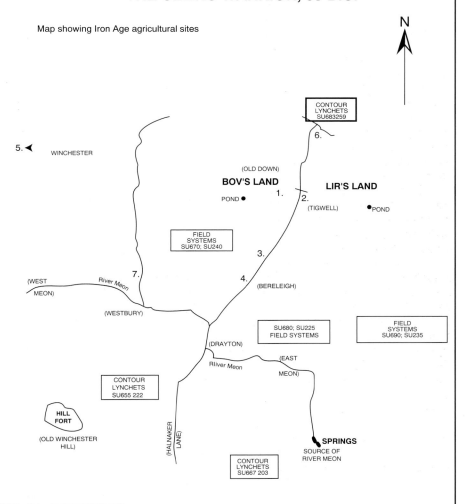

THE CELTIC WARRIOR, 55 B.C.

Map showing Iron Age agricultural sites

N

CONTOUR
LYNCHETS
SU683259

6.

5. ◄   WINCHESTER

(OLD DOWN)

BOV'S LAND   **LIR'S LAND**

POND ●   1.   2.

(TIGWELL)   ● POND

FIELD
SYSTEMS
SU670; SU240

3.

7.

(WEST   River Meon   4.
 MEON)   (BERELEIGH)

(WESTBURY)

SU680; SU225
FIELD SYSTEMS

FIELD
SYSTEMS
SU690; SU235

(DRAYTON)

(EAST
River Meon   MEON)

CONTOUR
LYNCHETS
SU655 222

HILL
FORT

(OLD WINCHESTER
HILL)

(HALNAKER LANE)

SPRINGS
SOURCE OF
RIVER MEON

CONTOUR
LYNCHETS
SU667 203

(DRAYTON) = **Modern Spelling and Settlements**

1. Pit near Old Down Farm. Site of Iron Age/Roman Farm. Abandoned c.150 A.D.
2. Gold Coin found from time of Verica, c.A.D.40
3. Bronze Age Round Barrow
4. Bronze Age Round Barrow
5. (Winchester) Settlements of Belgic Celts, between St. Catherine's Hill,
   Hockey Down and higher ground to West of present City
6. Bronze Age Round Barrow
7. Bronze Age Round Barrow

As the warriors mounted their steeds, Fionnuala called out, "May your ancestors protect you!" but the riders seemed not to hear, for the geese were again protesting at being disturbed.

After they had gone, their dust-cloud following them, Lir turned to Fionnuala. "O daughter", he began, "let not your heart fly after such a one as Phelim. He is a warrior and clearly of high status and far beyond your reach. Moreover, we have no knowledge of him nor of his clan and it is safer by far to cast your eyes upon one of our own tribe, even upon Bov our kinsman."

"Phelim is a Hero," she answered proudly. "One of the great. If the Gods so decree, he will return and claim me for his own." With that she turned away, and retrieving her pitcher, returned to the stock-enclosure to continue the milking.

Two days later the air became breathless and still, the heat hugging the earth in a close and stifling embrace. Then black clouds began to mass and the family watched them with dread. "The Gods are angry," Lir declared. "When clouds are as black as ravens and the great sun no longer shines, then mankind must fear." When a blaze of lightning sprang to their sight, followed by the noise of thunder, Lir spoke again. "The silver spears of the Gods are thrown," he said "and their chariot wheels crash through the sky. The Gods are angry and punishment must surely come, but I pray not to us."

Many days later came news that the enemy from over the seas had been caught in a terrible storm. Many ships and men were lost, the remaining attackers being driven from the land. Fionnuala welcomed the news and waited patiently for the return of Phelim, her bright Hero, and sang as she worked on the homestead. At last word came that the triumphant warriors had indeed returned. They were gathered with a growing multitude in the hill-fort where, it seemed, there was to be a great feast to celebrate the victory, and to which all the clan were invited.

On the appointed day Lir, Usna and Fionnuala set off to walk the few miles and, having climbed the hill, lay down to rest. The crowd was immense and the noise already splendid. The fine, aristocratic warriors on their horses were yelling their war cries and shouting boastfully of their valorous deeds, galloping the while around the feasting site and weaving in and out of the groups of clansfolk. They had donned their fighting armour again and flattened back their long hair with lime-wash and, with their billowing cloaks, looked a triumph of young manhood. A single tall trumpet, its mouth in the shape of a boar's head with a wooden clapper-like tongue, brayed harshly over the gathering, producing a din that caused a frenzy of excitement in all who heard it. The battle honour had been great: the feasting would be truly good.

And so it was. The roasting-fires sent up appetising smells of cooking pigs, deer and sheep, while great iron vats of freshly brewed ale stood ever full and frothing. All the clan, both men and women, drank and ate and drank again until many fell into stupors, and others into quarrelsome and bitter frames of mind. The worst quarrel arose when two warriors each claimed the succulent thigh-part of a roasted pig - the Hero's Portion. Each shouted his right to that portion because of his greater heroism in battle. Then each leapt to his feet to seek justification through trial by single combat. When the clan heard the challenge they gradually quietened and, as the two young men cast away their drinking vessels and threw down their cloaks, they gathered round to watch the contest.

No one shouted now and no kinsman leapt to his leader's defence, for all things had to be done in due order and according to the right-way-of-things. Only thus could the Gods decide between the adversaries, both seemingly worthy of the Portion and both of magnificent physique. It was then that Fionnuala recognized one of the combatants as Phelim, and her cry became a wail, quickly silenced by the onlookers. She fell to her knees and beseeched the Gods to grant victory to him of her choice.

The fight began with long iron swords being swung through the air. When this tactic failed, the opponents took to raising them with two hands above their heads and smiting downwards, throwing the whole weight of their bodies into the blows. After a while the sword blades became blunted and even bent, so the short, fighting daggers were snatched from their sheaths and used for closer battle. By now blood was pouring from wounds received by both men and each began to stagger. To maintain his courage, and to lessen that of the other, each was shouting abuse at his opponent, while proclaiming his own brave deeds and the greatness of his ancestors.

"My dagger is held by a God," cried Phelim "the very God of War - and he it is who will kill you."

"The Goddess of Sight will become an eagle," panted the other, "and will pluck out your eyes and you will die at my hands."

When both men sank to the ground, too weakened to fight more, the disappointed crowd returned to its feasting, deprived of a clear decision as to which should have the Hero's Portion. Only then did the kinsmen of the two wounded warriors carry them away to be tended by the women. Because Fionnuala was not kin to her hero, and thus could not go to him, she took another mouthful from the beer cup when it was handed round yet again, and rocked herself to and fro in despair. As the intoxicating fumes assailed her brain, she began to chant even yet more wildly, imploring her tribal God, Tutatis, to heal her warrior. Great offerings she promised should he live, and vows she made to go on pilgrimage to the shrine of the Mother Goddesses of Healing and All Life at the triple spring of the sacred river Meon. Finally, exhausted with weeping, she fell asleep where she lay. It was not until the dusk of evening that she was woken by her parents shaking her. Staggering to her feet, she wiped her salt-stained face with the plait-ends of her long hair, and followed them downhill towards their home.

News filtered through over the ensuing days and they heard that Fionnuala's hero still lived while his opponent had died. This was tragedy enough, but what was of greater importance was that they had been foster-brothers, for Phelim, the son of a lesser noble, had been taken at the age of seven into the household of a senior aristocrat for training in all things manly. Despite returning to his own home at the age of seventeen, the two young men had retained their devotion to each other, and now it was Phelim who had killed his foster-brother and had thus also cruelly wounded his beloved foster-parents. Only if Phelim should also die could the tragedy be set aside with no ensuing blood-feud, for both families would be equal in their grief. But Fionnuala was determined that Phelim should live.

"Father," she declared one day, "when Phelim lay wounded I vowed much treasure to the Three Mothers at the Meon spring. Now I must pay my dues so that my loved one may be recovered and return to me in strength. So now I ask you for my inheritance that I may cast it into the sacred waters, for in no other way can I ensure his health. Let me have now what you would have left me at your death - the horse-harness trappings, the bronze bowl, the torque of cast iron. And from you, Mother, a cauldron and the silver cloak-brooch."

These things were all given to her, for a vow should never be broken and, moreover, in those days women had equal rights with men and so could claim a son's portion.

With her pony laden with the sacks of sacred offerings, Fionnuala left the farmstead and took the track that ran downhill between her father's land and that of his kinsman Bov, passing as she did so two of the round burial mounds of the Old People. When she reached the river she turned east, and passing a number of scattered farmsteads, came to the source of the Meon. There, under the shade of a group of trees beside the marshy dell that held the holy springs, she found the shrine to the Three Mothers tended by a priestess in a robe of unbleached sheeps' wool. The shrine and dwelling-place was a simple wattle hut, with a sarsen stone as offering table, and it was onto this that Fionnuala unloaded her treasures.

"Bless them, O Priestess," she begged, "that my vow might be fulfilled and my hero, Phelim, be cured of his wounds. Bless them that the Holy Mothers may take him into their care and make him whole again. Bless them that the Spirits of the Water may accept my gifts and send him strength. Bless them that the Gods of the Otherworld may not yet claim him as their own."

The Priestess raised her hands and blessed them, calling on all the deities to witness the piety of the supplicant. Then she told Fionnuala to take the items one by one to the marshy edge of the pool and cast them into the water, while crying out to the triple Mother Goddess to grant her wish. This the girl did, and after laying a plucked goose on the offering-table by way of payment to the priestess, she returned home.

No word came to her of the health of Phelim but, keeping her faith in the goodness of the Three Mothers, she went about her work on the farm without undue anxiety. Harvest came, and after it, on the first day of August, the great seasonal market and the Feast of Lugnasadh. This was for worship of the God Lugh, the bringer of renewed fertility to the land, for the reapers had slain the corn-spirit when they had cut the corn. It was at this feast, held in the sacred enclosure near the shrine of the holy river-springs where she had so recently made her offerings, that Fionnuala heard that Phelim had died.

"My offerings were not enough!" she cried in anguish. "I am at fault! I have caused his death! I have not pleased the Gods and the Great Mothers failed to hear me!" Then she wept, wailing with a terrible wildness and tore off the enamelled brooch that fastened her cloak and undid the three plaits of her hair so that it covered her face. None should look on one who had failed a Hero in his time of need.

It was many, many days before she recovered a semblance of calm, and when she did, the youthful high spirits had gone from her. She became filled with an implacable determination to appease both her guilt and the spirit of her lost love. "Now I shall marry Bov," she declared. "My kinsman shall mate with me and I shall bring forth sons to equal Phelim. They shall be as brave as he in war, and as lusty as he in body, and as fearless as he before any sword or dagger brandished by an enemy. They, too, shall become Heroes, and claim the Portions at the feasts, and I shall love them fiercely and defend their honour with my life." So her father agreed to speak to Bov and their marriage took place.

Based on:

Everyday Life of the Celts by Ann Ross. Batsford/Putnam, 1970.

Iron Age Farm: The Butser Experience by P. J. Reynolds.
British Museum Publications, 1979.

Celtic Britain by Lloyd Laing. Book Club Associates, 1979.

The Celts by Frank Delaney. BBC Publications, 1986.

Iron Age Agriculture Reviewed by P.J. Reynolds.
Wessex Lecture I, Council for British Archaeology, Group 12, 1983.

The Celts by Norah Chadwick. Pelican, 1970.

Celtic Warriors by W.F. & J.N.G. Ritchie. Shire Archaeology, 1985.

Ancient Agricultural Implements by Sian Reer. Shire Archaeology, 1981.

The Celtic Tradition by Caitlin Matthews. Element Books, 1995.

Salvage Excavations at Old Down Farm, East Meon, by Richard Whinney & George Walker.
Proceedings of the Hampshire Field Club & Archaeological Society, Vol. 36 for 1980.

Folklore of Prehistoric Sites in Britain by Leslie V. Grimsell. David & Charles, 1976.

Shrines & Sacrifice by Ann Woodward. Batsford/English Heritage, 1992.

Chapter Three

Stroud Roman Villa, 340 A.D.

A S Ertola sat at her weaving-loom she could see her eight year old son, Valerius, leading the plough-oxen in the field nearby. Both she and his father, Justus, were slaves on the villa but, being slaves, had not been allowed to marry legally. Unfortunately, they had produced only the one child, causing the last villa owner to express extreme annoyance, for the children of slaves were slaves themselves, belonging totally to the master. The more babies a slave bore, the richer the master became. Slaves were property to be bought and sold as he wished.

The estate had recently changed hands, however, being acquired by a young man from the Roman settlement on the nearby ridge of hills. His name was Carinus Marcus, a Deputy Surveyor of Military Roads, who was in charge of the upkeep and repair of the highway between Venta Belgarum and Calleva Atrebatum.

While Ertola was watching her son, she heard footsteps in the Courtyard. Returning to her weaving, she soon became aware of Carinus and his steward standing in the doorway. Embarrassed, she rose quickly to her feet but was waved back to work by her master. As neither man spoke, she became acutely nervous under their scrutiny, handling the shuttle with less than her usual dexterity. A few minutes later they left, still without having spoken. Her nervousness increased when the steward returned alone and told her Carinus wished to see her in the dining room, the main chamber of the house.

When she entered, he was standing by the window. "I am told your name is Ertola and that you live with the slave Justus and have one son. Is that right?"

"Yes, sir."

"Well, that relationship is to cease. I have taken a liking to you myself. I do not intend to set you up as my official concubine, seeing I am seldom here, but I'll arrange for you to live better than you do now. Justus, of course, I shall sell. With his sale your relationship with him will be legally broken. Ended. Do you understand?"

Ertola could not answer, the tears ran down her cheeks and she sank to the floor in despair.

"Furthermore," Carinus continued, "I intend to sell your son Valerius. Then your loyalties will not conflict, should you produce children of mine."

When she lifted her head to plead with him, she found he had already gone.

Over the coming months he did not return very often, but when he did, he would send a servant to fetch her to his room. She bore him four children during the ensuing years: Grata, Victor (who was the only boy), Flavia and Carina. As Carinus was a free-born Briton, Romanized and Latin speaking, it was socially acceptable for him to have a woman, and even one concubine, but only if their mother was free would his illegitimate children be free also. As Ertola was still enslaved, so were her four children.

Slowly the years passed and the children of Carinus Marcus grew up and she bore him no more.

Inevitably changes were made on the estate, including many alterations to the villa buildings, for Carinus was making progress in his career and wished to have a home worthy of his status. He told Ertola that many years ago, when the place was first built, it had been little more than an aisled barn. The present living quarters of nine rooms had been inserted at some later time and the southern-most aisle turned into an enclosed corridor. He had already added a fine room to the south-west, installing underfloor heating to both this and the adjacent smaller room from a new hypocaust system, fed from an outside stoke-hole.

Even with these new additions, the house was still small and unpretentious, despite having mosaics on some of the floors of the living-quarters. Carinus declared himself dissatisfied with these, as they were of coarse red brick from local clay, and not of a very high standard. Later he intended to modernise the large bath-chambers on the western side of the courtyard and to buy additional land when it became available. His wealth – apart from his salary – came from agriculture and the sale of surplus grain and animals, some going to local market-dealers and some to overseas merchants for export. To farm on this scale he needed a considerable landholding, for now he had a large household of slaves and servants to feed. In addition, many sheep were needed for their wool, for all the estate clothing was home-spun and woven by Ertola and other slaves. Cattle, too, were needed to provide oxen for cart and plough. When these animals were unable to work through age, their hides were tanned on the estate and the resulting leather used for footwear and jerkins as well as for the many buckets, jugs, harness, saddles, belts, and other necessary articles.

Ertola's children were developing well and she became increasingly proud of them. Grata was proving successful in the kitchen and was learning to produce the spicy sauces so beloved by Romans and the Romanized Britons, such as Carinus Marcus. Victor was proving an eager pupil in the vegetable garden, while little Flavia and Carina had been put to work carding the wool for her weaving. Then came the day Ertola had been half expecting. One afternoon Carinus entered the weaving-shed and stood watching her work.

"Ertola" he said gently. "I am to marry. I am now thirty-four years of age and need legitimate heirs to whom I can leave my estate. You, therefore, must not come to my bed again."

"I understand," she murmured. "I have been expecting this long since. You have been a good master to me and I have been proud to bear your children. Now I am content to retake my place among the other slaves."

"But, no," Carinus said, and hesitated before he continued: "I would like to reward you for these last years, so I have decided to free you and to settle you on a small property of your own."

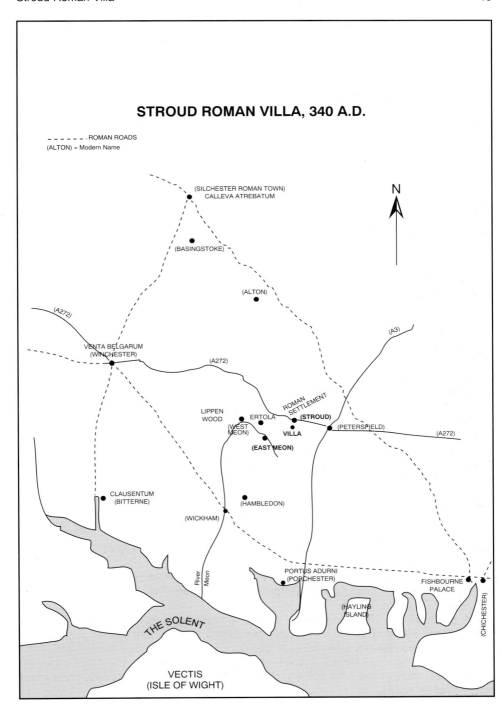

STROUD ROMAN VILLA, 340 A.D.

– – – – – . ROMAN ROADS
(ALTON) = Modern Name

N

(SILCHESTER ROMAN TOWN)
CALLEVA ATREBATUM

(BASINGSTOKE)

(ALTON)

(A272)

(A3)

VENTA BELGARUM
(WINCHESTER)

(A272)

ROMAN
SETTLEMENT

LIPPEN
WOOD

ERTOLA

(STROUD)

(WEST
MEON)

VILLA

(PETERSFIELD)

(A272)

(EAST MEON)

CLAUSENTUM
(BITTERNE)

HAMBLEDON)

(WICKHAM)

River
Meon

PORTUS ADURNI
(PORCHESTER)

FISHBOURNE
PALACE

(HAYLING
ISLAND)

(CHICHESTER)

THE SOLENT

VECTIS
(ISLE OF WIGHT)

For a moment Ertola could not reply. Then she sank to her knees and laid her forehead on his sandals. "Master!" she whispered with tears in her voice. "Master!"

He went out quickly, leaving Ertola still on her knees. Never had she dared to hope for this! Reaching out blindly for her weaving-stool, she raised herself from the floor, the tears pouring down her cheeks. To be freed! Freed! Release from slavery was the dream of all slaves, but that it should happen to her was unbelievable. Before many days had passed she was summoned to the main room of the house. Entering, she found her master with three of the senior slaves, a neighbouring villa-owner and an official of some kind. She was led forward to stand in the centre of the room and Carinus cleared his throat.

"I declare before you all, who are my witnesses, that this woman Ertola, lately my slave, is now freed from that slavery and is from this day forth a freed-woman and released from my jurisdiction, becoming merely my client. Furthermore, I declare that her four children by me are also freed but that, as I am now patronus to their mother, they shall remain in this villa under my control."

When the brief ceremony was over she went back to the weaving-shed. Freedom was a great thing but she was frightened now it had come. All her life she had been given orders and all her life she had known her duties. But now? How would she manage? And what had Carinus Marcus in mind for her future? Several days passed before she knew.

"Ertola," he said, meeting her in the courtyard. "Would you like to move to a new area - a settlement where there are many people of your Celtic kind, and where you could become a person of consequence? I'm thinking of a few miles west of here, on the river called Meon, and not far from where the old track comes off the south hills and travels north towards the great town of Calleva Atrebatum."

"But, Master," she began, "how would I live? I have no man to support me."

Carinus smiled and replied gently, "You'll still have me. As my ex-slave, I'll be your patronus and you will be my client. As patron and client you will owe me certain dues – and these in exchange for my continuing protection." He put out his hand and touched her shoulder. "And the due I require from you, Ertola, is one of your beautiful lengths of cloth each year, so that I may always have a resplendant tunic."

"Yes, yes! The best I can weave". Then a thought struck her. "But I would have no loom! This one is yours and I have no other."

Carinus laughed. "I shall send this loom with you and some of my own linen thread and fine-wool fleeces from my sheep. Then you can set up as an independent weaver, and if the cloth you make in the future is as beautiful as the cloth you've made me, you will soon be a rich woman. Have no fear. I have arranged for you to be lodged near the house of another freed couple, and have asked them to look after you. And that's not all, Ertola," he went on. "I have instructed the scribe to draw up an addition to my will, declaring that should I die before you, I desire that you keep these goods -the loom and so on. Despite being your patronus I do not look for their return to my estate. And - and - " he went on, holding up a hand to prevent her interruption, "I have instructed my steward that every three months he is to release your four children, so that they may visit you for a day or two. You lost your first son only because I took you as my woman, and I know how you grieved."

Ertola's departure took place three days later. Her loom, the working tools and her basket of belongings were packed into the ox-cart, which an old slave had been instructed to drive. She did not see Carinus Marcus again but she was given the opportunity to say farewell to the children.

The journey to her new home took nearly three hours, for the ox covered no more than two miles an hour. The way led first across the marshy land near the villa and then by higher ground, just south of the isolated hill on which the Old People had been buried. From there the track ran downhill to join the small river Meon, with scattered farmsteads along its banks, and so to her new abode, two miles or so further on. The slave, who did not know where exactly she was to be set down, asked a man working in a field. "Julius and Emilia?" he replied. "Why, yes. Their home is the one on the north side of the river, with beehives by the gate."

When the beehives came in sight, she saw that all the houses thereabouts were mere rough cots. They were set a little above the river track and were just native British roundhouses of the old fashioned sort, made of wattle on a timber frame, daubed with clay, and thatched. Her heart sank at the sight of them. As the ox was pulled to a halt, the slave called out to attract attention and almost immediately a man appeared at the run, with a woman following behind. Julius and Emilia, no doubt.

"Welcome, Ertola," the man called cheerfully "and may the gods bless your coming!".

Shyly she clambered down and stood uncertainly on the dusty track.

"Welcome, Ertola!" called the woman. "I have looked for your coming all day!" She smiled in such a friendly way that Ertola relaxed.

"I am come," she said, "and may the gods bless my coming."

Julius and the slave unloaded her belongings from the cart and she saw they were not carried into a roundhouse, but to a small separate building, a little to one side. "That's your house!" Emilia declared proudly. "You have it all to yourself, and with room also for the loom. It was made clear to us by your master that you were used to better living than we poor countryfolk. He said you were a great craft-worker and were to be well cared for."

Ertola turned to the woman. "I shall be happy here," she said formally. "I have been much favoured."

"Well, that's good," the other replied, "but you'll be wanting to set out your possessions. I told Julius to put the loom in that corner because of the wall opening. You'll have light enough, I think. And here's a bench to sit on and a platform for your bed. The straw palliasse is well filled – and with sweet scented herbs mixed in –- for I've made all as well as I can. But I'll leave you now, as I've the meal to see to, but I'll call you when it's ready, for you'll eat with us tonight." She turned to leave the hut and then added, "The latrine is down the hill a little. It's well sluiced by a small stream so you'll find it quite fresh. And there's a goodly pile of soft moss for your use should you need it."

She bustled out of the hut and shortly afterwards the two men brought in the bundles of wool, her basket of tools and other belongings. When they, too, had left, she slowly set about arranging her things until she was overcome with terrible longing for the villa. Being free was not as safe as being a slave. She sat down on the bench and wept, for now she had no familiar home, no Carinus Marcus, no children, no security. Being freed was very frightening. Gradually, though, as the days passed she became more settled. Once her vertical loom was threaded with its warp, the weights attached, and she had spun all the fleece that Carinus had given her, she began to feel more at ease.

She soon arranged to eat the one daily meal with the older couple, in exchange for weaving their cloth, but she found their poor diet very difficult to become used to for they existed mainly on bean porridge, green vegetables and flat cakes of coarse wheat-flour, cooked on a large stone pushed near the fire. There was seldom meat for they were too poor, and only occasionally did they have weak barley beer – mostly they drank river water.

Her children came in the month of July and it took them less time to walk than it had the ox-cart that brought her here in April. All day she had been in and out of her hut, scanning the road from the east, looking for the dustcloud that would be made by four pairs of feet. Then she had seen them, rounding a bend in the river, and had run to greet them. When she led them into her hut she was glad she had decorated it with some of her checked cloth in the bright colours favoured by the local people, and had strewn the floor with scented wild mint from the Meon's edge. Her little abode looked friendly and cheerful and, after a drink and some of the special honey cakes that Emilia had made, the children began to talk of their doings.

Grata was now ten years old and full of her prowess in the kitchen. "And when the wife comes – that's the Lady Aurelia" she explained, "there'll be all sorts of changes, they say. And great big feasts! And if I do my work well I may be allowed to serve at table. And do you know what?" she went on. "I've even been allowed to dust and polish the shrine, as well as the statue of the goddess Ceres, so that when the Master goes each day to pray to her (for a good harvest and fruitful cows, I think) it's all clean and ready for his next offering of salt and bowl of food. I feel quite creepy doing all of that. Suppose the Lares of the hearth, or the Penates of the food cupboard think I haven't dusted well enough! I might be struck dead or shrivel away or something! It's really creepy."

"Ah, well," Ertola remarked. "I don't think the gods of the Romans are so very different from our own. Just different names, that's all. Look! I've made a little model of the Three Mothers out of river clay and set it up over my bed. They'll watch over me and bless my home, and I expect the household gods of the Master do the same for him." She turned to Victor. "And the gardening? Is that good?"

"Oh yes!" he sighed happpily. "I like it. Hard work, though. But the other slaves do the digging because I'm too small. I do things like weeding and all the easier things - but I have to do them for hours and hours and hours. And there are some of the new kind of bushes called roses that prickle me. I don't like them much!" He paused and then added: "And the new herb beds! I look after them, too, but some of those plants smell really horrid." He wrinkled his nose and they all laughed. "But they're for medicines and things, so I suppose it doesn't matter."

That night the children slept on straw that Ertola had brought in from the farm. From the silence that greeted her small morning offering of cold bean-porridge with a beaker of water, it was clear that they did not think much of her living – there was no bread and no fruit. The slaves at the villa ate better then she did now.

The brief visit of the children was soon over and Ertola returned to her work at the loom, weaving now with both brown and white sheep's wool from the new season's clip, which she had exchanged with a villager for one of her check blankets. Many hours she put in, for now she had to do her own dying and fulling as well as the spinning and weaving. She knew that only after harvest would people have enough surplus corn or salted meat to be able to trade with her. By then she needed to have enough woven material ready for their new tunics, trousers and shawls, as well as large pieces for blankets and the double-thick rugs for use on saddles or bed-boards. Although most of the women in the scattered settlement wove at home, people were beginning to wander up to see what she was doing, for she had a growing reputation for quality work. Once she was even given a coin in part-payment for a decorative wall-hanging.

On many occasions she was lonely, of course, but she was working so hard and so long that she was deeply tired at the day's end. All those about her worked equally hard, and the only times when labour ceased were the occasional feast days. The festival of Lugnasadh had just passed, falling on the first day of August, when a wild feasting had taken place in honour of the god Lug. Soon would be the great and dreaded festival of Samhain on November the first, when the new year began for her Celtic peoples. This was a time of gloom and sacrifice and divination, for all the inhabitants of the underworld might appear in an attempt to cause distress and destruction to human kind. Only by wild dancing and playing of music and much propitiation could disaster be averted.

The festival to which she looked forward the most was that of Imbolc. It would fall on the first day of February, when the lactation of the ewes was said to begin, and all the feasting would be in honour of fertility and the springing earth. She had already been in the settlement for the feast of Beltane on the first day of May but, having been newly arrived and shy, she had not participated fully in the light-hearted frolicking to celebrate the strengthening sun. She had enjoyed the lighting of bonfires, through which the cattle were driven to ensure their fertility, and which was reinforced by the people dancing in a sunwise direction in a great circle round the blazing logs.

The Celts, as Ertola knew, had always been renowned for their wild and extravagant feasting, as well as for the vast quantities of food and drink they consumed on these occasions. At their festivals there was always much music and singing but also, of course, much drunkenness. For all the domination by Rome, the people alongside the river Meon were still the native British, many living in the outlying and isolated Celtic farmsteads and continuing to celebrate the gods in the old ways. All these people were free-born, never having been slaves, but most were very poor. Ertola could see that if she were able to sell her high quality cloth, it might come about that she, a freed slave, could end up more wealthy than those born free. She knew, of course, that having once been a slave she was considered of a lower social class. Nevertheless, she felt that a talented craftworker could surmount this stigma and be respected more than an ordinary peasant.

During the following year, her children continued to visit her every three months, and it was with them that she sent back the new lengths of fine wool cloth for Carinus. Now that he had risen in his official position, he was permitted to wear the white toga with a narrow purple band along its edge on ceremonial occasions. Ertola was very proud to be making it, and she struggled hard to keep the wool clean, although this was not easy in the dusty hut. The cloth lengths she had woven previously for his tunics had all been coloured, without the distinguishing stripe of high office. They had also been considerably less cumbersome and lengthy than this one.

When the children came in October, Grata was full of talk of the Lady Aurelia and all the alterations she was making to the property, following the marriage between her and Carinus. "New couches in the dining-room!" she exclaimed. "And when they have guests I'm allowed to carry in the dishes, which are all new from the forest pottery."

"But I thought you worked in the kitchen?"

"Oh, I do! But the Mistress lets me serve sometimes when the cooking's done."

"And I'm allowed to cut up the meat!" Victor declared proudly. "I cut it up into such little bits that they're easy to pick up. Then the house-slave puts them in dishes on the table. But I sprinkle my herbs over them first."

"And I make all sorts of things," Grata continued, "I really do like it, Mother, although the chief kitchen-slave is very strict. But oh! It's so hot! All that burning charcoal! Sometimes, when I'm stirring and stirring a sauce, I don't know how I can go on standing up. Pounding the herbs in the mortaria is worse, though. My arms ache so much they go all quivery! And do you know, at meals they have so many courses you wouldn't believe! And so many little tiny dishes to each course! It take us days and days to get things ready for a really big feast. Then I have to make medicines out of some of Victor's herbs. I have to make lots and lots of a borage drink to help the slaves' rheumatism – and to make them more cheerful! And I have to dry off caraway seeds and put them on the table for guests to chew after a meal – stops them feeling sick if they've eaten too much! Like lettuce leaves. They chew those, too, after a big meal. And valerian, to do away with wind – and to send them to sleep. And another thing I do is to make garlands – the Lady showed me how – for the guests to wear round their necks at a feast to stop headaches in the morning."

Ertola laughed. "It all seems very grand," she remarked.

Grata nodded. "And all sorts of people come to stay. They spend ages in the bath-chambers – the men go in the morning and the ladies in the afternoon and no end of wood has to be brought down from the hills to keep the fires going. They're in there for hours and hours. Just gossiping!"

During the midwinter visit the children were full of excitement. Carinus Marcus had at last been persuaded by his wife to enlarge the villa fully, concentrating first on the old bath-houses. They were now to be very splendid and very large.

"And all red inside," explained Flavia. "All the walls in the tanks are to be red."

"That's only coloured plaster," Victor explained condescendingly. "A layer of opus signinum – which is a special kind of concrete – and they're putting new tiles on the floors."

"And tiles on the walls of the other chambers," Flavia added. "I go to have a look sometimes. It'll be lovely when it's all done."

"And another thing, Mother – and this is really strange – a funny little building is being squeezed in between the house and the store sheds. Do you remember? There was a gap there before, on the east side of the courtyard."

"Yes," Ertola nodded. "I remember."

"Well, a very little room with eight sides is being built there for the Lady Aurelia. We don't know why exactly, but the bricks are very neat – not rough at all – so they must be expensive. They've put glass in the windows, too. It's somewhere very special."

"What I've heard," Grata said grandly, "is that the Lady doesn't believe in the Roman gods any more and has a new god. One called Christus, I think. In the kitchen we think she's building a shrine to him. Somebody told the cook that even the Emperors believe in him now, and that we're all meant to. But we have the Celtic gods and the Roman gods, so why do we want any more? It seems a bit silly to me."

So Ertola watched her children grow up. Victor, at nearly twelve, was put as an apprentice to the wheelwright, and although he was very sad at the thought of giving up his gardening, he knew that to be a craftsman was much superior to being a mere labourer. Grata continued in the kitchen but was allowed more and more time to work at her herbals. Flavia and Carina were now house-servants, cleaning and sweeping and occasionally being used in the kitchen to prepare vegetables.

Then tragedy struck. Carinus Marcus became ill while in Londinium – some pestilence had struck him down – and he died. When the news reached Ertola she mourned his death more deeply than she had thought possible. Now she worried about the position of her family for, being still bound to the villa, they would be at the mercy of the Lady Aurelia. She was very apprehensive, therefore, when a week or two later she caught sight of all four trudging through the rain, with Victor pushing a loaded handcart. Throwing on a cloak, she ran to meet them, fearful of what she would hear, and so was puzzled when she saw that they were smiling and calling to her.

It was little Carina who broke the news when she splashed through the mud and puddles and hurled herself at her mother's skirts. "We've been freed!" she shouted. "We've been freed!"

Ertola stopped. Bending down she eased the wet and straggling hair from the child's face. "You've been what?" she queried.

"Freed! Freed! Freed!" shouted Victor and Grata and Flavia all together. Then they just stood there grinning, waiting for her to say something.

Hesitantly Ertola asked, "Is this true? You've been freed? You're no longer bound to the villa in any way? Not even as clients?"

Wanting to hear more, Ertola hurried them out of the rain and into her hut. There they explained how with Carinus Marcus and the Lady Aurelia away in Londinium, the steward had been in charge and it was to him that the news of the death had been given by a messenger on horseback. It seemed that the widow Aurelia would not return to the villa. The land was to be leased out to neighbouring farmers, the slaves sold and the buildings cleared and left empty.

"And then a few days later we four were sent for," Victor explained. "And the steward read from a scroll which made us free of clientship. While he was dying the Master had made a declaration before witnesses – like he did with you, Mother – and – here we are!"

All evening, as the rain beat down on the hut and dripped steadily through the smoke-hole, she and the children discussed their new situation and made plans for the future.

"There are other villas round about," ventured Grata. "Couldn't we all get work at one of them? I could cook, Victor garden again, you could weave and Flavia and Carina – well, they're eight and six now, and are quite good as house-servants."

"Yes," chimed in Victor eagerly. "There's a villa I heard of west of here along the river and another one a bit south of us. Then there's the big Roman settlement to the north – "

"And big ones at Clausentum and Portus Adurni. And the huge one at Calleva Atrebatum."

"And Venta Belgarum, don't forget! I'm sure we could get work at a villa somewhere."

"Well," Ertola said, slowly and carefully. "I don't think we'll get work at any of the villas hereabouts – not all five of us at the same place. That's too many. But I do think that going to Venta is a good idea. I've heard there's quite a large cloth-weaving centre there, and if we could find a little house to rent, I'm sure I could make my way with the weaving. Especially as I could concentrate on quality cloth, instead of having to weave coarse blankets and cloaks in exchange for food."

Later she went across to Julius and Emilia to tell them the news and arranged to give the couple her hut and small garden. The old hand-cart that the children had brought from the villa was then exchanged for a bigger one that would take the loom. The following day they left the settlement as soon as it was light, Victor and Grata pulling a shaft each and Flavia, Carina and Ertola pushing the cart from the back.

"May the gods go with you!" Julius called.

"And may they bring prosperity and good harvests to you!" Ertola replied.

Then, without looking back, they began the long journey to Venta, following the river westward, then southward and finally leaving the valley to climb slowly over the smooth-sided hills. After they had gained the high ridge they began the slow descent towards their new life, and the fulfilment of all their hopes.

Based on:

Article by A. Moray Williams, B.A., in *Archaeological Journal,* 1909, on excavations of Romano-British Villa, Stroud.

Rome, Britain & The Anglo-Saxons by Nicholas Higham. Seaby, 1992.

Later Roman Britain by Stephen Johnson. Routledge & Kegan Paul, 1980.

The Romans by Karl Christ. Chatto & Windus, 1984.

The Romans: A History of Britain by Tim Wood. Paperbird (Ladybird) 1989.

Women in Roman Britain by Lindsay Allason-Jones. British Museum Publications, 1989.

The Gods of Roman Britain by Miranda J. Green. Shire Archaeology, 1983.

Food & Cooking in Roman Britain by Marion Woodman. Corinium Museum Publications, 1985.

Roman Crafts & Industries by Alan McWhire. Shire Archaeology, 1988.

Roman Herbal by Michael Hoadley. J. & P. Bealls, 1991.

Chapter Four

The Wandering Youth, 680 A.D.

A T last the great oath-giving night arrived. Resplendently seated at the end of the mead-hall, the lord Hardulph had his hearth-companions about him, awaiting the newest of his war-band. As each came to him, they kissed him, then knelt to place their own hands and head upon his knees in dutiful subjection, swearing eternal fealty. Hardulph raised each brave warrior to his feet, giving him a ring of shining gold and his newest battle-friend, a gleaming sword. Those of lesser courage and younger age received a slender ashen spear, taller than a man, with a deadly and polished tip which gleamed in the firelight.

Then the rafters of the hall echoed with joy. Songs rang out among the benches as the cup-bearers, all lively maidens, carried the drinking horns to each in turn. Alnoth was filled with soaring happiness, glad his lord was such a mighty ring-giver, sparing nothing from the treasure of his life-hoard. Hardulph, proving such a gold-giving thegn, was truly fit for lordship, for a leader sparing of gifts, would not attract retainers, and Alnoth had no wish to serve such a one. In gladness, then, he drank deeply of the horn when it was brought to him again, and his voice rose hoarse as the mead befuddled him. His ring he kept safe upon his finger and his newly-given sword close by his side, for these were now his own treasures and his own war-gear, marking him out as a favoured warrior.

Later, replete with roast pig and coarse-grained bread, he rolled himself in his cloak and slept beneath the bench. This reception had been very different from that of a few months ago, when he had been so cruelly turned away from the hall.

Hardulph was lord of the lands that lay along the Meon river and his stoc was very large – it was that great farming estate which made him powerful. His tribe had once been led by Jutish invaders who had arrived in the area later than the Saxons, who had already occupied the land to the east and the west for many years, but there had been little friction on their arrival. The Jutes and their bands of followers had moved mostly up the river valleys, for these marshy lands had not been appreciated by the sheep-farming, pastoral Celts, nor their Saxon overlords, who preferred the drier hill-tops. Now, after much inter-marriage, there was little difference between the tribes, and to Alnoth a Jute seemed much like a West Saxon – or a South Saxon, such as himself. Basically, most of the people were still Celtic Britons.

His father, Edwold, held a fair-sized area of land on the high downs, and his dwelling was one of the eight great halls in the settlement of Chalton. There his sheep-flocks were among the finest and his woven-cloth the best. His wife had been Wendreda, dead now these two years and buried in the cemetery which, as was usual, lay on a hill-crest and a little way from the settlement. She had been placed in a chalk-cut grave, linen-shrouded, and with her chain-linked pins fastening cloak and headress. Her amulet bag had been laid with her, as had three iron rings, a bronze bracelet and her iron knife. The infant, whose birth had killed her, lay by her side unadorned except for an iron knife. The ceremony had been one of full burial, not of cremation as was the custom in some tribes, so the mound was strewn with flints to keep their spirits from wandering.

Many were the tears spilt at that burying. Gloomy was the dirge sung in hall at the funeral feast, the minstrel grieving over the loss of so fine a lady, beloved of all, and the death of a son whose warriorship would never now be known. Since those sad days, Edwold had taken as his new wife the widow of his brother, as duty demanded, but she proved to be filled with a sneering animosity, jealous of Alnoth and his father's love for him. This jealousy became beyond bearing and the cruelty of her tongue without support. The youth endured many hateful abuses and, knowing himself ill-starred, was filled with heartache for the times of peace and warmth of mother love. No longer was he stout-spirited, hiding any sorrow with a smiling face, but was choked with misery and became a burden to all about him. It was thus that his father, that earlier loving Edwold, pressed him without mercy to leave the hearth's side. So Alnoth began his exile, far from kin and boon companions, masterless and with no lordship protection, having nothing but a spear and one iron knife to commend him to a future lord.

Much hardship he suffered in his wanderings, the hoar-frost often white upon his hair, his limbs racked with cold and grief uppermost in his mind. Occasionally he found shelter and food in exchange for small labours. Once he was befriended by a shepherd who shared a hare with him, skinned and roasted on a hazel spit; once by a woodman who gave him a portion of hedgehog, which had been coated in clay and buried in the glowing embers of a fire. When the clay had dried and cracked, the spines of the creature had come away from the succulent flesh and the sparse meal was full-enjoyed. Mostly, however, he slept hungry, the demon-filled darkness of night drowning him in fear while his heart was ever pierced by thorns of sadness.

When howling winter truly came, he was desperate enough to accept the task of nightly deer-scaring on a thegn's patch of autumn-sown barley. This entailed the whirring of a wooden clapper from the chill of evening through to the bleakness of dawn, listening the while to the harsh barking of vixens in the woodland and the eerie screeching of owls. From this unwelcome work he gained the right to sleep the day away in an out-building of the farmstead, to be fed daily but be scorned by all. He was usually hungry, but he lived. Only when spring came again, with its exuberance of birdsong and a warming sun, did he leave the thegn and come to a small settlement at the ford near the bridge, where the land was raised a little and thus drier. Here, away from the bogs and marshes of the river, he was taken into the household of a farmer in need of a cowherd. Of the original buildings only a few timber and thatch cots were still standing, and it was clear from the tumbled state of the others that this was a site of dwindling prosperity and influence. Most of the villagers had moved on – there was, after all, plenty of open river-land as yet unoccupied. The man who gave him work had stayed, perhaps, because his reverenced dead lay in the cemetery across the river and only a short way upstream. There being no apparent lord or protective kinship, Alnoth saw it as a hamlet abandoned by the gods. Surely Eostre, the bringer of spring, had passed by this place, for it seemed damp and desolate.

Finally, of course, the sun did shine and the grass spring joyful in the pastures. The sheep produced their bounding lambs; the larks – those lovely sky-masters – sang overhead, and the fish awoke from their winter sleep. Alnoth recovered his strength, his spear arm growing eager to hurl its weapon and his legs to run to the battle fray. Yet his adversaries were but the slinking foxes which snatched at lambs, or the horny-beaked ravens which swooped across the slaughter fields of March and April, crying for carrion, with death in their wings. Despite the increasing warmth, Thor, the sky god, occasionally sent down malevolent hail, that coldest of grain, or such torrential rain that new-hatched partridge chicks died of cold and young leverets shuddered in their forms. He remembered then the great mortality of birds that had hit the countryside for two seasons when he was a boy. Perhaps this was yet another? He remembered, too, tales of the day when the shining sun was swallowed by darkness and a great pestilence befell the country. In the cold and wet, death was even now coming swiftly to many creatures, without mercy. Then Thor relented and sent days of balm, a warming sun and springing growth. Alnoth was able to feast on the young green buds of the hawthorn bush, known from his childhood as 'bread and cheese', and to tip raw egg-yolks from birds' nests down his throat. He lived, and grew to young manhood, waiting for the gods to reveal their next intent.

When this came it was not auspicious. He met a man in strange clothing with a rope round his waist which had knotted ends. Moreover, he carried no weapons or tools and his hair was clipped short, from ear to ear and from his forehead to the crown, leaving only the back part a normal, if straggling, length. Clearly he was a madman and Alnoth slipped his knife from his belt and held the spear in a firmer grip. Madmen were unpredictable. However, the man came towards him with a friendly smile.

"May God be with you" he called.

This was a variation of the usual greeting when all the gods were called upon. Perhaps the man was dedicated to one god only?

"My name is Brioc," he went on. "I come in peace."

His voice was strange, too, having a lilt that could be heard in some of those of pure Celtic descent. Cautiously, Alnoth smiled. The man was old, and therefore would be more easily overcome in combat. Besides, only one of them was armed.

"I am a priest," the other said. "A monk, and I come from the west, seeking those who have not yet heard of Our Lord the Saviour. Are you such a one?"

"What saviour is this?" Alnoth asked. "And from what would he save me? I am in no danger."

Then Brioc sat on the grass and seemed so at ease that Alnoth sat, too, but keeping his weapons near to hand. "I am a priest", the monk repeated, "and I come from far away, an exile from my homeland for the sake of Christ. I was born in the north of the land your people call Wales – the land of the foreigners – although we Britons were on this island long before you. I was taught in the great monastery of Bangor Iscoed, in the kingdom of Clwyd, and later crossed the sea to the isle of Iona, where the holy Columba had founded a monkish community some years before. That saintly man, our venerable father, was from Ireland and Irish taught, and his monastery followed the rulings of the Irish Church."

None of this made sense to Alnoth. He understood but little of such a speech and feared the man was indeed mad. Why else the shaven head, lack of weapons and this strange talk?

"From Iona I crossed the sea again to my native place, but was inner-driven from there by my need to wander in the service of God. I arrived at Malmesbury and the hermit's cell of Maildulph, its founder. He, too, was of the Irish Church, but it was Abbot Aldhelm who accepted me into his school. Under his teaching and guidance I became a priest, for he was a man of much learning and persuasive power. So keen was he to draw the people to his abbey and a proper love of God that he would take his lyre to the river bridge and sing to passing crowds, although he was an aristocrat and of the royal house. Also he believed that to teach was as important as to preach, for without Latin none of the holy books could be read. By the end of my time there, Malmesbury was the chiefest place for education in all the lands of the West Saxons."

He turned to Alnoth and smiled ruefully. "My troubles began when the holy Maildulph heard that the British Church (but not yet the Irish) had to bow to the authority of Rome. The great synod at the Abbey of Whitby, twenty-four summers ago, decided that. Why, I cannot tell. Our Church has been here since the time of the Romans, and successful, until your people came into this country. You, with your many gods and foolish sacrifices, have won supremacy over us by defeating some of our leaders in battle. But you have never reduced the ordinary people to servitude or full obedience, and even now the British are thick upon this land. Only in my native Wales and other western places do they live in total freedom. And, of course, in Ireland, which you never won. Then the Roman pope, Gregory, sent the monk Augustine to make us all adopt the Roman usage, the Roman tonsure and the Roman date for Easter."

"Eostre?" queried Alnoth, this word at least, making sense to him. "Do you worship the goddess of springtime and new life, as we do?"

Brioc smiled again. "No, my friend. But we have given her name to the great day of our own faith, when the Saviour rose again from the dead. As wild nature rises in the resurrection of spring, so the Lord gives us eternal life in Heaven."

This was meaningless to Alnoth and he stirred restlessly. "But this lord, this great war-prince, where is he? Is he a glorious ruler of earls, a generous ring-giver, protector to his companions and the kin? Has he won many battles at the spear's point? At the sword's edge? Fighting from the shield-wall of his noble warriors?"

Although Brioc expounded the Christian story, Alnoth was unimpressed. He could not see the need for such a leader, who was not only a weakling but had already been overtaken by the inflexible fate of death. His battle-glory had not even fallen to the next great warrior, the next man leader-worthy of the tribe. Brioc made no sense. However, as the day progressed and the monk stayed with him and Alnoth herded the cattle along the lusher pastures beside the river, he found himself glad of the companionship.

Later, Brioc continued with his own story. "When I could not accept the ways of the Roman Church, for they were placed upon us quite without need, I left Malmesbury Abbey as both Maildulph and Aldhelm became obedient to this new ruling. They even grew their hair again – and four months it took them – so that they could shave only the crown of their heads as was now required. But I kept mine as it was. And left. There is no place for me in the Roman Church, any more than there was for the followers of Bishop Aiden, founder of Lindisfarne, for they were all of the Irish Church. Rome has too much pomp and glory, placing an over-emphasis on the dignity of bishops. Why should I care for wealth in the abbey, for gold croziers, for processions banner-led on feast days? I am of the Celtic Church. We admire simplicity and goodness, humility and prayer – as did the holy saints Patrick of Ireland and David of Wales. And Columba, founder of Iona. All Celtic."

Alnoth, uninterested in this talk, watched a kestrel hovering and waited for the bird's dive to its prey.

"Look at all the holy men we have had," Brioc went on. "Even in my life-time have lived Cedd, Colman, Chad, the great and holy Cuthbert, and the Abbess Hilda of Whitby. All worked in Northumbria so you won't have heard of them, but all were of the Celtic Church, either Irish-trained or from my own country of Wales. But now they follow Rome. Our day for Easter is recalculated and our tonsure is changed – as I've already told you – but, worse still, the Church is under the ruling of a foreign pope instead of our own good and holy abbots."

Alnoth asked, "But where was the battle? Why do you not kill these interlopers, ruling you when such a ruling is hateful?

"No battle," the monk replied sadly. "Except with words. Our Lord has told us to forgive our enemies, and so we must. No battle, then."

In exasperation, Alnoth exclaimed, "No battle? No vengeance? No blood feud or settling of scores? That I could never accept. Never! A feeble faith and a weakly king, for the chief duty of any prince is to lead his men to battle."

Patiently Brioc told him how Augustine came to this country, not knowing, perhaps, that the Christian Church had long been active both here and in Ireland. He spoke, too, of Paulinus of York and of Bishop Birinus, working in the southern regions, who had founded a minster at Winchester forty-odd years ago. They were all of the Roman persuasion, as was Theodore, Archbishop of Canterbury, who was from Tarsus in a far away country, and his abbot, Hadrian, who came from a place called Africa.

"I could tolerate these foreigners," Brioc added, "but I find it hard that our beloved Saint Cuthbert of Lindisfarne has changed his allegiance. Betrayed our Celtic Church. As has Bishop Agilbert of the West Saxons and, worst of all, Maildulph of Malmesbury and my own teacher, Abbot Aldhelm. Since the Synod of Whitby, at the great double monastery of Abbess Hilda these twenty-four years ago, the Celtic Church is forgotten. Overlooked. Ignored. For three hundred years we have been in these islands but now we count for nothing. Only in the remoter regions does our ancient usage continue. And it was we, all those years ago, who converted so many from following the heathen ways of the Druids. Yet we receive no credit."

He sighed and then went on thoughtfully, "I remember hearing of a holy saint in Ireland, Fintan of Clonenagh, who came across a party of heathen warriors. They had the severed heads of their enemies. You must know," he explained, "that in those times Celts believed the spirit of a man resided in his head. Possess his head and the spirit of that man becomes your slave. So Fintan persuaded the men to give him the heads and he buried them in the monks' cemetery, hoping that by Domesday they would have benefited from the prayers of generations of monks, and so would find God's mercy. And I don't believe that Fintan was alone in doing such a thing. There must be many such heathen heads lying buried close to a chapel's walls. Perhaps on the south side, which is the holiest of all."

The two remained in silence until Brioc continued, "I can understand the arguments of Rome. It does seem foolish to have two forms of Christianity – without unity between the Churches it would be difficult to convert the heathens." He told how Oswy, King of Northumbria, had listened to both sides of the argument at the meeting in Whitby, one party led by Colman, the Celtic bishop of Lindisfarne, and the other by Bishop Agilbert, who now followed the Roman usage. This last was assisted by Wilfrid.

"And it was Wilfrid," he declared, "who was the persuader. Agilbert was Frankish, you see, and didn't speak good English, so Wilfrid put his arguments for him. And won everyone over – including King Oswy. He said it was ridiculous that little Iona should set itself up against the rest of the western Christianity when only Lindisfarne, Northumbria, Wales and the north of Ireland still practised the Celtic ways. Such an alliance was too small and too remote from the centre in Rome. So, says Wilfrid, it must bow to the Pope and accept the Roman way of doing things."

Alnoth snorted in disgust. "So you gave up without a fight? Could you not have killed at least some?"

"No, no!" Brioc replied. "The difference between us is only one of practice – we Celts try to live simply, spiritually, without grandeur. Our bishops will only walk among the people, refusing to ride, while theirs insist too much on their dignity and have the best of horses. Celtic saints live in meagre hermitages, often in lonely places, tending the people gently, while theirs go about in pomp and glory."

"Oh, I side with them!" Alnoth declared. "All leaders must be proud gift-givers, lords of the mead-hall, brave shoulder companions to their warriors! I could follow them!" He looked at Brioc dismissively. "Your gods seem poor things. I prefer ours." Then, his long patience exhausted, he herded his cattle away and left the monk by the river's edge.

The talk of bravery, however, of gift giving and battle glory, filled him with restlessness. After all, he was not a ceorl but of noble birth, a warrior by right. He must leave the cow-herding and find a lord. Enjoy once more the warmth of hearth-companions and the protection of a prince. In return he would protect his lord in battle, never leaving his side even though both died. Only shame fell on those who deserted their lord. No glory could come to them, for faithfulness was all. Never could a man return to the hall and the safety of kinship while his lord lay dead, the rest of his war-band about him.

A few days later he left the farmer whose cattle he had guarded and turned south-west, braving the wolf-slopes where those fierce grey wanderers lived unmolested in the Forests of Bere. He had heard there was a great settlement called Hamwic on the edge of the river Itchen and thought someone there might be glad of a warrior. When he finally reached that river he followed it south. After many miles he met a man who pointed out the remains of old buildings, which, he said, had been a town called Clausentum when foreigners had owned it, long years before. Further on he could see a settlement on the opposite bank and persuaded a boatman to carry him over. The Itchen was not deep here, and no doubt he could have waded, but the boatman laughed and said the tide was coming in – whatever that meant.

Alnoth found Hamwic a large and thriving place, far bigger than anywhere he had seen before. There were even ditches surrounding the many cots and large halls. For a while he wandered about, seeking the leader of these people so that he might join his warband, but failed to find him. He was amazed to see the number of boats tied up on this west side of the river and was overawed by their size, having seen only the

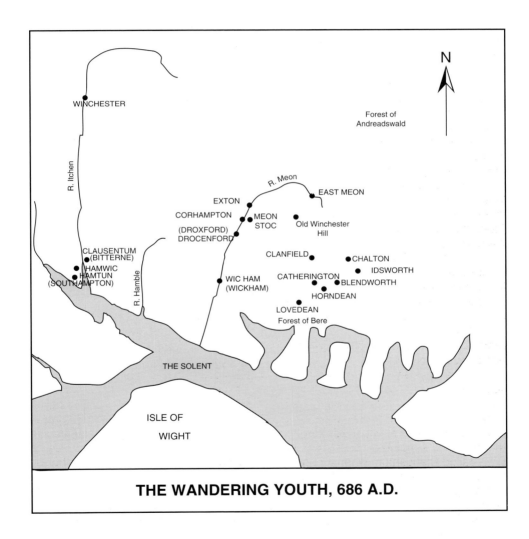

THE WANDERING YOUTH, 686 A.D.

small, flat-bottomed vessels on the shallow Meon. Standing on the rough wooden walkway, built to ease the loading and unloading of goods, he watched men bring ashore a crate of pottery, packed in straw and of a fineness that was new to him. Glass items were coming in from the area of a great river called Rhine, and he saw heavy quernstones for the milling of corn. Away from the river he found open-fronted workshops where ironware was fashioned - knives, axes and tools for both farm and wood-workers. He saw nails and rivets, locks and keys, all being hammered out with a din that put him in mind of the god Thor, son of Woden, and the noise his chariot made when raging through the sky. Surely the Thunderer could not be more noisy than this?

Further on he came to a shed which was nearly empty. In one corner was a small pile of indifferent fleeces, perhaps rejected by merchants needing high quality wool for cloth. He thought of his home with a sudden longing. Was this where the best wool from his father's sheep ended? He knew that many of the quality fleeces went over the sea - over that great ship-mere that he had never seen but could now smell. Perhaps they had been shipped from here? Filled with an unexpected weariness, with no joy in his life, he lay down on the greasy pile of skins and slept.

He was woken by a snarling dog. Cautiously he stood up, fearing its gleaming teeth, and edged out of the shed. By now he was in great hunger. If he did not find a war-leader soon he would starve. Stumbling a little, he saw a small wooden building ahead and wandered in. A rushlight burned on a table at the far end and a figure was moving about.

"Is this the mead-hall of a great prince?" he called. "I would serve him gladly if I could but eat at even the lowest bench."

"Nay," the other replied. "This is the minster church. It is the Son of God who is the great Prince, fighting evil where he finds it."

He was dressed in a long robe, womanish in style, and a cowl lay behind his shoulders. Sighing in disappointment, Alnoth leant against a pillar for support. "I am hunger-faint," he explained. "I seek a great lord to serve, for I am noble-born but turned from my father's house. I have no kinship protection in these parts."

Silently the priest retired, returning with half a loaf and a beaker of water. While Alnoth consumed these in ravenous haste, the long-dressed one told him of much fighting in the countryside. "Led by Prince Caedwalla, a fierce fighter and a mighty conqueror. All this land hereabouts he has taken very recently and we are now part of the kingdom of the West Saxons, or the Gewissae, as they call themselves. Caedwalla gathered to himself a large war-band, many being from the great forest of Andreadswald that stretches from the Meon River, eastwards across the land of the South Saxons and towards the kingdom of Kent. That great wild wood is filled with robbers and outlaws, dispossessed Britons and criminals – as well as bears and wolves. Caedwalla found it easy to bring these men to him and, with those from Bere, which is an impenetrable oak forest stretching from Itchen's edge along the shoreline for many miles east, he has a veritable multitude of fighting men. For three years he has battled, and now holds Hamwic and all the valleys of the Test, the Itchen and the Meon and their inward lands. More recently he has fought the South Saxons to the east and that land he has ravaged. The devastation was such that I hope never to hear of again. This year their king he killed, although he, too, was a Christian, and took the island of Wight – which you could see if you stood on the waves' edge against the Solent. Two princes had their holdings on that island, but Caedwalla drove out both and slaughtered many that lived there. He then gave one third of those lands to a bishop called Wilfrid, to make into a Christian community, and began to lay out this fine port of Hamwic. A mighty, valiant battler he is. A man to be feared, for he has retaken for the Gewissae the lands that King Wulfhere of Mercia took from us twenty seasons ago. That was in the time of Cenwealh, son of King Cynegils, who had moved his centre to Winchester because of the Mercian invasions of his land in the valley of the river Thames. Although Winchester holds the chief royal residence, it is Hamwic that is the leading town in all this part. There is no town greater, and the king's officials work from here. Also," he added proudly, "we're all Christians now. Only far to the west, where Bishop Birinus did not reach, are there still heathens. There, and in the hidden places of the forest of Andreadswald and in some benighted settlements up the river valleys."

Alnoth had no wish to hear more of Christians, for he remembered his bemusement at the ramblings of Biroc, but he did want to hear about the fighting. "I have heard of no battles," he declared, puzzled. "I have spent many weeks alongside the Meon and I heard of no great warband or fine leaders."

"Ah!" said the priest, "in the river valleys there are no kings – they have their great estates on higher land. When a war-leader is killed, his land passes at once to his enemy and with it the people who occupy it, whether they be British, Jute or Saxon. There is no quarrel with farmers or their serfs, so why fight in a boggy river valley such as that of Meon? Only hand-to-hand combat between chieftains might be fought at a river crossing. When the waters run red at a fording-place, then those downstream know that a great contest has been held between powerful ones and that their own allegiance may have to be given to another lord."

"And Caedwalla? Where is he now, for I would seek him out and offer my own life's blood in his service?"

The priest thought for a long moment and then suggested Alnoth forgot about Caedwalla, aiming first to serve a lesser prince but one who was nearer at hand. "For it is rumoured in the market-place that Caedwalla is fighting far to the north-east, conquering lands of the river Wey and beyond. It is said, moreover, that he has given a great estate to the Church at a place called Farn Ham, perhaps because he was sore wounded in the battles against the South Saxons and, fearing he may not have long to live, is thinking of going to Holy Rome to die there. If this occurs we may have Ine as our next West Saxon king. He, also, is a Christian and a man of much ability."

"Then Ine," Alnoth asked, "where is he?"

The priest shrugged. "Who knows? The great ones keep their own counsel."

The two supped together and, in return for his food and drink, Alnoth felt obliged to listen to talk of religion, of a man called Christ, and of a monk in exile from his own northern lands. This monk loomed large in the conversation, for his name was Bishop Wilfrid and he had spent long years in this south country, having been given land at Selsey for his see. Brioc had spoken of him, too, but with disapproval, blaming him for changes in the Church. When Alnoth mentioned this the priest smiled a little and raised an eyebrow.

"Wilfrid is a good and saintly man," he stated. "A great persuader of people to leave their heathen gods, but – " and here he paused. "But – well, he is too over-bearing for many of us. An austere man, but proud. I follow the ways of Rome, as I must, but I can remember the days of the Celtic Church when humility and gentleness and poverty were what counted. The bishops were all monks then, owning nothing and hoping only to take the people to a faith in the true God. Now religion has become the province of aristocrats and kings, drawn by the promise of eternal life." He paused again. "When a leader becomes a Christian many are the baptisms that follow, but few understand the faith. They rely quite blindly on the new prayers to protect them from harm, just as they did when they were pagans. And now there is little idea of solitary meditation – those of the old Church would seek out aloneness so they might know God's will, but today –" he shrugged. "A priest insists upon his dignity as a great one, and a bishop is made to ride a horse and have a retinue. When I was young, monks and priests would walk among their people, helping where they could, consoling those in distress. There is little you can do from horseback."

Sighing, he added: "Ah, well. I suppose it's better to have but the one Church, even though the rules come down to us from Rome instead of our holy abbots. And with distances so great and the diocese so vast, no bishop could make his peregrinations on foot. Change had to come and at least there is now one system and one usage for all. And the actual teachings haven't changed."

As when Brioc had talked to him, Alnoth expressed his increasing irritation at the weakness of these men, but the priest replied, "No, my son. Not weakness. Submission to God's will."

"And my own people? Are they now Christians? The people of the high chalk-lands to the east of here?"

"I do not know, but Bishop Wilfrid, before he returned from exile here to his See of York, spread the Gospel along this coast and up the river valleys, so he may have reached your people. I know he is one of the greatest founders of churches but I think he was inspired at least a little by grandiose ideas. Hereabouts, we thought he had something of personal ambition, too." He turned to Alnoth with a smile. "As for you, my son, if you also have personal ambition then become a Christian. All the great men are converted, and a heathen, such as yourself, would not be welcome in their mead-halls. You might bring ill-fortune upon them."

The next morning, before Alnoth left the town, he wandered through another busy area which had many dwellings and bustling people. He was told this newer part was called Hamtun, and being a little to the south of Hamwic and further from Itchen's shores, would be easier to defend from any sea-borne attack. Finding little to interest him, he turned east, recrossed the Itchen, waded the river Hamble, then climbed the hills until he saw another river below him and a small settlement. This was called Wic Ham and lay on the remains of an ancient road, built by the Romans. As nobody knew of a war-leader nearby he continued up the river valley, trudging through the low-lying, marshy land.

Eventually he came to an area he recognized – the hills where he had pastured the cows near the Meon ford. He ignored that scattering of homesteads, avoided the extensive cemetery for fear of the dead, and so came at last to a great farming estate known as the Meon Stoc. This was possessed by Hardulph, a noble warrior. Filled with hope of finding security, Alnoth approached a young man and enquired about the chance of joining the war-band. The other laughed.

"No chance at all!" he declared. "Look at you! The war-band is for warriors - not ragged youths such as you!"

"But I'm noble born!" Alnoth retorted. "I am Alnoth, son of Edwold, lord of Chalton, and I have the right to be a warrior. Take me to your own lord. That, at least, cannot be refused."

Shrugging, the young man passed him over to another, who showed little interest. "You have only the spear of a freeman," he said. "Where's your warrior's shield and sword? Your ring of honour? We want no imposters here. The lord Hardulph is too great a fighter to need to take on beggars – he has the pick of the best. Be gone with you!"

But Alnoth stood his ground. "I am indeed noble born. In exile from my father's house. I have a right to speak to your lord."

Grumbling, the man took him to the timber-built hall where many people were gathered, awaiting the coming of Hardulph. Here Alnoth was left, intimidated now by the splendour of the gathering.

"And who is this?" a voice enquired at his elbow. "A stranger in our midst?"

Alnoth turned quickly and dropped to one knee, explaining who he was and how his exile came about.

"And what would you of me? Those in exile are of uncertain use, for I know nothing of their honour or their trustworthiness in battle."

"My lord, if you would but let me join your companions in arms, I would serve you faithfully - until the ravens of Thor strike me down in untimely death."

Hardulph stroked his drooping moustaches, first one side and then the other. "And proof?" he asked. "Who have you served before and what battle-glory did you win?"

Shamefaced, Alnoth admitted he had never fought, his father living peacefully with his neighbours and no attacks having been made on the settlement. "But I am well-trained with a sword and eager to fight. I only lack my oath-helpers to prove the truth of my words, for here I am in exile."

Hardulph dismissed him with a wave of his hand. "I do not take a stranger as a companion in my hall – a stranger who can prove nothing. If you joined my war-band I would become responsible not only for your behaviour, your survival and your well-being, but for your kin also. I would have to fight your enemies should you be killed in my service. And, as I do not know you, I am unwilling to offer you this protection. These men about me I know well. They are true warriors, faithful to my following and my life. You I dare not trust."

So saying he entered the hall, leaving Alnoth still on one knee, filled with despondency and a sore humiliation. After he had regained his feet and was standing, miserable and ill at ease, a serf of some lowly class came through the skin-hung doorway, handing him a hunk of mutton and a half-loaf of gritty bread. "Now be gone," the man said. "You'll get nothing more."

Gratefully Alnoth ate his meal, only wishing he had a horn of ale instead of the river water he presently moved downhill to drink. On the way, he glanced into some of the cots and was astonished to see that one had a paved floor, decorated with little coloured stones. He did not stop for a closer look for the woman of the house was staring at him in disapproval. The settlement was quite large and seemingly new-built, the roof-thatches neither wind-torn nor moss-grown. He guessed the people had been here for only a few years, shifting from another site, perhaps.

Wandering on, he eventually found a track leading steeply up a hill to the east, and this he climbed, pulling himself up by the lower branches of scrub. When he was on the very highest point he saw it was surrounded by great banks and ditches, with burial mounds in its centre. An ancient place - a place of the dead. Hurrying away, he found on the eastern side a track that was clearly much used. By the time he finally reached a heavily wooded area, night overtook him, and he sheltered between the roots of an oak. He was woken by the sound of many voices, and feared they were those of the long-dead from the hill-top, whose spirits must surely be all around. Crouching as low as he could, he waited in apprehension. His relief was great when he heard ordinary talk as the men approached. They must be robbers, hiding in the woods from justice, or outlaws who had escaped from their master's wrath. Or perhaps they had been defeated in battle and run shamefully from their lord's side, valuing safety above honour.

As he listened, he became aware that they spoke of the lord Hardulph. Straining to hear more clearly, he decided they were planning to attack the settlement near the Meon which he had so recently left. He remained hidden until they had passed, then, seeing his chance to gain the approval of the scornful lord, he crept from his hiding place. By listening always to where the men were, he gained the hill-top and ran down the farther slope, pushing through the underwood until he reached the settlement. There he checked, for he was afraid of being taken for a robber himself and slain. How could he alert the lord and his warriors without risk? He had no wish for a dagger in his back, but neither did he look to shouting his arrival as quietness was clearly necessary. The war-band could not be far behind him.

Quickly he laid down his spear, pushing it into a bush, and his knife with it. He approached the first hut with empty hands on his head. "Awake!" he called softly. "Awake! The lord Hardulph is in danger. Awake, awake!"

A man stumbled through the door-opening, thrusting his spear at Alnoth. "The lord Hardulph," Alnoth repeated. "He is in danger. Evil night-attackers approach. Take me to him quickly. I am quite unarmed."

The man grunted, fully awake now. "Go before me," he ordered. "Keep your hands on your head. And woe betide you if this is a trick."

In this manner they came to the fire-hall and he was hustled into the lord's presence at the far end, where he lay beneath sheepskins with his wife. As soon as Hardulph became aware of the intrusion he sprang up, demanding to know what was occurring. Eagerly, Alnoth explained how he had heard the plotting of evil strangers and had come here as fast as he dared. At once Hardulph called for his weapons, and for his warriors to be roused from their sleep. When they were gathered, all fully armed with swords and shields, Hardulph led them out into the darkness. For fear of knavery, Alnoth was tied with hempen rope and left in the charge of a slave.

Dawn was near to breaking when the party returned triumphant, some with bloody weapons and a few with wounds. Hardulph ordered Alnoth to be released, be given a horn of ale and allowed to rejoice noisily with the victorious warriors.

"Tomorrow," the lord declared "you shall take your oath to me. You, and two other brave youths who have proved their worth. You may join the heroes in the hall, eat at the mead-benches and fight in my shield-wall. You have done well."

Full of happiness, Alnoth awaited the ceremony and, true to his promise, Hardulph presented him with a ring and a sword amidst much feasting. His excitement increased when he heard that Hardulph was planning a return raid on the camp of the evil-doers and that he was to be included in the war-party. It seemed that before the prisoners were slain they had admitted they were South Saxons from over the eastern hill, trying to regain the tribal lands lost when Caedwalla of the West Saxons had conquered them a few years before. Two days later, when the small army had been increased to thirty by men from Exton and Corhampton who owed allegiance to Hardulph, they left the Meon valley. Having climbed the downs to the east, they went first to the settlement of Clanfield, seeking plunder. They slew as many men as was necessary, finding this easy as the land was open, having long been cleaned of scrub. Then they moved to Catherington, the mother settlement of Clanfield, Horndean and Lovedean. In all these places they left men dead, for they were South Saxons and deserved to die. Alnoth rejoiced at the thought that their cemeteries would soon be full. Driving on, in a glory of triumph, they crossed the valley, retraced their steps and slew more below Blendworth Down. They then turned south and plundered the few farms at Blendworth itself, followed by Idsworth, and came at last to Chalton.

Here Alnoth's heart nearly failed him, for this was the land of his father, Edwold. He shrank from attacking his own kin and from burning the great halls, huts and barns of his old home. Despairing, he saw that the sheep, those splendid wool-bearing beasts, pride of his father, had been herded into an enclosure for shearing and that Hardulph's men ran among them, slitting throats. This was the penalty for rising up against the lord Hardulph with plans to kill him. Rebellion had to be punished. Of his father or step-mother he saw nothing, nor any of the ceorls he had known. Thankful he was, and feeling freer in his mind he slew ferociously what animals he could, loyalty to his lord over-riding any loyalty to his kin. That was the rule of fealty, and as he had accepted the golden ring and the splendid sword from Hardulph it was to him, and to him alone, that he owed duty.

When the killing was done and the hall-plunder piled high, Hardulph gathered his band about him and joyfully distributed the mead he had found in an outbuilding. While the horn was still passing from hand to hand great shouts were heard behind them. They saw a group of men, women and even children running down the hill from where he remembered the cemetery had been. Hardulph shouted to his own men and they took up their swords and shields, ready to repel this meagre onslaught. Then they realized other men, well-armed, had run towards them from the shelter of the woods on the other side. Having been distracted by the first group, Alnoth and his companions were at a disadvantage, particularly as their sword arms were tired from the earlier fighting.

Gradually the attackers slew first one man and then another, and then with a howl of horror, Alnoth saw that Hardulph was slain. Death was now the only course open to him. To live when one's lord lay dead was the greatest dishonour possible. Warriors must die by their lord's side, body piled upon body, until all the gallant band was life-extinguished. Raising his sword above his head, Alnoth drove down on a man before him. Only as he did so did he realize he had been attacked from behind and that his own life's blood was gushing forth. His death, at least, would be honourable.

But he did not die. Regaining consciousness later, he found his wounds had been covered with cloth, tight-pulled about his chest. Moaning a little, he knew that life was still in him, while his lord lay dead. Anguish and pain filled his mind and he fainted into blessed oblivion.

When next he opened his eyes he realized he was still lying on the bloodied grass, corpses of sheep and men all about him. That he should live while his lord did not was a horror to him. He was disgraced. He would now have to die without achieving a man's highest reward - that of leaving a proud reputation for greatness and glory. He had failed.

A man's voice then instructed him to lie still. "You're sore wounded," he was told.

Alnoth turned his head and looked at the speaker. Edwold, his father, from whose home he had been banished, was kneeling beside him. Bewildered, he closed his eyes again. A beaker was held to his mouth and he drank clumsily. "Father," he said. "The lord Hardulph is dead. I must not live." Then weakness overcame him and he drifted into a strange half-world in which he felt himself being carried a short way and laid on straw in an outbuilding. There he stayed for many days tended only by his father and a small child he came to know as his half-brother, Wistan, who he had last seen as an infant in his mother's arms. In his mother's arms! That had been Lewinna - the woman whose jealousy had caused his exile! Where was she?

When he asked, Edwold explained that she had died in the last onset of the plague. "Many others died. And I did not know if you were smitten also. Son, your departing from here was an evil, and now I would make recompense. When you are well, we will shift our settlement and what animals remain to beyond Clanfield, into a valley of which I have heard. If needs be, we can exchange our treasures and gold rings for sheep and land. If the gods be willing, we shall begin again. The grassy goodness has gone out of this chalk upland and the Meon valley is rich and fertile. A small gathering of folk has settled not far from the river's spring and I am minded to join them."

Then Alnoth remembered the rows of dwellings he had seen in Hamwic, and smiled. "Let us place the cots carefully," he said, "with lanes between. We'll have everything orderly, in blocks and straight lines. I would like that."

So it was that Edwold moved his people – his family, warriors and ceorls – to a new home near the river. Their overlord, they discovered, was the great law-giving Ine, the new king of the West Saxons, and the land they held of him was royal land. It had once belonged to King Ethelwach of the South Saxons, who had held land both here and downstream to the west, but he had been killed by Caedwalla and so it had fallen to Ine. Proud were Edwold's people to be there. Even when they heard that Ine was a follower of Christ, they did not demur when requested to change their allegiance from the old gods to the new, for they hardly noticed the difference. The whole settlement submitted to baptism, standing knee-deep in the Meon, and Alnoth knew that both the monk Brioc from Wales and the minster priest from Hamwic would rejoice.

Based on:

Wessex to A.D. 1000 by Barry Cunliffe. Longmans, 1993.
(A Regional History of England.)

Anglo-Saxon England by Martin Welch. Batsford/English Heritage, 1992.

The Foundation of England, 550 - 1042 by H. P. R. Finberg. Paladin, 1977.

The Beginnings of English Society by Dorothy Whitelock. Pelican History of England, 1977.

The Coming of Christianity to Anglo-Saxon England by Henry Mayr Harting. B. T. Batsford, 1972.

Rites & Religions of the Anglo-Saxons by Gale R. Owen. David & Charles, 1981.

Oxford Dictionary of Saints by David Hugh Farmer. O.U.P., 1992.

Settlement Mobility & The 'Middle-Saxon Shift': rural settlements and settlement patterns by H. F. Hannerow. Anglo-Saxon England, XX, 1991.

Saxon and Medieval Settlement-Patterns in the region of Chalton, Hampshire, by Barry Cunliffe. Medieval Archaeology, Vol. 16, 1972.

Hamwic: Southampton's Saxon Town by Sharon Pay.
Southampton City Museums Archaeology Series, 1987.

The Meon Valley Landscape Project by Michael Hughes and Elizabeth Brooks.
Newsletter No. 4, Autumn, 1985, Hants. Field Club & Arch. Soc.

Droxford Anglo-Saxon Cemetery, Soberton by Fred Aldsworth.
Proceedings of Hants Field Club & Arch. Soc., Vol. 35, 1979.

Early Burials & an Anglo-Saxon Cemetry at Snell's Corner, Horndean by G. M. Knocker.
Proceedings of Hants. Field Club & Arch. Soc., Vol. 19, 1955.

Chapter Five

The Reeve of East Meon Hundred 967 A.D.

'M doing my best and I don't see how I can do more. Or to put things another way, law and order won't improve until I'm given an additional assistant, a better horse and more in the way of pay. It's no use them grumbling at me, for with this new charter of King Edgar's my work load has increased yet again and the Hundred is now very, very large – far too large for one man – and I feel extremely put upon.

I grant that the prestige of the job is great, and in that I feel honoured, but a man of notability, social position and some power (such as myself) should surely have more comforts and a life of greater ease than I do?

Let me tell you just how big the Hundred has become. There's the Tithing of East Meon itself, of course, and now there's the whole of Froxfield, Langrish and Steep, part of Privett, the Tithings of Westbury, Peak, Riplington, Bereleigh, Bordean, Ramsdean, parts of Stroud Common and Oxenbourne and Coombe. If that isn't too big for a single Hundred and too much for one man to manage, I don't know what is. And I certainly don't thank King Edgar for this charter he's just made in favour of the Lady Winfled. Now I have not only her property to look after in the west and north of the Hundred, (which has increased my work considerably) but that of the King's grandmother, Queen Eadgifu, who was granted land in the Hundred seven years back. With two such noble ladies having land here I feel my work is under constant scrutiny by the King's Ealdorman – and this I don't like.

It's not just the actual size of the Hundred that makes my life difficult but the numbers now living within it. People seem to have bred and prospered since they came here, and now we have a good number of households in this village alone, instead of just the few and scattered farmsteads of my great-grandfather's time. Keeping order in his day must have been easy.

The thing that really takes up my time is running the Hundred Courts. I suppose these Courts are good things, otherwise they wouldn't have started them up a few years back, but holding them once a month is a bit often, don't you think? Surely law and order isn't as urgent as all that and people used to manage perfectly well with the old Folk Moots – not those held by the Shire, you understand, but our local ones –

meeting every now and again where the preaching-cross used to be before we had our new church.

But there you are. Progress is progress, I suppose, but what with the laws of old King Ine, then those of King Alfred, King Athelstan and now King Edgar, we're all tied up with rules and regulations and a man has a hard job to know what he can do and what he can't. And everything has to be written down for Winchester now. As my clerk is ever behind with the scribing I can scarcely find my way round the lists and the summonses, the fines and appeals and judgements. It's all written work, I tell you, and nothing left to commonsense or local knowledge like it used to be. It's one of the worst things about working for Kings and Bishops – in ordinary Hundreds nobody bothers to write anything.

I will grant you this, though, and despite my dislike of laws, old King Edmund did a good job in stopping blood-feuds. All that revenge, from generation to generation – what good did it do? Just a lot of deaths, with young men killed and a multitude of women-folk weeping. I'm not saying that this new business of paying wergild is perfect but it's better than killing – and once a man's wergild (that is, his blood-price) is paid in money for his murder then that's the end of the matter. When a man knows he's going to be hit in the purse then he thinks twice about losing his temper or starting a feud. With all the penalties for crime laid down to accord with a man's wergild – so much for killing a thegn's son, so much for dishonouring a ceorl's wife, so much for cutting off a slave's forefinger on his right hand and so much for that on his left – well, folk do know where they are.

(The only fault with the wergild system that I can see is that the very rich can still afford to commit murder, but I wouldn't like to say that in public!)

It's a pity, really, that King Edmund's reign was so short, just the seven years, and it's ironic that he was murdered by an outlaw in 946 when it was he who was so against all murdering and bloodshed. A good king, Edmund was. And holy. I think it was he who started up the interest in monasteries again. It was years since the monasteries had counted for much because of the wars with the Danish Vikings. When you're fighting for your freedom against marauding pagans you don't put your sons to be monks – the bonds of loyalty to one's King, one's lord and one's kindred count for more. But since the great days of King Alfred when he halted the invaders, and Winchester became his capital, we have been at peace – the Danes now live north of here under their own Danelaw and we see little of them.

It's because of the peace, you see, that men's thoughts can now return to the Church and monasteries. I suppose King Alfred carried on in holiness where Edmund had left off – he had, after all, been taken as a boy of four to Rome by his father, King Ethelwulf, where he met the Pope. He had a good beginning, therefore, so it is not surprising that it was he who both rebuilt the Old Minster at Winchester and made plans for the New and did so much to increase learning and culture in the country – and especially among the clergy. Alfred was a good king, but I can tell you we've had some terrible ones since his day! However, all things pass and now we have Edgar who makes up for them all, despite his marital goings-on.

He has a good eye for men as well as women, has Edgar. For instance, he recalled Bishop Dunstan of Worcester from exile on the Continent and made him Archbishop of Canterbury. He made Oswald the Bishop of Worcester in Dunstan's place and now has installed that great and holy monk, Ethelwold, as Bishop of

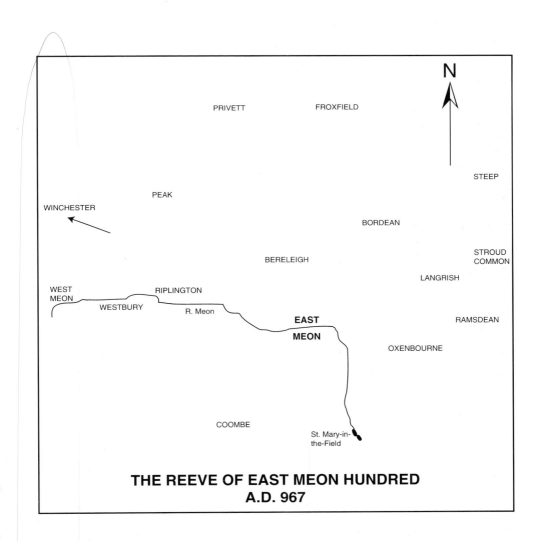

PRIVETT   FROXFIELD

N

STEEP

PEAK

WINCHESTER

BORDEAN

STROUD
COMMON

BERELEIGH

LANGRISH

WEST
MEON   RIPLINGTON

WESTBURY   R. Meon

EAST
MEON

RAMSDEAN

OXENBOURNE

COOMBE

St. Mary-in-
the-Field

**THE REEVE OF EAST MEON HUNDRED
A.D. 967**

Winchester. Even out here in East Meon we can feel the reforming zeal of those three saints, Oswald, Dunstan and Ethelwold, for our own priest, Wulfric, is much better educated than the one we had before. (That last priest was a good man, although married where Wulfric is not, but he spent more time farming his bit of glebe and tending his pigs than he did looking after the souls of his flock. He was a simple ceorl, really, with a wergild of no more than a hundred shillings, and knew very little Latin.)

I think it must have been Wulfric who stressed to Bishop Ethelwold in Winchester our need for a proper church. Years ago, it seems, the villagers had met for Mass in the open air at the preaching cross. Then a small shack was erected over the altar-stone itself to protect the Holy Eucharist from the rain, and after that the people built themselves a bit of covering, too. In this way our first ramshackle church was created, with the visiting priest from the Minster (who came to baptise people and celebrate Mass) being responsible through the Bishop for his bit of roof and the people for theirs. (This arrangement still continues, by the way.)

As you know, much land in Wessex belonged to our Kings who granted it out to nobles or churchmen or members of their families, sometimes for one man's lifetime, sometimes for his son's and even his grandson's. Sometimes the King would grant the family a new lease of a life, or lives, and sometimes he would refuse to do so and take it back into his own care. Our village has been kept much in royal hands (at one point, King Alfred gave it to his younger son, Ethelwerd, who died young) but there have been several grants to the Bishops of Winchester, so we've never been quite sure who our landlord actually is. All we know is that all our scots are paid to Winchester, but as the man who collects these taxes is a churchman, we can't be sure whether our money and goods go to the King, Bishop Ethelwold or the monks at the Minster.

They say he's a strict man, Bishop Ethelwold, and won't stand for laxity in his diocese. I heard that three years ago (in 964, that is) he became tired of the slackness of the Minster canons and marched into the Cathedral with one of King Edgar's chief men, while the priests were in choir and celebrating Mass. He then announced that because of their laxity and their married state they would either have to become celibate monks or be turned out of the their comfortable homes, and their wives and children with them. It seems they all left – protesting – and Benedictine monks from Abingdon were installed in their place and we've had monks there ever since. (It seems most bishops are monks nowadays.)

Ethelwold is strict, too, about the taxes due to him from his estates here – and they're another thing I have to grumble about, for I have to collect them in this Hundred. Getting payment out of free farmers is bad enough but out of unfree cottagers or even freed men or tenant husbandmen is terrible. There's a lot of poverty about at the moment. Sometimes I can't blame those men who give up the struggle and sell themselves into slavery to a local lord – at least then they're fed, housed and protected. We have quite a number of such slaves hereabouts. With things as they are, not all of them want to be freed and those that do are mostly young. The numbers of slaves are slowly declining, though, due to emancipation being so often granted in the wills of their owners.

But these taxes – I truly dislike their collection. Recently I've bullied the Tithingmen into helping me for they are, after all, responsible for the good behaviour of the households in their Tithing (and by whom they were elected) and I do feel the payment of dues is part of good behaviour. But it's not just the rendering of ale, barley, timber, sheep or whatever else they pay by way of rent that I'm responsible for – I have to see that the land-workers perform their week-work as ordered. It's surprising how many slow and lazy sons we have in this area! Few fathers will despatch the more energetic members of their families to do the lord's bidding, whether that lord is King or Bishop! I'd do just the same if I had a son who was a little simple and a lord's work to be done.

Tithes are the worst to collect and supervise, for so much depends on the honesty of the man concerned – I can't blame people for cheating a little on those, either, although it's commonsense that we should all go some way to supporting our parish priest and the church itself, as well as the needs of our poor. But tithes are truly resented. After all, to lose one-tenth of what we gain from our land is to lose a great deal. However, with Wulfric as our priest, and with the Bishop over him, no-one in this community escapes that tax – no-one goes scot-free – and I do feel that's right, for how else would we keep a fine scholar such as Wulfric in the new priest-house or be able to help our widows, orphans, sick or aged? If the village doesn't help its own needy, no-one else will.

There are, of course, other scots to bear, such as the soul-scot or, as some call it, the burial scot. That's offered to the clergy by a dead man's heirs to secure prayers for his soul. I'm very glad I'm not responsible for collecting that tax because half the time the family of the dead man can't pay – the harvest has failed, or the sheep have suffered the murrain, or the son has died before the father or some other tragedy has befallen them.

The King has paid Romescot to the Pope for years, of course, and I have heard that we villagers may be made to pay it, too. A penny for each household, I believe, to provide oil for lamps in the great churches of Rome, and especially St. Peter's – which is why it's known as Peter's Pence – but although I don't begrudge the oil I'm not looking forward to having to collect the pennies.

But to go back to Wulfric and our new church, we're sure he has had a lot to do with persuading the Bishop that we needed one. That first ramshackle building had become a disgrace and we're very proud of its replacement. The dedication is to St. Andrew the Apostle, so our patronal festival falls on the thirtieth of November. This is not a good date for the processions, the weather being often wet and cold, so there are plenty of running noses and hacking coughs. It's a fine church, though, built straight onto chalk on a site tucked under the hill, with a course or two of stone at the wall bases and good timbering above. We would have liked a roof of oak shingles but it seems the bishop's money didn't run to more than thatch.

Such a splendid building has made a real difference to the village. We're beginning to get weddings there, rather than in ale-houses or barns, and plenty of burials in the new churchyard. But I'm sure, though, that some of the old folk are still half-heathen in their ways for they prefer to journey to the little chapel of St. Mary-in-the-Field, near the source of the Meon, to offer up their prayers to the Holy Mother of God. (They can't be married there, though, nor buried, because field-chapels have no burial grounds.) With country folk, change doesn't come easily and I wouldn't be surprised to hear of occasional heathen offerings being made at that chapel. I don't enquire too closely, though. It's none of my business. I just go there with the rest of the village to our one big fair on the first day of August, although as like as not I'll call in to say a Hail Mary or a Pater Noster if I'm passing. That chapel's a poor place, really – no stone at all. Just timbering with wattle and a clay daub and a rather thin thatch on the roof. I doubt the building will stand for more than my lifetime and then will have to be rebuilt, for with no stone footings, wood rots in little more than forty years.

It's a good thing we have that fair because we don't have a market in the village. I can see it wouldn't be worthwhile for the King to grant a market charter – the tolls on the animals and produce coming in would be too small to give much profit. Instead, people sell what they can after Mass on Sundays outside the churchyard fence – and sometimes inside, or even right outside the church door – which our priest doesn't like but finds such trading on a Sunday difficult to stop. Still, he doesn't object too much, unless there's riotous behaviour or blood is shed.

And speaking of the church door, my daughter was wed there last Sunday. She's a good girl, so although her mother and I and all our near kindred had discussed with her the man she had chosen, we did not try to influence her against him, although he does strike us as one of the lazy sort. However, his kin are prosperous folk being free farmers, well-known to us and of high wergild. We all talked over the bride-price, or "wed" as it is called, that he pledged himself to settle on her. When we were all agreed and my daughter was happy with the arrangements, he gave her a token wed of a golden ring – which I was glad to see was of good quality metal. I was also glad to note that his kin were numerous, for thus there were many witnesses to this wedding, which could be important should the legitimacy of her offspring be challenged. I am, as I think I've said, a man of at least a little wealth and land and, being my only child, she will inherit these.

Two days after the wedding agreement we had the bridal itself, with much feasting and the usual ceremony of escorting the bride to the groom's house. The day after, when the union had been consummated, he offered her a very handsome morning-gift of a fine cloak and a carved coffer in which to keep her bed-linen. As she was pleased to accept these things we knew that she also accepted her husband, so our anxiety was allayed and all was rejoicing in the two parental households. I think the only one who was not pleased with the situation was Wulfric, for he would have liked to have given the couple the Church's blessing or even to have said a nuptial Mass for them. However, at the time he was away in Winchester to see the Bishop so we didn't bother with him. Everything is quite legal, having had so many witnesses, and I am saved the price of the Mass.

My land which, as I've said, will go eventually to my daughter, is not extensive but is of good quality. The enclosures and infields near my house are fertile, well ditched and fenced and I have several staddled granaries secure against the rats. I also have rights in the woods to the north of the village where I put my pigs in autumn. My cattle are kept on the common pastures but are brought into the stockade at night for, despite the strict laws of our kings (Athelstan, Edmund and now Edgar), cattle-lifting is still very commonplace, although the penalty is death. Of sheep, of course, I have many and these the shepherd brings off the hills at dusk and pens on the arable overnight, so that they dung the land and maintain its essential fertility. My main wealth, though, lies in the oxen, for they pull the plough, harrow and carts, provide meat for my hall and skins for leather. On this last I make a goodly profit as the wooden shields of fighting men are by a new law covered with ox-hide (sheepskin covering now being prohibited) and as this vill of East Meon has such close connections with both King Edgar and the Bishop, I have been able to obtain a worthwhile contract for hides. There are certainly advantages in being the Hundred Reeve!

There now! I must have cheered up to have said that! Only a few minutes ago I was full of resentment because my duties are so onerous. But now I'm more content. It's done me good to talk. It's made things clearer. Not, mind you, that my duties are not onerous, because they are. A heavy burden to me and I truly feel the weight of my responsibilities. I think I'm growing old before my time and would like to be given fewer tasks – not more, as with this new charter. But I am content with my lot. And being favoured by the Bishop I have little to grumble about. I just wish, though, that tomorrow wasn't the day for the Hundred Court. It looks like rain, too, so we'll have to meet in the church – it's the only building large enough to hold us all. I hope that the witnesses turn up, and especially the oath-helpers, because the village can only judge a man by the quality and number of his friends who are willing to make an oath on his honesty. (That's why it never pays to commit a crime in country where you're not known – no oath-helpers means no success, however hard you swear your innocence.)

I dare say there'll be more disputes over land and property-rights tomorrow and I really dislike those, for if a man moves his neighbour's boundary-marker even a foot or two it's very difficult for us to prove. Then I'm sure we'll have the usual complaints against drunkenness, and bawdiness in church, and watering of ale, and the taking of honey from another's beehive, and the affray that took place behind Aelfric's house when he was thrown into the river, and the non-payment of those fines we imposed last time. And so on and so on. A full day's work as you can see and very little thanks for it. Very little gratitude and no understanding of my labours on behalf of the King and the Bishop. I feel despondent again. Quite cast down. I'm a very unhappy man after all – especially as only today I had a message from Winchester saying law and order in this Hundred is not as good as it should be.

But what can I do? I'm already doing my best and I don't see how I can do more. Not unless they give me another assistant and a better horse and an improved arrangement about pay. I can't work miracles.

Based on:

A History of East Meon by F. G. Standfield. Philimore, 1984.

Rome, Britain and the Anglo-Saxons by Nicholas Higham. Seaby, 1992.

Anglo-Saxon England and the Norman Conquest by H. R. Loyn. Longman, 1991.

Unification and Conquest: A Political & Social History of England in the Tenth and Eleventh Centuries by Pauline Stafford. Edward Arnold, 1989.

The Beginnings of English Society by Dorothy Whitelock. Pelican, 1952 (Reprinted 1977).

The Formation of England, 550 – 1042 by H. P. R. Finberg. Paladin, 1976.

Anglo-Saxon England by David Brown. Bodley Head Archaeologies, 1978.

In Search of the Dark Ages by Michael Wood. Ariel Books, B.B.C., 1981.

Anglo-Saxon England by Martin Welch. Batsford/English Heritage, 1992.

Chronicle of the Royal Family editor Derrick Mercer. Chronicle Communications Ltd, 1991.

Chapter Six

Anarchy and War, 1140

HALDRED, aged twelve in this year of 1140, was employed by the Bishop's Bailiff to help his men carry heavy timbers from the carts to where alterations were being made at the Court House. And heavy those timbers were – solid oak, and all from trees that had been felled in the Meon woods belonging to Henry de Blois, Bishop of Winchester and brother of King Stephen.

Only after Stephen had taken the throne in 1135, had Bishop Henry managed to have the Manor of Meon returned to the bishopric to join his Manor of Meon Church, for it had been seized by Stephen's grandfather, William the Conqueror, and not given back. Now, with Bishop Henry not only of royal blood but also the richest and most powerful prelate in England, it stood to reason that he would want to improve his Court House in this eastern part of Hamtunshire, or 'Hantescire', as the Normans called it.

Haldred's grandfather had worked on the same grand building for Bishop Walkelin, when the Court House was new built, and he had told the boy how, during the winter months before the stone had arrived, men, women and children had been out on the land collecting flints for the walls. Great piles had been made in the yard, ready for use, and many were the sore and bleeding knuckles endured by villagers struggling to loosen flints from the often frozen soil. They had been paid, of course, for Haldred's grandfather said the Steward had been very fair, but in the cold and misery of winter the few pennies had not seemed over generous. Still, those had been the days when the Normans first held power and for Saxons life had been very insecure and even a quarter penny, cut or broken from a silver coin, could make the difference between a family eating or starving for weeks on end. When they were paid, quarrels and disputes had sometimes arisen because the breaks did not always match the quarters of the cross that was moulded on the reverse of a coin. Although some broken pieces were larger than others, it seemed nobody gained because each supposed quarter penny was weighed, and then calculated against the size of the pile of flints. The Normans were nothing if not methodical.

Haldred could also remember his father grumbling about those pennies. In the reign of Stephen's uncle, King Henry, the old way of counting five silver pennies to a shilling had been changed to twelve pennies to a shilling, and this had caused great confusion. Nobody had then known what a penny was worth or whether a new shilling would buy more goods than an old one, or fewer.

Now, with both his father and grandfather dead and no-one to speak for him, Haldred had been lucky to be taken on as a day-labourer for the carpenter working at the Court House, especially as this was paid work. Previously his time had been fully occupied with working on the family's strips of land, farming as best he and his younger brother could, when, that is, they were not required by the Bailiff or the Reeve to work on the demesne of their lord – in this case, the Bishop himself. Haldred was indeed grateful for the paid work but wished most deeply that helping to carry the heavy oak planks was not so exhausting. He was always hungry, and the one meal he had in the evening was seldom more than a sloppy mix of green vegetables and oatmeal made by his mother in the old black pot that hung above the fire. Only occasionally did he find a piece of pork floating in the gruel, and even more rarely a bit of chicken meat, so he was always in need of the lump of dark rye bread she gave him when he set off for work. The grown men working with him fared as badly, but they disguised their constant hunger by taking gulps of the barley ale they carried in earthenware pots. They could seldom afford to fetch much of even the cheapest ale from the alehouse but it was essential to do so, for without adequate liquid a labouring man could not keep going – especially in the summer – and with the River Meon constantly fouled by cattle and house-slops there was little alternative.

Haldred's mother remembered better times. Those had been when Henry, the Conqueror's youngest son, was king and his word had run the length and breadth of the land. He had been strict and quick to punish but, with the peace that he brought, it was said that a woman and child could walk the length of England and not be molested, so great was men's fear of the King's anger. Punishments were harsh – hands and feet could be lopped off, as were the sexual organs of an offender, such as a rapist or a cheating moneyer, but people learned to obey the King's ruling and peace came to the country. No wonder they called him the 'Lion of Justice'. She said, too, that for years the weather had been much better than now – no excessive heat or cold and an adequate amount of rain. A just reward, she considered, for a just king and an obedient people. Food had been plentiful in those days and people had eaten well and even had meat perhaps twice a week. The summers had been so good that the Bishop's Steward had begun to experiment with growing vines at the Court House, for the Normans were a fastidious and wine-drinking people, despising rough Saxon manners and their huge consumption of ale.

But now King Henry was dead and, with Stephen having seized the throne (largely due to the backing of his powerful brother, the Bishop of Winchester), life had changed and war erupted. Nobody in the village understood this war although they did hear it was between Stephen and his cousin, Matilda, the late King Henry's daughter, widow of the German Emperor. Furious at being denied what she saw as her right to the English throne, she had landed with her forces on the south coast in late September, 1139, determined to claim it back.

News began to reach the village of armies clashing in battle and of soldiers burning villages and stealing livestock; of farming disrupted and trade reduced. Word came that even the Bishop had felt it wise to fortify his Palace of Wolvesey in Winchester, for he was siding with his brother, Stephen, despite their both having vowed years earlier to put Matilda on the throne when her father died. Most of the magnates and powerful men had taken that same vow to make her queen, although many had been reluctant to see a woman as monarch. The tragedy was that young Prince William, King Henry's heir, had been drowned when his White Ship foundered in 1120, leaving only the girl to succeed her father. The war was thus essentially a family squabble but, with both Stephen and his brother having broken their vows to the old King, people were apprehensive. Perjury was a grave sin: vows made before God must be kept.

"This is a bad, bad time," one of the carpenters remarked, pausing in his work on the Court House. "Can't tell where it'll end." He was named Robert, in the Norman fashion, even though he was a Saxon. "Fighting's no good for anyone. Certainly not for the likes of us. When rich men and prelates are jostling for advantage and taking bribes to change sides, then justice is of no account."

"But will the fighting come this way?" Haldred asked with a touch of eagerness.

"I pray the Heavenly Father it won't", the older man replied. "My wife and children are in Winchester and I fear for them. Already King Stephen's writ is ignored and bad men do what they will. He's well enough liked but he hasn't the makings of a real king. Not strong enough, see. Gives way to people too much and forgives their bad behaviour with a laugh. He's a good soldier, mind," Robert went on, "and brave with it, but there's no strength to his ruling. So look what we've got – barons all at odds with each other, trying to gain advantage, and nobody's word to be trusted. And now war."

The boy did not feel it wise to say he was excited by the war. Grown men were fearful for their homes and livelihoods, while he wanted to see the fighting. He decided, therefore, to speak to the old tally-man who kept count of the work the men had done, for he had once been a soldier and would surely understand. But, instead, Haldred was rebuked.

"Don't you go for soldiering," he was told. "Soldiering is terrible. I went on a Crusade when I was barely your age and look at me now – one arm withered where a sword bit into it and one leg crooked where my lord's horse kicked me as it died. No, don't you go a-soldiering. Not unless you're ordered to, like I was, being in France with my lord as horse-boy. He was caught up with the Pope's calling for a Crusade, to get back the Holy Land from them infidels. Took us three long years to get out there and then win back Jerusalem and Antioch. In the summer of 1099 that was, for we'd left after harvest the three years back." The old man closed his eyes. "Terrible, it was. We won the Holy City for the Pope, but the cruelties, the massacres – you've no idea, boy. We Christians were without mercy when we were in those Jerusalem streets. Blood lust, it was." He paused again. "And the heat! It was July, see, and we wasn't used to heat like that, coming from France and Germany as most of us did. Those men in full armour near enough cooked in it, the metal got so hot. Some of the knights who was wearing helmets went mad. Others fainted clean away and the Turks beheaded them where they lay. No, don't you go a-soldiering, boy. Leastwise, not in hot countries. Not in our kind of armour."

Haldred wanted to ask about the war-horses and the mules and whether they had also suffered in the heat, but the tally-man had shut his eyes again and the boy did not like to disturb him.

"But there'll be another Crusade soon! Mark my words!" The old eyes had opened suddenly and stared at Haldred with ferocity. "Them infidels is on the march again I've heard, and I can't see no Pope letting Holy Jerusalem go back to them Muslims. There'll be war again!"

As abruptly as he had opened them, the old man closed his eyes once more and Haldred left his side to find Robert. He would go on a Crusade, he thought, despite the tally-man's warning. He would save the Holy Land for Christendom and win the special blessing of the Pope! Glory would be his! Filled with excitement he returned to his work and forgot the ache in his shoulders and the blisters on his hands.

"What are you smirking at, then?" Robert asked.

"I'll go on the next Crusade," Haldred answered happily. "The tally-man says there'll be one soon."

"Go?" Robert snapped. "That you won't! Let the rich ones go on those – they can afford to lay out the money and leave their families and estates behind. The likes of us is better here. If you want to save your soul, then be a lay-brother in a monastery. No crusading for you!"

Disappointed, Haldred continued his work in silence. It had not been his soul he had been concerned about, only the chance for adventure. Determined not to give up, he later found himself alongside Edwin, a big, bony woodworker, and asked him about being a soldier.

"Ay," Edwin replied, straightening up and easing his back. "I've thought about being one, too. It seems the barons are hiring extra men now for money-wages, instead of just using their villeins as fighting men. But it's not a life I'd take to willingly – only if I had to." Then he smiled. "But there's other ways to go travelling to them foreign parts, you know."

"Oh, what ways?" Haldred asked.

"Well, you could be a pilgrim to Rome. Or Compestella in Spain. Or Walsingham – only that's in England, like the shrine of Holy Swithun in Winchester. All sorts of people are being pilgrims nowadays". He rubbed the back of his head with a rough hand. "Times may be full of cruelty, what with Stephen and the Empress fighting, but we still like holiness, you know. I've heard there's a wonderful Bible written out by the monks in Winchester and Bishop Henry's having a Psalter made. All bright colours and little pictures, as I've heard. And there's his new Hospital of St. Cross for old and sick folk. Oh, yes! We're still keen on holiness and good works!"

Edwin bent to his work again. "This badness and war will pass, you'll see." Then he paused. "But travel and holiness together? Now I come to think of it, I've heard tell of a new lot of monks – soldier-monks, they are – who go to the Holy Land to protect pilgrims on their weary ways to Jerusalem. The Pope's favoured them no end with special rights and dues. They don't even have to pay church-scot! No tithes, no taxes, no nothing! Scot-free, they are. His special soldiers, see." Then he smiled. "You could join them, boy! Travel as well as be holy, like I said! I've heard them called the Knights Templar – but that seems a silly name to me. Some of your local knights might have joined them but I'm not from these parts, so I don't know. Ask someone else."

So he did, and there were no Knights Templar in the locality, but he did discover that certain lands in the village owned by the Bishop had been set aside by him to provide an income which went to the Templars. 'Temple lands', they were called. There was another lot of soldier-monks, he then heard, also not long since founded, and called 'The Knights of St. John'. Most people knew them as the 'Hospitallers' as they provided hostels and care for poor and weary pilgrims. Sadly, Haldred realised that both groups were of the knightly class, and that if he joined either it could only be in a humble capacity and as some kind of menial. This was not at all what he had in mind.

Then luck changed for him. Edwin, the woodworker, was sent to finish building the new latrine block on the north side of the Bishop's Wolvesey Palace, and he asked for Haldred to go with him as labourer. The boy was delighted and even his mother was pleased, for this was a step in the direction of better things and the move boded well for the future. All Edwin's woodworking tools were placed in a rough handcart which Haldred then pushed or pulled the fifteen or so miles to Winchester. When finally they crossed the Town Bridge over the River Itchen and through the East Gate, the Palace was immediately visible to their left. Haldred had never seen such a vast building and was greatly awed. For lodgings they built a shack near their work place but ate their dinners at the Bishop's expense in the West Hall. Edwin fed at one of the trestles while Haldred had to make do with a benchless table along the wall, where he shared a mess with three other young workers. He was annoyed to find they would often take more than their share of the helping which was handed to them on a square of coarse black bread. With mess-mates not only older but greedy, Haldred often went hungry and envied the senior workers and officials whose mess had only to be divided among three or, for the truly important, two. (The very senior men of the Bishop's household had a mess each and often left part of it uneaten, and this would be passed to those lower down the social scale or set aside for the poor.)

The Palace never ceased to amaze Haldred: it was so vast. There were two Halls now, for Bishop Henry had built a new East Hall, which was not only for eating and sleeping in, but for ceremonials and great meetings. Since he had been made Papal Legate in 1139 he had needed a larger space to hold his Legative Councils. The huge, older West Hall held a number of chambers, including the private rooms of the Bishop, and so it was that Haldred occasionally caught sight of the great man as he came or went, surrounded by his entourage of churchmen and foreign dignitaries. So far King Stephen had not been seen and it was rumoured that the Bishop was now on bad terms with his brother.

"The Bishop didn't get the job he wanted, that's why," a stonemason explained. "When the old Archbishop of Canterbury died our Henry thought he'd be made the next one, but Stephen said no. I don't blame him, either – an Archbishop, such as Henry de Blois, would have had too much power and Stephen wouldn't stand a chance against him. The Pope gave the job to Theobald of Bec instead, but the joke is that Bishop Henry was later made the Pope's Legate and so is now Theobald's superior!"

"It may be a joke," another man broke in, "but it was a bad mistake of Stephen's. Bishop Henry has changed sides in the war and is now backing the Empress to take the throne."

"That's not the only mistake Stephen's made," another added. "Look at the way he's treated the Bishop of Salisbury! And Salisbury's nephew, who's Bishop of Lincoln, and the other nephew who's Bishop of Ely. Shut them all up in prison! Fancy laying sacrilegious hands on anointed bishops! I don't wonder Bishop Henry changed sides. You can't trust a King who does that. Besides, those three just about ran the country, what with Salisbury being Chancellor and all. I don't know what sort of mess we'll be in without them. They were the real rulers".

Haldred listened entranced, revelling in this new life and the feeling that he was part of great affairs. Winchester was so large and had so many people he thought he would never go back to the little village beside the Meon. All he wanted now was to join the fighting and to see the King. However, he knew this was unlikely as Stephen was attacking the Empress largely in the Midlands and so was many miles away. Stories did come back to Winchester, though, and terrible they were. Tales of house burning and plunder, brutality and rape, cattle-stealing and the destruction of corn-mills, farms and hay-ricks. Poverty and misery were said to be everywhere and the common people suffered appallingly and without respite. It seemed that the barons were running wild and acting without the approval of either King or Empress.

One servant of the Bishop who had been on business for him in Stamford, had seen the devastation wrought in the countryside and described it on his return to Wolvesey. "There's so many castles now," he declared, "and few of them legal. It's every baron for himself and no matter whose side he's on. Those castle-men are wicked devils and cruel beyond telling. Brutality seems second nature to some Normans. I tell you, innocent people are put in prison and tortured until they give up their gold and silver. Hung up by their thumbs, they are, or by their necks, with their mail shirts hanging from their feet to give extra weight and pain. Or knotted ropes are tied round their heads and twisted until the skull cracks and the brain's damaged. Or they get thrown into dungeons with adders, to be killed like that. And I've heard some are squashed into small, narrow chests with sharp stones on the bottom. Then the lid's pressed down so all their limbs are broken on the flints and their flesh gashed to pieces."

The man rubbed his eyes in weariness. "Oh, I've seen terrible things, I tell you. And it's not just the torture. They levy private taxes on villagers, and when the wretched people have no more to give they just burn down their houses. I've been riding for a whole day – twenty or thirty miles – and never found a village with people in it. Just charred remains and dead bodies. And the stench!" He shuddered, and went on, "And the land's not tilled. No one left to work it. Corn too expensive to buy and meat stolen for the armies. No eggs, no butter, no cheese. Nothing. A few do escape the massacres, of course, but they just die of starvation. All along the roadsides, they are. Where they fell. I tell you, the heathen Danes of long ago did not do worse when they invaded, for these men hold no respect even for church or churchyard. They just steal the crosses and the candlesticks from the altars and then burn the buildings down. No respect for anyone's land, either. Not a bishop's, nor an abbot's, nor a priest's. For all that the churchmen keep excommunicating them, they pay no heed. They're utterly accursed and I tell you this, Christ and His Saints are asleep and no longer come to our aid. We're all accursed, I tell you. Damned for our sins."

Then news came to Wolvesey of a fierce battle at Lincoln, fought in the mud and cold of February, 1141. The King had shown great personal bravery, but was struck down by a stone and captured. This loss of the battle at Lincoln was the turning point for Stephen as his army and his party now collapsed and, even in his lands in Normandy, the nobles were restless and threatening to surrender to Geoffrey of Anjou, the second husband of Empress Matilda. Taken to Bristol, Stephen was put in chains in the castle of Robert, Earl of Gloucester, the illegitimate son of the late King Henry. He was half-brother to Matilda and her greatest and most competent supporter. He even had lands at Mapledurham, a few miles from the Meon.

At Wolvesey everyone expected the Empress in Winchester, to be followed by a declaration that she was now Queen and Stephen deposed. And come to Winchester she did, on the third day of March, 1141. She was given the King's crown, his castle and the royal treasure that was kept there. Then she was escorted into the cathedral by Bishop Henry, who called her 'The Lady of England', which was her correct title

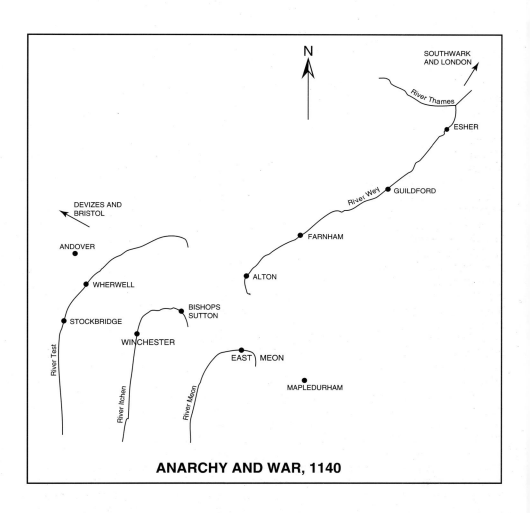

N

SOUTHWARK
AND LONDON

River Thames

ESHER

River Wey   GUILDFORD

DEVIZES AND
BRISTOL

FARNHAM

ANDOVER

ALTON

WHERWELL

BISHOPS
SUTTON

STOCKBRIDGE

WINCHESTER

EAST   MEON

MAPLEDURHAM

River Test

River Itchen

River Meon

ANARCHY AND WAR, 1140

until the coronation and annointing in Westminster. But, having achieved her aim of being recognized as the lawful monarch of England, she then revealed her true nature, becoming overbearingly supercilious and arrogant, upsetting all about her, including the Bishop. Much muttering could be heard, especially about the fact that her new husband, Geoffrey of Anjou, was an Angevin and thus a direct enemy of the Normans, and nobody wanted him to share the throne as consort. To Haldred and Edwin, both of Saxon stock, such niceties meant little, but what did astonish the boy was that when the two had been betrothed Geoffrey had been only fourteen years of age while Matilda was already twenty-four.

When spring came and the roads were drier it was decided the time had come to proceed to London for the coronation of the Empress, for that must take place at Westminster and before the people of London. On a fine sunny day Haldred was crossing the Inner Courtyard when a voice hailed him. "Here, you! If you're the carpenter's boy fetch some timbers – we've a fractured shaft on one of the Bishop's baggage carts. Get it mended."

Haldred hurried outside to where the cavalcade was assembling to see what was needed and found that a shaft had indeed splintered, although it was not broken through. "I'll get the wood," he said and dashed off, feeling immeasurably important for no such job had come his way before. As there was no time to replace the damaged piece, he laid lengths of wood on either side of it and bound all three together with strong hempen twine.

"That won't last!" the carter remarked scornfully. "It'll break at the first pot-hole."

"It won't! It won't!" retorted Haldred. "Look! I've plenty more twine and any hedge-bough will do as a splint."

"Then you'd best come with us, boy. Can't afford to hold up the Bishop."

Dashing back to Edwin, Haldred explained the situation and, gathering up an assortment of tools, ran back to the cart.

Slowly the long procession, headed by the mounted clerics and Empress Matilda, wound its way over the Town Bridge, up the hill and along the road to the Bishop's estate of Sutton. There they paused to spend the night before travelling on to Farnham, then on again to Esher, and finally to Southwark on the south side of the River Thames, which was the London residence of the Bishops of Winchester. With such a large and creaking baggage train, it was not customary to travel more than fifteen or twenty miles a day, and it was for that reason the Bishop had residences conveniently spaced along the route. Throughout the journey Haldred had walked beside the cart, only occasionally having to renew his repairs, and was filled with delight by all he saw. When they reached the wide Thames he was afraid, used as he was to the little Meon river and the gentle Itchen, but as the days went by he lost his amazement and, having few tasks given to him, was able to explore the muddy river banks and the strange phenomenon of tides.

It seemed that there was some delay about the Empress entering London, and Haldred learnt that negotiations with the citizens were not going well, for many still supported Stephen. However, on 24th June, 1141, she was allowed into the City but there repeated the disastrous mistakes of Winchester. Her discourtesies were said to be unbelievable – she was intolerably haughty and rude to the citizens, crudely demanding very large sums of money from them, seemingly acting from sheer pride, wilfulness and obstinacy so that even her own followers were ashamed. It was then that Stephen's queen, the other Matilda, who was in Kent and hoping for a chance to release her husband from prison, sent her army to ravage the districts round London. Haldred heard that in many outlying villages few houses were left standing. Londoners now faced a choice between the supercilious Empress and Stephen's loyal and courageous Queen. They chose the Queen, and so on that same day bells were rung to bring hostile Londoners swarming out to attack the Empress at Westminster, for they refused to see her consecrated as Queen. The Empress, however, had wisely abandoned her coronation banquet, and had fled to her castle in Oxford.

Haldred, in a lowly position though he was, again became aware of muttered conversations and faces filled with consternation. Bishop Henry was now in a difficult position for, with Stephen still in the Bristol castle of Earl Robert, and Empress Matilda scorned by the all-important London citizens, he had no real candidate for the crown. Disconcerted and now obviously regretting abandoning his brother, the Bishop and his party returned to Winchester.

The Wolvesey latrines were now finished and Edwin had been moved to repairing the woodwork of the four well-houses that lay within the Palace precincts, so Haldred worked alongside him there. Then word came that the Empress had arrived unexpectedly in Winchester and was occupying the royal Castle on the west hill. From there she had sent an imperious demand for the Bishop to attend her but he, with only a small group of horsemen, secretly fled. His allegiance was now openly given back to Stephen. His Palace of Wolvesey, however, he left well garrisoned with soldiers loyal to him. Other men were sent to occupy the site of the old royal palace of William the Conqueror which stood in the city centre, and especially the strong tower, for this gave a commanding view westwards to the Castle. Haldred was very excited by all this activity but when troops of the Empress laid siege to Wolvesey, life became considerably more dangerous. He was now very glad of the moat that lay on three sides of the huge area of the Bishop's residence and of the great curtain wall on the south side that had only recently been completed.

Earl Robert of Gloucester, half-brother to the Empress, was in charge of her troops and much feared by the Bishop's men, for he was a gallant fighter. Then they heard that the Bishop had beseeched Stephen's Queen for help and that her army, consisting mainly of Londoners, had arrived. Fighting within the City of Winchester now became ferocious and men fought, hand-to-hand, up and down the streets. The Empress held not only the Castle but the north end of the High Street, where many of Winchester's leading citizens lived, and many of these houses were burnt to the ground. In other streets, too, houses were ransacked, the occupants killed and goods stolen – sometimes by one army and sometimes by the other – and before the soldiers left they would put the wooden buildings to the torch, filling everywhere with billowing smoke, crashing timbers and great confusion. From the Conqueror's strong tower the Bishop's men were able to lob fireballs over the Castle walls, causing more fire, death and destruction to the forces of the Empress. Even the recently built Hyde Abbey, outside the City walls, was completely sacked and it was said that the Abbey's great wooden cross, reputedly given to Winchester by King Canute in the early eleventh century, was burnt to cinders and the monks were left sifting through the ash and charred remains for the gold and silver with which it had been adorned.

As well as Hyde, St. Mary's Abbey, near the river and known as Nunnaminster, went up in flames and the nuns were left frightened and homeless. Although the Cathedral and St. Swithun's Priory were left unscathed on the orders of Earl Robert, it was said that twenty churches had been destroyed as well as the two abbeys and countless houses. After seven weeks of fighting in the City most of its inhabitants were left destitute and homeless and could be seen flocking to the countryside to escape the flames and misery. But even there security was not assured, for Haldred heard to his alarm that the Queen's army was already in control of all the roads from the east that led to Winchester, and he feared for his home in East Meon. It seemed that her soldiers had been instructed to lay waste all crops and villages that surrounded Winchester, for by this means the Empress would be truly cut off from help.

Indeed, with the supply routes from her more northern castles also under threat, the Empress was in a dire situation. Even her small garrison at the great Nunnery at Wherwell was surprised by the Queen's men and most were killed, while those remaining took refuge in the Nunnery church and did their best to fortify it. Only when firebrands were thrown in on them and the building caught fire were they forced to surrender. The Queen's soldiers then rampaged in full armour all through the church, killing, maiming and dragging half-burnt prisoners along the floor by their clothing. The nuns, too, were driven by fire from their cloister and were seen running about in fear of their lives, not knowing in which direction their safety lay.

After Wherwell was sacked, the Queen's army went further north to Andover and sacked that too, so that no supplies or reinforcements could get through from the direction of Gloucester or Bristol, which were the main centres for the Empress' army. Still in Winchester Castle, but with support for her cause waning, food and water supplies running short and her army's retreat cut off, the Empress herself managed to escape. She left on Sunday, 14 September, in that troubled year of 1141, and many were the stories about the manner of her going, one being that she had been taken from the Castle in a coffin by her heavily disguised supporters. What did become clear was that her carefully planned escape turned into a rout, for the Queen's men attacked her fleeing party with such violence and in such great numbers that they had to scatter in total disarray.

Some of the soldiers who had joined in that attack later returned to Wolvesey Palace and recounted how they had seen knights fleeing in every direction, throwing off their coats of mail, flinging their shields and arms behind them, anything to lighten the burden on their horses to enable them to gallop faster. It was total chaos and the Queen's soldiers rode after them and struck them down.

"What a sight!" one of these men exclaimed to an admiring group at Wolvesey. "There were riderless horses galloping loose all over the place. Others lay gasping to their deaths on the ground while their riders tried to escape on foot. Some of these hid, but we soon discovered them and plunged our daggers in. The ground – well, it was strewn with shields, fine wool coats and all kinds of weapons. And costly robes and gold and silver cups and priceless ornaments – you've no idea what it looked like! Covered, it was! Some of the nobles we'd captured bribed us to let them go free – so we did, but killed them just the same, half a mile on. Oh, it was something I doubt I'll see again! A great, great day it was. And on the way back here, we was all picking up what we could and laughing. We all got rich, see, for a man with a horse and armour and a weapon is all at once well up in the world. Felt like knights, we did!"

"But what happened to the Empress?" someone asked.

"Oh, she escaped! Jumped on a horse, hitched up her skirts and rode astride in the male fashion, galloping at full speed in the direction of Devizes. But we caught Robert, Earl of Gloucester! He'd protected his sister's escape by hanging back to ward us off, but some Flemish mercenaries of the Queen's caught him at the ford on the

River Test at Stockbridge. A fine catch he is, I can tell you! Locked up in prison now. Puts an end to the war, I shouldn't wonder."

Now that it was safe to leave Wolvesey Palace, Haldred and Edwin went carefully into the still smouldering city and were deeply shocked by what they saw. It was not just the ruinous houses that upset them but the bodies of their occupants, still lying sprawled and bloody and now fly-covered where they had fallen, for this was September and the weather warm. The stench in the streets was almost unbearable for no-one had been able to bury the dead. A few dogs were roaming the area, tearing at rotting flesh, and rats had seemingly multiplied beyond counting.

"I'm going home," Haldred declared suddenly. "I can't stand this. I'm going home, with or without my pay."

So he went. Walking up Magdalen Hill he breathed the fresh air and was thankful. As he went, he passed pathetic groups of people creeping back to the city to see if anything was left of their homes. He saw others sitting abjectly by the roadside, too exhausted to go further, and others desperately begging food from all and sundry. He saw a women giving birth in a ditch and an old man dying as he sank to the ground. He saw all these things but he closed his mind to them and strode on. All he could think of was his need to reach home and the safety of his village. He had done with the wider world.

The war and the anarchy did not end, however. There were reports of continued fighting, for the imprisoned King Stephen had been exchanged for the captured Earl Robert, and both were once again leading their armies. Stephen had been taken to Westminster, though, and had been recrowned King in the Abbey by the Archbishop of Canterbury on Christmas Day, 1141. During the last few months he had been defeated, captured, deposed, then freed and restored to power, and was still having to fight the Empress and her army.

Mercifully for Hampshire, most of the battles were now away to the north, in the regions of Oxford, Cirencester, Bath, Nottingham, Peterborough and York. Inevitably the two main armies lived off the land and great famine ensued, for plough-oxen were slaughtered by soldiers, seed-corn taken to feed their horses and there were few men left to harvest what crops there were. Those who were homeless built themselves rough shacks in the churchyards, hoping that this would give them safety, but they were reduced to eating the forbidden flesh of dogs and horses or, in desperate hunger, raw weeds from the hedgerows and the grubbed up roots from abandoned crofts of the long-gone villagers. The situation became so bad that the Bishop held a council as Papal Legate in London in 1142, in the presence of King Stephen. There it was resolved that ploughmen and ploughs should, during the war, be held as sacred as clergy and churches, and a solemn excommunication announced upon all who should attack or injure those occupied in agriculture, for they were esteemed to be in sanctuary in their fields as if in church.

Occasionally news came of peace negotiations between Stephen and the Empress but as they always failed, the war continued. When the Second Crusade was finally preached in 1146 many knights and nobles thankfully 'took the Cross' and went to the Holy Land, for at least there they would see right from wrong and know who was their true enemy. However, in England in that year there was a very severe winter that kept the armies largely immobilised. The emphasis then changed from simply defeating the opposing army to the matter of the future succession to the throne. Stephen had one son, Eustace, while the Empress and her second husband, Duke Geoffrey of Anjou (known as 'Plantagenet') had Henry, now aged fourteen.

When Earl Robert died at the end of October, 1147, the Empress lost all hope of winning the throne for herself and she left England for good, retiring to Normandy, while leaving the young Henry to fight on. Small items of news came through, such as that Stephen and the whole of the Kingdom had been laid under an Interdict by the Pope. Even Richard, who was the parish priest, could not tell what this meant. People were more interested in rebuilding their lives than in following the doings of popes, kings and magnates. They were, however, truly sad to hear in May, 1152, of the death of the Queen, faithful and courageous wife of Stephen, and even more so when they heard of the death a year later of Eustace, his eldest son and heir. Not long after this double loss Stephen finally agreed to negotiate peace and on the sixth of November, 1153, terms were agreed between him and the young Duke Henry Plantagenet in a document known as the Treaty of Winchester. This stipulated that Stephen was to remain king for his lifetime but that Duke Henry should take the throne after him. When Stephen died in October, 1154, the young King Henry the Second, began his rule. The Bishop of Winchester, the lord of all the Meon lands, felt it expedient to flee to the monastery of Cluny in France where he had first become a monk, for he had openly supported Stephen, the new King's enemy. His rich lands in the Meon valley and other places were confiscated by the King during the exile and these, once more, came under royal jurisdiction. When his short exile was over he returned to his old position as Bishop and a leader in both church and state affairs, remaining powerful and rich until his death in 1171, although the King continued to hold the lands of Meon Manor.

By that time the new church of All Saints had long been built in the village and Haldred, the woodworker, had been employed to help with its construction. With the building of something so fine and re-assuring, religious faith seemed stable once more, for peace lay over the country and men prospered. Haldred certainly did, becoming a carpenter of much skill. Not that he totally approved of the Norman way of building only in stone, nor of the design of the new church for it had a square East end, rather than a rounded apse in the Saxon style. The villagers were also reluctant to accept this new design, especially as the old way of having a single candle at one end of the altar and a cross at the other (which left a clear view of the priest standing behind it to deliver the blessing) also became changed. Now two candlesticks and a cross were used, the priest standing in front of the altar. Nor were they accustomed to seeing the elevation of both the host and the chalice during the Consecration, and they resented having no north door to the new church. Always, at a baptism, that door had stood open, for when the baby cried the Devil left it and fled through the opening into his own dark, damp northern part of the churchyard, and the door was slammed, barred and bolted after him. Nobody could understand why the old ways were abandoned. Change for change's sake, was the general opinion.

Even so, all agreed it was a fine church, built by the Bishop as an offering to God, and they marvelled at the new font of Tournai marble. The flints, as always, came from the fields but the high quality of the stone was much appreciated. Some of it was brought from Quarr on the Isle of Wight, which had the best quarries, while the rougher stones in the tower, doorways and the nave crossing were from the Langrish quarry or from Stodham, a few miles away. Richard was no longer the Presbyter of the church, for he had died, and in his place was a young priest named Roger. He was seldom in the village because the new King, who still had the governance of the Meon lands, had appointed him so that he could be used on royal business. This was especially so at the consecration by the elderly, Henry de Blois of Thomas à Becket, the King's Chancellor, as Archbishop of Canterbury in June, 1162. The church and the parish of East Meon were then served by a curate, who was badly paid and not well educated.

Haldred had married long before that time and now had four children, the eldest of whom was working as a scullion in the Court House and hoping to be apprenticed as a cook. The second son, Peter, was following his father's trade and working in wood. Haldred was amused to find that the boy was hoping for another Crusade so that he might fight in the Holy Land. East Meon was, after all, a quiet little village and held few excitements for a boy.

Based on:

The Reign of Stephen : Anarchy in England 1135 – 54 by H. A. Cronne. Weidenfeld, 1970.

King Stephen by R.H.C. Davis. Longman, 1990.

Empress Matilda by Nesta Pain. Weidenfeld & Nicholson, 1978.

Henry of Blois, Bishop of Winchester: A Patron of the Twelfth-Century Renaissance by Nicholas Riall. Hampshire Papers, No. 5, H.C.C., 1994,

Wolvesey by Martin Biddle. English Heritage, 1986.

The Twelfth Century Renaissance by Christopher Brooke. Thames & Hudson, 1969.

The Norman Kings by James Chambers. Weidenfeld & Nicholson, 1981.

Anglo-Norman England, 1066 – 1166 by Marjorie Chibnall. Blackwell, 1987.

The Chartulary of Winchester Cathedral by A. W. Goodman. Warren & Sons, 1927.

Unpublished notes by Tim Tatton-Brown passed by Edward Roberts, December, 1993.

The Knights Templar by Stephen Howarth. Collins, 1982.

Chapter Seven

The Occasional Chronicle of Justin, Priest of East Meon, 1191-1207

From Godolphin, Curate of East Meon.
Father Justin is now permanently in Winchester with the Bishop and I have joined Father Simon here as second curate. The 'Chronicle' was left by Father Justin for our interest and information, and we have preserved it with great care.

April, 1191
Great feasting in Court House. Prince John, Count of Mortaine, paid visit on way to estates at Mapledurham, east of here. Travelled with wife Isabel and large party. Couple were married two years ago at John's castle at Marlborough in Wiltshire. Isabel is daughter of William, Earl of Gloucester, and Countess Hawissa who owned Mapledurham estates. (Earl William is son of Earl Robert of Gloucester, half-brother to Empress Matilda and her chief supporter in war against Stephen.)

Mapledurham is extensive estate. Once belonged to William the Conqueror. Includes Weston, Nursted, Sheet and Buriton (which has parish church). When these lands come to Prince John through his wife, will add greatly to his land holdings. Old nickname of 'Lackland' will no longer apply.

Prince John affable and friendly during his visit here. His marriage of great interest locally as Mapledurham so close, especially as Earl William recently founded new Market Town in small settlement of Petersfield. Will provide outlet for our farm produce as well as attracting merchants and craftsmen. (*Note*: Archbishop Baldwin very distressed by John's marriage as couple second cousins. Forbade them to co-habit owing to rules of consanguinity. So far no offspring. Not surprising.)

Wish that Richard, Duke of Aquitaine and now King of England, would produce heir. Is dashing and popular knight, keen on Crusades, but is seldom in England. Is taller and more striking than brother John – more like their father, Henry II. Although John sturdy and well-built. Hope he comes here again. Rich eating on last visit.

June, 1191
Am becoming increasingly tired of cases brought against Peter of Le Strood. Has shaved his head to a tonsure and insists he is a priest. All know is not. But in crisis, if neither myself nor curate is available people ask him to administer last rites to dying or to perform marriage. At most he was an acolyte when lived in Reading. Even when brought before me at Bishop's Court and been punished with increasing fines, he returns to criminous activities and personal attacks against me. My house door has several times been smeared with foul and stinking mess. Can't prove he did it. Have heard his own house now broken into and all his chattels thrown out. Probably done by brother of girl for whom he recently performed 'marriage' ceremony. She now deflowered and worth less, so father cannot find good suitor. Sent for young couple. Remarried them without fee. Hope next time Peter Le Strood gets his head broken. Tired of him in court.

Late Spring, 1193
King Richard in captivity while returning from Third Crusade. Huge ransom to be raised. Can't see how.

April, 1194
King back in England after captivity. Been away so much is to have another but smaller coronation ceremony in Winchester. His mother, Queen Eleanor of Aquitaine, to attend.

May, 1196
Pestilence and famine throughout England. Hot weather continuing. Unseasonal. Very unhealthy. Said that a hot May makes for fat churchyard. (Memo: Visit Daw family. Old man ailing, others sickly.) Little grass in fields. Sheep, lambs suffering. Oxen hungry and lean. Losing strength. Very serious. No Spring-bite to grass. Few men truly fit to work. Already river nearly dry.

27 May, 1199
John crowned King in Westminster Abbey, Richard being dead. Queen Isabel not beside him. Rumours that he wants to divorce her. Ten years of marriage – no heir. King to ask Church for advice. Almost certain decision to declare John a single man owing to second cousinship. Is thought he'll look to Portugal for bride while overseas.

16 August, 1199
Very hot. Manor Court held outside. Bishop's Steward, Bailiff, Parish Clerk and I sat at long table in shade. Plaintiffs, defendants and witnesses all glad to come to us out of sun to swear their oaths on the Gospel Book.

Geoffrey atte Ford very plausible rogue. Undoubtedly stole six chickens from Alys, wife of Robert, but as had more witnesses than Alys, all swearing his innocence, case dismissed. Can only hope the buying of witnesses cost him dear. Other cases of usual kind. Had no need to refer any to one of King's Courts. By end, sun had moved and jury was in full blaze. Several nodded off. Clerk wrote slower and slower. Don't imagine cases very accurately described. Besides, ink kept drying on quill and parchment rolled up in heat. Glad to go indoors and find goblet of wine.

26 December, 1199
Good news – Christmas gift. King John returned Manors of East Meon and Hambledon to bishopric of Winchester and the cathedral church of Saints Peter, Paul and Swithun. Had been in royal hands since Henry II. (The other manor, of East Meon Church, has always remained with Bishop.)

4 May, 1200
Watched wonderful commotion in village. Emma, wife of Leofric, fell in river. Was chasing hen she wanted to kill. Hen, clucking loudly, flew over water. Emma tripped, slid down mud bank into river. When had clambered out, hen seen to have gone into Stephen's house. Went after it. No sign. (Suspect Stephen rung its neck and at once buried it in dungheap.) Emma picked up neighbour's hay-rake. Railed against Stephen and beat him with rake. Head of rake flew off and Stephen threw it into river. Emma, wailing and shrieking, followed stream to retrieve rake-head. Cheers from villagers, all now gathered round to watch. Rake-head recovered and banged onto shaft. Good as new. Just as well, otherwise her husband would have beaten Emma in her turn, for damage to a neighbour's property serious crime. Hen never seen again, despite close watch for feathers and smell of chicken in stew-pot. Good amusement for all.

June, 1200
Bishop Godfrey de Lucy making success of planned settlement on manorial estate at Alresford. Given it a Market. Seems good number of building plots taken up by merchants and traders for money-rents. Newly-freed villeins also welcomed. Must provide Bp. with good cash income. (Cash now better than labour services and goods in kind.) Seems King John has granted annual Fair as well – he is certainly friend to traders and commerce. Is leading country out of old way of just nobles and serfs – although nobles naturally resent these middle people. King also encouraging education. Have heard his father, Henry II, read for pleasure. Now said an unlettered King is a crowned ass – doesn't apply to John. I believe he's forming a theological library. New Alresford bound to succeed. Especially as Bp. has dammed river Alre to make huge fish ponds to supply fish to his residences. Old Alresford now across causeway between lakes.

14 July, 1200
Bishop to pay 3-day visit here. (Usually comes in hunting season so entourage can amuse themselves.) Hope weather's dry tomorrow for his arrival. Am keeping eye on gnats. These swarming up and down in open, so good sign. Also found spiders drifting on long threads. Am now quite sure tomorrow will be fine. But not too hot? Still, will be cool in church. Have told villagers to present themselves without fail at Mass on Sunday. Have to bully them. Seem to think religion's more for landowners than villeins. Except when in trouble or distress. Then are very devout. But they do like splendour of Bp.'s visits. Services full of drama, mystery and beauty. They don't have much beauty in their lives so am glad Church provides it. Otherwise life largely hardship. Need to know splendour of God as well as authority. Must go out and check gnats again. Praying tomorrow will be fine.

21 July, 1200
Bishop's visit went well. Seems pleased with running of Manor by Steward and Bailiff

and with my work here. Invited me to his chamber after we had eaten. Great honour. Told me Southampton now building fine new Town Gates. One at north end to be called Bargate. Also Eastgate. Both to be finished this year. Will add to impressive town earlier laid out for commerce. Strangely has two communities – the French along French Street and the English along English Street. Hope all are bilingual.

4 October, 1200
This week village been over-run by pedlars. Can tell it's Fair time in Petersfield by number of women keeping watch on road. All waiting to see what pedlars' packs contain. Villagers' only real chance to buy household extras and pretty things. As now more money-wages, are able to pay coinage.

20 October, 1200
Strangers passed through village. Told me King John has remarried. Bride aged 12 – and not from Portugal as expected. Is Isabelle of Angoulême. Wedding was out there and now both back in England. Both crowned on 8 October in Westminster Abbey. King said to be besotted but marriage also political – broke up unwelcome alliance of magnates in Aquitaine. Has taken her to Marlborough Castle. Must hold memories of first queen, Isabel of Gloucester. Have heard he's very generous to her. Isabel now married to Geoffrey de Mandeville, to whom King grants Manor of Mapledurham. She owned it, of course, before her marriage to John. King now on royal tour of Midlands.

6 September, 1201
Am plagued by imposters again. These rogues pretend to be Saints. Swindle poor and ignorant. Take coins and goods as gifts on pretext of pleasing God. Most pretend to be Saint Nicholas or Saint Andrew. As Saxon church here was dedicated to Saint Andrew, folk-memories remain and villagers believe he has 'Come Again'. These men seem to be everywhere. Have applied to Bp. for advice. So far none given.

   Promise of big crop of walnuts. Hope hazel crop not as good – when young folk go nutting, get up to mischief. Have heard saying "A great nut year is a great bastard year". We'll see. Maybe it'll rain every evening and especially hard on Holy Rood Day, 14 September, which is usual nutting day. Still, nuts are truly great blessing. Free food, for a start. Also keep well so useful in winter. Make good money in markets so extra coins. Some sold for crushing, I believe, for certain useful oils. I feed nuts to my pigs. Had a look at them today. Fattening nicely. Gales may be threatening, though, as animals very agitated, tossing straw about with snouts and rushing in and out of shelter. Pigs can smell the wind. Maybe gales and rain will last until nutting day. (Memo: Must remember to have my window shutters fixed. Rattle and bang in wind.)

10 January, 1202
Severe frosts continue. Hope Bishop's vines all right. Weather very unpredictable despite recent general improvement. Have heard that wolves again troublesome in forest areas. Harass farmers, take sheep. King John offering 5 shillings for each wolf head. Very generous sum. Also King has reduced his own afforested areas – much to relief of those living there. Forest Laws very severe. As Chases of bishops not subject to these Laws, won't make much difference over the Bishop's Havant, Hambledon and Waltham Chases. King has had trouble, though, with all 12 Cistercian Abbots through-

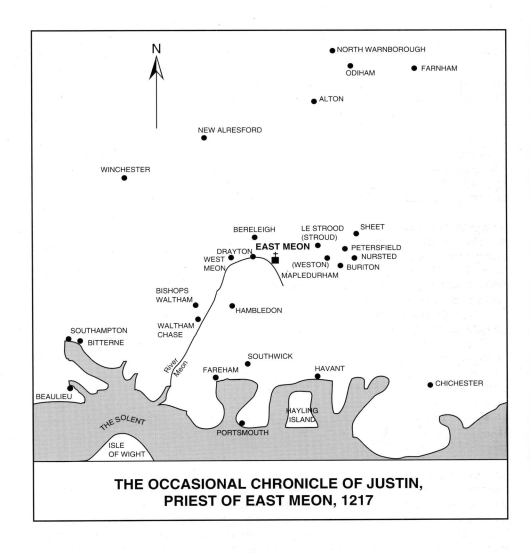

N

NORTH WARNBOROUGH

ODIHAM

FARNHAM

ALTON

NEW ALRESFORD

WINCHESTER

BERELEIGH

LE STROOD
(STROUD)

SHEET

DRAYTON

EAST MEON

PETERSFIELD

WEST
MEON

NURSTED

(WESTON)

BURITON

MAPLEDURHAM

BISHOPS
WALTHAM

HAMBLEDON

WALTHAM
CHASE

SOUTHAMPTON

BITTERNE

River Meon

SOUTHWICK

FAREHAM

HAVANT

CHICHESTER

BEAULIEU

THE SOLENT

HAYLING
ISLAND

PORTSMOUTH

ISLE
OF WIGHT

THE OCCASIONAL CHRONICLE OF JUSTIN,
PRIEST OF EAST MEON, 1217

out England over strictness of Forest officials. Heard he promised them redress and offered to give them land in New Forest for new abbey. This now building. To be called "Bellus Locus Regis" or Beaulieu for short. Excellent site. On river. Near Southampton port.

March, 1204

Case in Manor Court today. Theft of shovel from Lord Bishop's yard by Wigbert. Caught on Bp's land, was taken "hand-having", so this gives right to hang him. Last hanging in village was of Etheldreda, who stole 24 eggs from croft of Roger the Mason, also on Bp.'s land. She accused in Bishop's Court, convicted of theft and hanged. Thieving a grave crime. All our hangings from great ash tree in village centre. Have heard that Crown trying to take over right of erecting gallows. We have none – tree suffices. Didn't want to hear confession of Wigbert so curate Simon did so. Several unsolved thievings now accounted for. Wonderful what nearness of death does for consciences. Have complained to Tithingmen that control of law and order gravely lax. This Hundred not very law-abiding. Still, thefts not really their fault – times are hard.

May, 1204

War in King's lands in Normandy against Philip II of France going badly. John spending untold sums to equip army. England's wealth draining away.

Note: By end of month, Normandy lost. **TRAGEDY.**
BUT – English barons relieved. No more fighting or costly expenditure.
BUT – Now find their lands in Normandy lost also. Are **NOT** relieved. Blame King. No longer have faith in him. See him as cause of their loss of wealth and lands. (This true, but barons very bitter and are turning against King. No longer trust him. Have nothing good to say of him.) England drained of money – Richard's Crusade, his huge ransom, then continuing French wars by John. We will all be destitute.

1205

Richard Poore's election to Bishopric of Winchester quashed. Not sure of reasons. Peter des Roches new Bishop. Is stout supporter of King.

Southampton growing in importance despite loss of Normandy war and embarkation of troops. Is now more mercantile port than navy harbour. King John's own ship, exceptionally large and fast, captained by Alan Trenchemer, normally berthed there. William of Westham is Keeper of King's Ports and Galleys. Is organizer of new navy. Is also Archdeacon of Taunton.

King's reform of currency most welcome.

Bishop des Roches transferred West Meon from Bishopric lands to ownership by Prior and Convent of St. Swithun, Winchester. This good idea. Meon as a whole was huge area. The Winchester Prior is Stephen de Lucy – extra work for him but good revenues.

July, 1205

Archbishop of Canterbury, Hubert Walter, died. Question of replacement. King has put forward his Secretary, John de Gray, Bishop of Norwich, to Cathedral Chapter of Canterbury as new Archbishop. Quarrel seems to be increasing between Bps. and the monks of Canterbury Priory. So King has postponed all consideration of Archbishop's election until November. Both parties have appealed to Papal Court in Rome. Delicate situation.

December, 1205
King furious. Seems monks of Canterbury held secret election, chose their Prior, Reginald, sent him to Rome where he announced was properly elected as Archbishop and sought Pope's confirmation. John gone to Canterbury to challenge monks. They subdued by famous royal temper and declared no election had taken place after all. So king held another. Monks unanimously elected Bishop John de Gray, King's nominee. When asked for approval, Bps. agreed.

January, 1206
Second delegation of monks to Rome to seek Papal confirmation of de Gray. Pope (Innocent III) then refused both Prior Reginald and Bp. de Gray. Suggested his own man, Cardinal Stephen Langton. He's English and distinguished scholar. Canterbury monks have accepted him. Pope seeks John's approval. King explosive. English sovereigns have long had say in Church appointments and consider Archbishops of Canterbury as highest and most favoured advisers. Now Archbishop to be appointed in foreign capital by a foreigner and without consultation with him. Refuses to recognize Langton. Won't back down. Pope consecrates Langton as Archbishop nevertheless, ignoring John.

1207
King has no choice except to compromise. Accepts Langton as Archbishop but on condition that in future he and his heirs should not have this instance treated as precedent. Is face-saving formula. Honour on both sides. But Pope not satisfied.

End of August, 1207
Land at Liverpool, given by Henry II to Warine, his favourite falconer, exchanged by King John for better farming land. King astute and far-seeing. Will make harbour and port at Liverpool. Has issued letters patent giving town statutes of free borough. Subjects can now settle there with guaranteed protection and trading rights. Will no doubt prosper. Founding of towns and freedom to trade obviously important to King.

King now building castle in flint at North Warnborough, in parish of Odiham. Will have unusual octagonal keep. Probably take 5 years to build.

Bailiff tells me he's insisting Widow Cynthryth remarries. Understandable. She is third recent widow in Manor to inherit husband's holding but has no man to work it. (This loses profit for Bishop.) Bailiff concerned that Cynthryth should marry younger man than late husband – one fully able to render services due to manor. (And to father profitable villeins?) If she is unwilling to marry, will forfeit her landholding. Problem is Pope Innocent ordained in 1205 new Canon Law forbidding even distant relatives to marry as this would be incest. In village like this, most people related to every other. To comply with new law, Widow Cynthryth must take a husband from elsewhere and pay fine to do so, and he must pay even larger fine for moving onto our Manor. No wonder with our increasing population and resulting marriage fines the lords of English manors grow rich.

1 October, 1207
Queen Isabelle gave birth in Winchester to first-born, Prince Henry. Royal marriage seems successful. Thank God something is.

February, 1208
Simon, brother of Stephen Langton, now with King in Winchester to negotiate Archbishopric. But Simon demands King's total surrender of all royal rights in matter of election of future Archbishops. Threatens Papal Interdict if John won't agree. John does not agree.

23 March, 1208
(Passion Sunday) Interdict proclaimed in England and Wales to take effect from tomorrow. Appalling situation. Never known worse. All Church's services to be withdrawn from people. Only allowed to administer baptism of infants and to hear confession of dying. Everything else disallowed.

Am furious myself. Cannot understand justice of Pope's declarations. Bishop John de Gray was worthy choice of King's. Totally unjust that King's chief counsellor should be forced on him by papal decree. If Archbishop can be appointed this way, what hope for the rest of us? Will foreigners now appoint our bishops? Or even priests? Much anger about. Not only among churchmen but also people. Nearly everyone sides with King. If Pope hoped to turn England against John, has failed. All are rallying behind him. Who wants foreign interference?

April, 1208
Most churchmen including our Bp., Peter des Roches, refusing to obey rules of Interdict. Why should we close and lock our church doors, preach only on Sundays and then in the biting wind of churchyard, refuse Christian burial? This last is real sorrow – a grave in consecrated ground is first step to Heaven and soul's Salvation. Our dead are now buried without prayers in ditches, woods, holes in corners of fields. Marriages in church porches but no nuptial Mass in chancel. No Masses at all, in fact. Churching of women also in church porch. And that in today's freezing cold. Villagers flock to my door in distress. I think I've been over cynical about their faith. They are now truly unhappy and bewildered.

May, 1208
Some good news at last. King very far-sighted – before Interdict even pronounced, had arranged for royal officers to confiscate property of any clergy unwilling to celebrate Divine Office, who lock church doors and who refuse comforts of religion to people. Seems Pope had appointed 3 Bishops to see his orders carried out – Bps. of Worcester, Ely and London – and these now fled England in face of King's threats and anger. Their lands have indeed been confiscated. Most other English prelates remain, refusing terms of Interdict. Cistercians at Beaulieu ring church bells as usual, defying Pope. How much of defiance is genuine outrage and how much fear of losing property, only they know.

June, 1208
Some clergy now being attacked by angry people as being seen to blame for closing of churches. Heard of riot in Oxford between scholars studying for Church and

townspeople. King has given ruling that anyone molesting or insulting a monk or priest should be hanged from nearest oak tree. Seems effective. Have also heard that King has issued decree that all mistresses, hearth-mates and concubines of clerics should be detained by Sheriff's officers and held to ransom. Many priests said to be very eager to hand over ransom money to reclaim their women. So much for celibacy.

King very fair with those few churchmen who are obeying Interdict and suffering confiscation of property as result. Individual negotiations. Most already allowed resumption of estate management (which essential in countryside). Some pay fines to regain possession.

30th September, 1208
New problem. Interdict cannot be lifted until churchmen who have lost property through confiscation are repaid by King. This now to be done in instalments.

October, 1208
Case heard in Manor Court. Stranger accused of stealing one hen and one piglet from Godwin. Refused even to plead as said accused of two crimes – and only one might be true. Was excused on payment of 2 pence and return of piglet to Godwin. (Could use such quick-thinking man.)

Case heard in Bishop's court – Bishop's bondwoman, Ethel, found to be unchaste of her body. Is young and unmarried so Bp. will lose money if he sells her, unchaste women being devalued on labour market. As unchastity is church matter, I had to deliver judgement. Fined Ethel on behalf of the Church but as fine goes to Bp. anyway (who is also her manorial lord) nothing is gained or lost. (Except by Ethel, on two counts.) Fornication and adultery profitable in fines but really too common to bother with. Country young are ever lusty. But I do object to lechery among their elders. Thomas the Wheelwright is in constant Court attendance for this and for over-drinking of ale and subsequent noisy behaviour. Is always unrepentant and does no more than raise the price for good cartwheels to pay off fines. Village now thinking to look elsewhere for cheaper wheels.

Bishop Peter des Roches visited. Is living very grandly. Gives impression that Hall here is too small for his liking. Prefers his three main seats – Winchester, Farnham and Taunton – although East Meon Hall bigger than some of his other residences such as Fareham and Bitterne. These last mainly used for distribution of wine and salt. (Very profitable.) Bishop obviously keen hunter, like King. One reason for his visits here. Has purchased many hawks and hunting dogs.

January, 1209
Is too mild. Spring in January is worth nothing. If we have March in January we'll surely have January in March.

Helped with drafting final charter made by Robert de Berleia concerning all lands of Burly and Drayton given to Southwick Priory for soul of his father, Anketill, his own salvation and of his mother, Olimpiadis, and of his children and friends. Am glad this business finally sorted out, even to satisfaction of Gilbert de Draitun who holds Robert's mill at Drayton along with 16 acres, for which he pays 12d. annual rent at Michaelmas to Robert and his heirs. Witness to this charter was Godfrey de Menes. Gilbert has also commuted all his services by payment to Robert of 1lb. of cummin a year.

Appears there is almost total disregard of Interdict. So Pope Innocent is threatening King with personal excommunication. King tries to buy time by offering to re-open negotiations. Meanwhile builds up navy into powerful and effective fleet.

November, 1209
King declared excommunicate. Virtual outlaw from Church. This very serious. Caused genuine difficulties of conscience for some clergy. Bps. of Bath, Lincoln, Rochester and Salisbury withdrew their relations with King. Joined exiled Bps. of London, Ely and Worcester overseas. Their estates seized and these ruthlessly exploited by King – to great financial advantage. These churchmen now writing bitterly about King. Call him a blasphemous despoiler of churches who scoffs at priests. Quite untrue but people ever ready to hear ill of a man. Seem to rejoice in easy condemnation. Bp. Peter des Roches remains in Winchester, still loyal to John, who seems to retain his orthodoxy. Constantly gives generously to religious houses. (But this noticed to be mostly when he has eaten meat on Friday or hunted on a Holy Day.) Is not irreligious – just loses patience with clerics, which annoys them.

With churches closed, some priests have too little to do. This serious problem. Tavern-going much increased. A number of clerics taken up secular work. Will be difficult to bring them back to priestly lives and duties when this trouble eventually over.

November very cold. Said to herald mild winter but October was very foggy and this said to presage hard winter. Weather contradictory, as so much else. However, with my horses having grown thicker coats than usual hard winter almost certain.

April, 1213
Now new threat. King Philip II of France declared intention to invade England. Possibly sees it as convenient Holy War on behalf of Pope against excommunicate King John. Is gathering army, supplies and large fleet on French coast. John reacting briskly. Has ordered all largest ships to assemble at Portsmouth. (King Richard's ship-repairing centre there is proving its worth.) Navy now formidable. Also ordered all owing him military service to gather on south coast. Even disaffected barons complying and seem willing to defend realm against foreign invaders.

13 May, 1213
Cunning move by King John. Meets Pope's Legate at Dover. Accepts Stephen Langton as Archbishop after all. Agrees to re-instate dispossessed clergy and recompense church for financial losses. King and Pope thus reconciled. (Thank God. Soon churches can be re-opened, Masses said, dead buried with full reverence.) John now Pope's favourite son in God.

BUT now Philip of France can no longer pose as Pope's champion. John has pre-empted that plan. But does France still wish to invade? Not known, but Philip and son Louis very ambitious and greedy.

20 July, 1213
Arrival in Winchester of cavalcade of churchmen – Stephen Langton (now fully confirmed Archbishop of Cant.) with recently exiled Bps. of London, Ely, Hereford, Bath, Lincoln and others. King knelt humbly at feet of Langton crying "Welcome,

father. Welcome." Langton could not embrace John as still officially excommunicate, so blew him a kiss. Then King formally absolved from excommunication and so did receive his kiss of peace.

September, 1213
I was required to attend Bp. des Roches in Winchester. Seems possibility that King will again go to war with France and des Roches will be made Lord Chief Justiciary of England in his absence. Thinks he may need me as Secretary. Am honoured. Would enjoy working within Council.

Heard in Winchester about King Philip of France and his crusade against Cathars in Albi region of South West France. Seems to be having success. Cathars are anti-sacerdotal heretics. Are too many free-thinking people about. Look at Abélard and his female pupil, Héloïse. No good can come of <u>that</u> relationship.

On way home noted signs of splendid harvest. Have had long period of good weather and this ideal for oats which are cut when still part green, so have to be left in stook for several weeks. Can't be carted until dried out. With plenty of sun during oat harvesting, at least horses will be well fed. In country round Winchester (and London?) plenty of oats grown as so many horses travelling between two cities.

Early February, 1214
King embarks with troops from Portsmouth. Good thing John enlarged harbour and built up defences. King seems determined to win back lost lands in Normandy and strengthen Flanders. (Still holds Gascony and Aquitaine.) I now join Bp. des Roches first in Winchester then London. He has been appointed Justiciar as expected and left to control country. He frets about this as would much rather be active on battlefield – have heard him called "Wintoniensis Armiger", the Warrior of Winchester. Still, he is getting older. And I've no wish to fight.

Late July, 1214
News arrived of King's total defeat in Flanders by Philip of France. King now lost Flanders as well as Normandy.

Early September, 1214
King back in England. Very depressed. All barons dissatisfied – especially those from North – and blame King. John dare not trust anybody unless bound to him through self-interest. Has been taking sons of barons as hostages to keep fathers loyal. Not good plan. Administration of country disrupted. Much bribery and seeking of advantageous positions of power. Talk by barons of deposing King – who now fears assassination. Has become touchy, less magnanimous and is sometimes cruel. Geoffrey de Mandeville now rebelling against King, so deprived of all lands. Manor of Mapledurham now granted to Savary de Mauleon.

I leave London for Winchester. Enjoyed my time at centre of things. Return to East Meon. Village seems excessively dull. While in London heard of new Order of Friars in Italy. Founded by man called Francis who lives simple, natural life, seeing God throughout nature. May his Order prosper. The Church everywhere becoming very rich. Too little simplicity today – London very sophisticated and worldly. Also heard of nun, Clare, who has founded associate Order of Poor Clares along same lines. I thank God for some goodness, visible and active.

March, 1215
Again sent for by Bishop. Serious feud arising between barons and King John. Probably only quarter of barons are rebels but these very vociferous. Most standing aloof. Feudal tenants and freeholders not involved. Certainly no mass upsurge of populace against King. Even Pope on his side and against rebels.

10 June, 1215
Stalemate between King and barons. King agrees to meet leaders of opposition at Runnymede, near Windsor, and leaves Odiham Castle. Rough outline document drawn up and Great Seal attached. This charter sets out practical reforms to protect baronage from over-mighty ruler. Almost nothing concerning liberty or reforms for common people.

15 June, 1215
Charter approved by both sides. Copies to be made.

19 June, 1215
Rebels now renew their original oaths of allegiance to the King and submit to his rule. Given copies of Charter. Pope angry. Declares Charter null and void. Condemns all who agree to it. Many excommunications.

Early October, 1215
Bad news. Prince Louis, son of Philip II of France, decides to invade England on his own account – but ostensibly at request of excommunicated barons. John's Flemish mercenaries were due at Dover at Michaelmas but storms delayed them. Many ships overwhelmed and soldiers drowned. Rebels took advantage and marched on Rochester Castle and occupied it. King recovered it with small force but had to resort to mining the Keep. Tunnel dug, filled with combustibles and fired with fat of 40 bacon pigs. Corner of Keep fell down.

January, 1216
King decided to set off to troublesome Northern and Eastern regions to harry main rebel strongholds. Caused much pillage and destruction. This confused many barons who had been wavering in loyalty to rebel cause and were thinking of rejoining King. Now turned away from him and back to rebels.

2 June, 1216
ENGLAND INVADED BY FRENCH. Prince Louis and army entered London. Many disaffected barons joined him.

6 June, 1216
Louis left London on way to Winchester.

7 June, 1216
Captured Reigate Castle.

8 June, 1216
Captured Guildford Castle.

10 June, 1216
Captured Farnham Castle. (Hardly any resistance.) More of King John's barons defect to Louis, including William, Earl of Salisbury, the King's half-brother.

Later
Now word has come that Louis has over-run Winchester. <u>Winchester</u>, of all places – the old Royal capital of England. King's men in Castle put up strong resistance. Hope to God our Cathedral isn't desecrated by soldiers. Thankfully, King John now in Devizes. Prince Louis and troops then turned back to take Odiham Castle. This held out for weeks before defenders allowed to march out with full battle honours. French amazed that garrison was only 3 knights and 10 men-at-arms.

King went to Corfe Castle to join family, then to Welsh Marches and Midlands. Seems that in rebel areas of North and East, French armies roam at will. Appalling situation. East Anglia over-run with them. Frenchmen all over the place.

July, 1216
Heard that so many English landed nobles are joining Prince Louis that French disconcerted. Had come to conquer English and win lands from enemies – now few enemies left so little land to conquer. So few spoils. French now behave arrogantly to English to prevent more defections from John. This successful ruse. More nobles returning to John.

September, 1216
King gathered army to attack French. Went via Oxford and Reading to relieve besieged Windsor. Then to Cambridge. This successfully divided French army into those North and South of him. King indefatigable but is sick man. Rides 40 or 50 miles a day. Then has to sit up overnight on administrative and government affairs. His military strategy proving effective. French disheartened. I fear King is wearing himself out and cannot continue in this life much longer.

October, 1216
King John left King's Lynn on 10th. Suffering from dysentery. Last part of baggage train which took short cut across edge of Wash was overwhelmed by sea. King had gone long way round via Wisbech. Was shattered by loss of men, goods, horses and some at least of treasure. Exhausted. Barely able to sit horse. In pain, fever and sickness. Had to be put on litter. Reached Newark on 16th. Went to Bp. of Lincoln's castle there.

King died there on 18 October. Aged 49. Death due to dysentery, fever and exhaustion. Was no longer plump and sturdy but balding and grey. Sad sight. He will be sadly missed, not least in Winchester, which he visited 51 times during his reign. Much misunderstood. Was immediately reviled by his enemies, both English and French, nobles and churchmen. Was embalmed. Taken to Worcester Cathedral for burial as he had requested, despite pleas from monks of Beaulieu Abbey to have his burial there.

Young Prince Henry, aged 9, crowned in Gloucester Abbey by Peter des Roches, Bp. of Winchester. Said as royal crown lost in Wash, gold circlet provided by his mother in its place.

March, 1217

Louis and French army still in England. Some barons hesitated to give support to new King until clear whether Louis would prevail. When French badly beaten at Lincoln by English, they flocked to give allegiance to Henry.

Prince Louis gave up pretensions to English throne. Left country for France.

12 September, 1217

Peace agreement finally signed. NO MORE WAR.

Based on:

King John by Alan Lloyd. David & Charles, 1973.

King John by W. L. Warren. Eyre Methuen, 1961.

The Book of Magna Carta by Geoffrey Hindley. Constable, 1990.

Life on the English Manor: 1150 – 1400 by H. S. Bennett. Alan Sutton, 1987.

English Society in the Early Middle Ages by Doris Mary Stenton. Pelican, 1991.

The Medieval Village by G. G. Coulton. Dover Publications, 1989.

The English: A Social History, 1066 – 1945 by Christopher Hibbert. Paladin, 1988.

Weather Forecasting The Country Way by Robin Page. Penguin, 1981.

The Chartulary of Winchester Cathedral by A. W. Goodman. Warren & Sons Ltd., 1927.

Chapter Eight

The Bishop's Fisherman of East Meon, 1246

RICHARD Combe was full of resentment as, grumbling to himself, he set off to continue the clearing of the Bishop's fishponds. It was bad enough having such a dirty job to do without the knowledge that Master Nicholas was being sent over from Alresford to supervise. Gave himself airs, Nicholas did, and that only because he was Bishop William's Chief Fisherman, and because Alresford's Great Pond counted as a Magnum Vivarium while those at East Meon were only ordinary vivaria, being smaller. The work in both places was the same, so what was Master Nicholas sent here for? To interfere, that's what.

Richard turned to shout at two of his workforce who were still crossing the Meon river by a shaky plank made slippery with frost. "What are you dawdling for? Speed up, I tell you, speed up! Else I'll be giving a bad report on you and then you won't be getting a penny a day, that you won't!"

"Yes, Master," the two men chorused but Richard knew that as soon as he walked on they would be winking and pulling faces at each other behind his back. As he plodded along he watched for the rest of his gang of men, all of whom came from Langrish, for most of the tenants there held their lands by service of finding men for the fishery on the Meon. How he was to have the pond cleared out before that self-important Master Nicholas rode up on his horse, with his stuck-up servant on another, he did not know. In irritation, he turned round and shouted again. He had no wish to be looked down on by such as Nicholas with his great pay of three-pence a day and the luxury of provender for his horse.

This 'breaking of ponds' was his least favourite job although, of course, breaking the smaller ponds was much easier. Still, they were nearly done now. Five weeks they had been at it – five weeks of barrowing and carrying the mud and silt and filth out of the Large Pond and tipping it onto the Bishop's garden-close, where he grew his worts and other vegetables, near to the Manor House. That it was good fertilizer there was no doubt, but Richard relished the knowledge that he had seen to it that the most smelly mud was tipped as close to the Great Chamber of the Lord Bishop as was possible. Even with the wooden shutters slid closed at night, the foul stink must penetrate the sleeping-room like a foretaste of the stench of Hell. Richard had no love for the higher clergy, and was only disappointed that the Bishop had not been in residence these last weeks. Still, he might come unexpectedly before the smell wore off. One never knew with bishops. Come and go they did, on King's business.

He remembered back to the last breaking of the East Meon Large Pond in 1231. As a boy he had worked on that, too, and had helped remove five feet of mud from its bottom. On that occasion they had left the pond empty all season and grown a crop of barley there. A good crop it had been, for the remaining earth was very fertile – just as the fish had become when they were finally returned after the pond-filling and fed off the many grubs and insects.

At last Richard's full work-party arrived at the nearly cleared pond and the men sat down on the overturned barrows to remove their soft leather boots, for it was useless to work in the mud except with bare legs and feet. Their long tunics they tucked into their belts, undid the tie-strings from below their knees and rolled up their breeches as high as they would go. Then, reluctantly, they slithered down the frosty banks while one of their number handed down the barrows. There had originally been other barrows but the Manor carpenter had had to make a total of twelve, along with stretchers for carrying the mud, for seven had disappeared mysteriously over the weeks. It had been a cold winter, with fuel scarce.

Having seen to it that the men were at least working, although having to squelch about on the pond bottom, Richard went a short way along the river to the Stew Pond. This was acting as a 'Holding Pond' and was full of the fish so recently removed from the Large Pond. He and his gang had used seine nets to catch these fish. One end of the long net had been attached to a tree-stump on the pond's edge, while he and two more men had rowed their small boat in an arc, playing out the net. When they reached their starting point, they hauled in the fish, then transferred them in straw panniers to the breeding or other ponds.

Richard was expert at this and handled both boat, nets and panniers with confidence. It was, after all, much the same method he used every time a message came from the Palace at Winchester that the Bishop needed fish, and he had a regular team of two men to drag the net into the bank. Now he busied himself at the Stew Pond, checking as best he could that not too many fish had been poached. He inspected the sluices placed at each end, where the small stream ran in and out, and which prevented fish escaping either up-stream or down. Although this smaller pond was now very crowded, the fish seemed quite unperturbed. Being winter they were lazy and moved about very little. They would come to no harm, he thought, provided storm water did not swell the stream and push over the sluices. He tested these very carefully but they seemed firm enough.

When satisfied, he began the walk back to the Large Pond to supervise the last of the mud-clearing. He reckoned it would be a full forty days from beginning to end before the whole job would be done and the fish returned to their previous home. Because they were breaking the pond and not just catching fish, he had needed longer nets and a bigger boat, and had had to send the Manor cart over to Alresford to fetch them. Again he felt resentment rise in him. If only the Meon Pond had been a little bit larger he would have qualified for a boat and long nets of his own. These he could have kept in the Manor outbuildings, instead of having to request the use of those in the possession of Master Nicholas – and then to wait until they were free of other use at Alresford, or Bishops Sutton, or elsewhere. Richard disliked acting humbly, but he knew full well that unless constant good reports of him were submitted by the Bishop's Steward, he would never gain a better job. It paid to be subservient if you wanted to rise in this world.

As he trudged back to the Large Pond, he began to plan the final stages of this breaking – provided that Master Nicholas came on time and approved the work so far completed – and to consider the speed at which he could allow the river to flow back in again. The lifting of the sluices against the by pass channel was a crucial moment. Lift them too high and the entrance banks might suffer from the watersurge. Lift them too little and the pond would fill so slowly that the return of the fish would have to be delayed. Then he would be in trouble for costing the Manorial coffers an extra day's wages for himself and the men. He knew from past experience that there would be trouble anyway, because all the time the river was being re-routed into the pond, with the sluices at the far end remaining in place, there would be little flow of water downstream. The millers would then complain. No water, no milling. The village mill below the church was little used now as John the Miller was old, so the worst affected would be Shutt Mill in Drayton Hamlet, and there was no doubt that its miller would come storming up to the Manor. Richard smiled to himself as he visualised how he would play his own innocence, blaming everything on the Bishop's Steward and his order to break the pond.

Nobody much liked millers because of the Bishop's monopoly they held for grinding corn from the villeins' field-strips but, even so, Richard made a mental note to send a man down to Drayton to warn of the impending water shortage. Courtesy in such a matter might count as a point in his favour when promotion was being considered. And he did want promotion. If he succeeded in being moved to Alresford, Bishops Waltham or even Frensham he would be in a different manor but, because all the manors were under the control of the Bishop, he would not lose his present benefits. Nor would he be penalised by the usual fine to be paid into the Manor Court for leaving his home village, for his appointment would be by the Bishop himself.

But what was of such immense importance was that as Chief Fisherman, at Alresford or elsewhere, he would not only have three pence a day throughout the year but could build himself a decent dwelling. His present one-room cot no longer pleased him. Besides which, he had noticed that the skin of Alice, his wife, was already becoming darkened and yellowed by the smoke that blew about the room before it managed to escape through the hole in the thatch. When the wind was in the wrong direction it even drove the smoke down again, so that it was scarce possible to see across the hut, and her cough seemed to be becoming permanent. Smoked skin, a rough cough and soot-blackened clothes were sure signs of poverty. He wanted a two-roomed dwelling at least, and a wife whose skin was pale again. And, by all the Saints in Heaven, he would get them!

When his workforce saw him coming they immediately began to busy themselves. To show that he had noticed their lack of work he clouted one fellow over the head with his fist and knocked another down the bank of the pond, into the remaining mud. So far he had been a gentle master to them, drawing blood only once when he had thumped an idle fellow on the nose and broken it. They could have no complaint against him. He was a better master than most and had never yet taken a cudgel to any of them – but he might yet, if Master Nicholas arrived and the work was not done. So he scowled and shouted angrily and made dire threats. The barrowing resumed.

While they worked, he studied the pond bottom which was now exposed over most of its area. Another two days, perhaps, and then they'd be able to re-fill it and bring back the fish. After that, he and his two regular underlings could return to the normal and more pleasurable tasks of just catching and carting the pond's occupants, and his extra helpers from Langrish could return to their own farming and their weekly-work for the Bishop.

It would be a relief to return to the easier life. Only occasionally, when grand folk were occupying the Manor House, would he receive orders from their cooks for a few dozen tench or a pike or two. More often his orders would come direct from the Palace at Winchester to provide vast quantities of fish for a great feast, for fresh fish were an important status symbol, being expensive. Then he had to work with speed and care for they all had to be delivered still alive. For this reason, episcopal vivaria were all within a day's journey of the palace they served. By wrapping the still flapping fish in wet grass and carrying them in sacks placed either in carts or, for shorter journeys, in panniers carried by yokes on the shoulders of villeins, they arrived in good condition for the cooks to deal with them. Sometimes the fish were transported by cart after being placed in canvas-lined barrels which were filled with water, but this was not done very often. Several of the men of East Meon Manor were liable for such carrying or carting service, owed as part of their rent to the lord, and many were the grumbles when Master Richard demanded that they leave their own fields to do his instant bidding. William Suk was the worst – perhaps because he preferred one of his other duties, that of carrying writs and documents, for he certainly let it be known that carrying fish about was beneath his dignity. He grumbled about every one of the services he owed to his lord, the Bishop – of turning hay in the meadow after the reapers, of carting wood at Christmas, of cutting it up at other times, of washing and shearing sheep, of clearing the corn from the Bishop's land. These duties were not really onerous, but he was a grumbler by nature and Richard despised him for that, although he could understand the pleasure of carrying writs, especially out of the county, for that would be exciting and all his expenses would be paid by the Bishop and the Hundred.

He remembered how once, in a cold December a few years back, and whilst there was a long vacancy in the Bishopric of Winchester, King Henry III (who had the right to all the fish in the episcopal ponds at such a time) had sent orders to have them all fished out. Richard was told he had to clear the ponds at East Meon and have the contents sent to Westminster without delay, to be delivered to the King's Serjeant by the Saturday before Christmas.

Because the journey was a long one and the fish were not needed immediately, orders came that the pike were to be salted down and all the other fish were to be preserved by cooking in pasties. That was a rushed job, all right. And didn't the carters resent it! In the middle of winter and over terrible tracks! Richard heard afterwards that the same orders had also gone out to Alresford, Marwell and Bishops Waltham. Some of their carts had broken down on the way, incurring the terrible wrath of the King's Serjeant for the late deliveries. Thankfully, the East Meon carts had survived intact and arrived on time.

Looking up from his scrutiny of the pond bottom, he saw two men on horseback approaching. Master Nicholas at last!

He ran to greet him and enquired with much solicitude as to his health and to the comfort of his journey. The niceties completed, he led his superior to the Large Pond

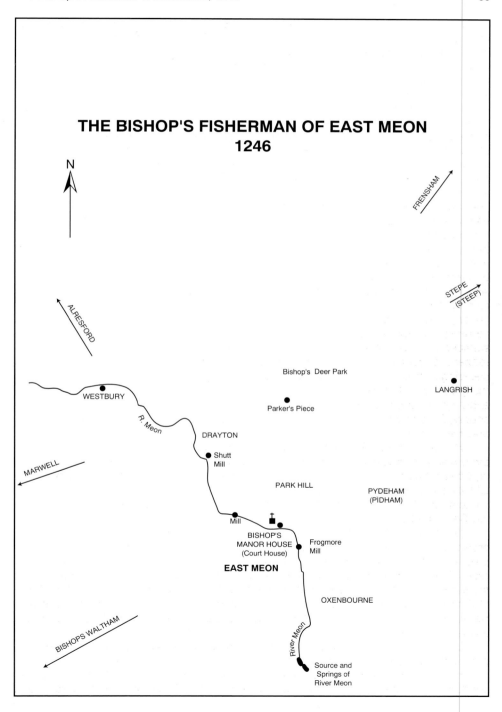

THE BISHOP'S FISHERMAN OF EAST MEON
1246

N

FRENSHAM

STEPE
(STEEP)

ALRESFORD

Bishop's Deer Park

LANGRISH

WESTBURY

R. Meon

Parker's Piece

DRAYTON

MARWELL

Shutt
Mill

PARK HILL

PYDEHAM
(PIDHAM)

Mill

BISHOP'S
MANOR HOUSE
(Court House)

Frogmore
Mill

EAST MEON

OXENBOURNE

River Meon

BISHOPS WALTHAM

Source and
Springs of
River Meon

and was amused to see the considerable industry being shown by his barrowers who, of a sudden, and seemingly becoming aware of the newcomer for the first time, threw down their shovels and stepped humbly aside (but nevertheless ostentatiously wiping imaginary sweat from their brows). Master Nicholas did not stay with them long. He grunted his approval at what Richard showed him, commended the labourers, rode to the smaller ponds to stare at the fish and then retired to the Manor for rest and sustenance, with his servant trailing behind.

Satisfied, Richard made his final arrangements for the refilling of the Pond, and then dispatched a boy to Shutt Mill to inform the miller of the future reduction of water-flow. When he reached home his satisfaction evaporated, for Alice was huddled before a dying fire and the front of her over-kirtle was stained red with blood. The cot was bitter cold and the first thing Richard did was tend the embers in an effort to produce a little heat. Then he carried her to the low bed, laid her on the straw-filled bags and covered her with what blankets he could find. As she was still coughing he sought for a rag or two so that she could cough into them, but found nothing but the winnowing-cloth which he pressed into her hand. This she waved away and pointed feebly to an earthenware bowl. When he had placed that near her, he tested the gruel in the cauldron to see if it was warm, and groaned when he found it nearly cold. Spooning a little into a beaker he held that as near the flames as his cold hands would allow and, after what seemed a long time, felt it was heated enough to offer her. She was very weak, and he realized now that she must have been ill for some days and had managed to hide it from him.

In alarm he knelt down on the earth floor, cold and damp though it was, and prayed for her recovery. After a time he decided he had left the prayers too late and should send for the priest immediately, for clearly she was sinking fast. After the curate had said the necessary prayers and left, Richard sat beside her all night long, constantly stoking the fire, concerned by the rapid disappearance of their small pile of wood. In the small hours of the morning she must have died, for when the late dawn of January began to lighten the sky he laid his hand on her brow and found it already cold.

A great sadness filled him for she had been a good wife, although ashamed she had produced no children. She had tried every remedy for barrenness the village knew, but all to no avail. Watercress she had eaten; she had plucked endless wild flowers; had drunk milk from a hornless cow that was all of one colour, and many, many other cures, but even so had not conceived. He had chosen her carefully, too, for although he was a villein he was ambitious and needed a fitting bride. He had scrutinized her parents for good health and breeding abilities, and had even looked at her fingernails to see if they had bread-making dough beneath them, for that was said to be a sure sign of a diligent and practical girl. And now she was dead.

Sadly he threw water on the corpse to prevent her from returning in ghostly fashion. Then he remembered that during a recent storm, rain had leaked through the thatch and landed on her – a sure omen of an impending death. After she was laid out by the corpse-dresser, she was wrapped in a blanket, carried to the churchyard on a hurdle and placed in the grave already dug for her. The prayers were brief, for the priest was shivering in the wind as he was wearing only an old cope and that was thin, clearly indicating that Richard was of small social importance. The mother of Alice muttered that half the service was left out, and that such a negligent priest deserved to be buried with a multitude of bags filled with all the words omitted from services.

"It's been a good winter for priests, too," she added. "Plenty of funerals. He'll be a rich man yet. But he shouldn't skimp on the words."

Then Richard returned to his task at the Large Pond. Private tragedy could not intrude upon his service-works but remarriage was now never far from his mind. He needed a wife to share the work with him, as well as to bear children, but he was not as prosperous as some of the younger widowers and so not such a good catch for a girl. (The newly widowed Thomas le Mathon, for instance, must have more land than he did, for he paid two shillings and six pence a year in rent.) He could choose Widow Champenaye, of course, who was as prosperous as Thomas le Mathon, but she was nearing the age when child-bearing ceased. Or the widow of Richard Wood of Langrish, but she was said to have a fondness for the ale-pot. Nearer home, Mabel, widow of Sheregery, was a possibility. Or Agatha of Oxenbourne – but she was not well-endowed with land for she paid only twelve pence in rent and reaped but three days and her only other yearly service was to give help in the Bishop's new deer park on the hill. She was fine-looking but her hair was red, and everyone knew that red headed women could be witches who it was wise to lock up on New Year's Eve, when witches were most about. Moreover, Judas Iscariot was said to have had red hair and that such people were deceitful, unreliable and had short tempers.

Finally he decided on Christina, widow of Toly, who belonged to the tithing of Church Meon like himself, and whose services to the Bishop were normal but not heavy. Besides which, her land carried the right to plough ten acres of her own land with the Bishop's plough, and to have six bushels of oats in Lent (just when oats were short) and even half a sheep at Christmas although it had to be an old one. She had to plough the Bishop's land, of course, but was at present paying a neighbour to do this, having no sons. Like red-haired Agatha of Oxenbourne, her tenancy required her to give occasional help in the deer park, but of Waltham, not of East Meon. However, this would not be onerous as there had been a park there since time out of mind, and it was now largely a matter of mending the enclosures and keeping the woodland cleared. Richard thought he could take on these extra responsibilities, so asked Christina to marry him. She gladly agreed, seemingly impressed by his position as Fisherman of East Meon.

After the Bishop's permission had been sought through the Steward and a fine of three shillings paid, the banns were called and the marriage ceremony took place in the church. Afterwards the wedding party and most of the village resorted to the churchyard. There a great bride-ale was held, until cold rain began to fall and they all moved into the church itself to finish the celebrations. All were encouraged to drink as much as they could of the specially brewed ale, paying their pennies as they fell due, and at the end they clapped and cheered when the profits were handed to the new bride. Christina conducted herself well and Richard was pleased to see that she was sure-footed in the dances, tuneful in the songs and cheerful and friendly with all, neither behaving lewdly as some there did, nor becoming morose with the ale. As was the custom, any bachelor who could still stand up at the end was allowed to drink without charge, and he was amused to see that Christina's two younger brothers were among that number. If she was as hard-headed in running their dwelling and properties as the boys were when in drink, he had married well. Feeling overcome with gladness he picked her up and, carrying her home, laid her down on the new-filled bags of straw.

After a week or so they left Richard's cot and moved into the larger one she had shared with her late husband. Richard was glad to leave the soot-laden hovel he had lived in with Alice and decided to knock it down, leaving the rotten thatch for the neighbour's hens to scratch in, and to cart the timber home for firewood. He felt that he was now moving up in the world, for their combined pieces of land amounted to a sizeable holding. Perhaps if the harvest was good they could afford to buy themselves out of some of their duties to their lord, the Bishop. Richard's own work with the fishponds was now less arduous, there having been few calls on his time to tend them, although the Bailiff had reminded him that many fish would be needed at Wolvesey Palace for the Easter Feast. This would be no trouble, for his other work-services were lighter than those of many tenants because he was the Fisherman. With Christina to help him, his customary duties on the Bishop's land were manageable, for the Bailiff did not often insist on him doing all of them – except for the harvest boon-works, of course, and again after ploughing when he was required to harrow the Bishop's oat-strip on the second of his boon days. He was thus left with adequate time to tend both his own and Christina's land.

On many of his normal days of duty for the Bishop he worked alongside John Tebald, who had many of the same services and boons to perform as himself, as also had Mabel, the widow of Sheregery, whom he had so recently wondered about marrying. She was a strong woman and handled the plough and oxen well but he was still glad he had finally chosen Christina. The villagers seldom had to work a full day for the Bishop, just from early morning until noon, on things such as ploughing, harrowing, building the cornstacks, carting wood for fencing, washing and shearing the sheep and weeding a half-acre of crops. Another task was the carrying of hurdles from place to place when the shepherd needed to move the night-time sheepfolds, so that all the bishop's land could be manured. Naturally they were also required to mow, carry the Bishop's hay and stack it in the summer, but only John Tebald had to repair the lord's farm implements and sometimes the great barn of the manor itself. On those occasions John could claim food once a day from the Manor House if he worked until Vespers, although he grumbled at the coarse fare provided. Richard, on the other hand, was allowed free fish from the ponds on certain days, and his own land owed only two shillings a year, whereas John had to find four shillings because he also had a cottage from the lord.

Several villagers had already commuted some of their services for money payments, and Richard planned to do the same, for he was reasonably sure that with Christina's thrifty ways and his own hard work they could make enough money to do this. He knew that the size of their holding was not large enough to provide a living – a holding of twenty-four strips of a half-acre each were barely enough and they had little more than this – but he thought he could hire himself out to the larger tenants for day-work, or even to the freeholders, of whom there were now quite a number in the Hundred. He had no wish to be a free man himself, for the risks and hazards of such a position were innumerable. Particularly was this so if the harvest failed. It was not to a lord's advantage to have his own villeins starving and unable to work, whereas nobody cared if a free man and his family died of hunger or disease. Besides, he was well aware that there were more people on the Manor than there had been a few years back and land was becoming harder to find. Even land on the Down margins that were part of the Bishop's waste and had never been cultivated were now, with his permission, being ploughed and cropped. So also were the new assarts, which had previously been scrub or rough woodland and of small value to the Bishop. Clearly there was a great hunger for more land. It was clear to Richard, though, that safety and a chance of good living lay in remaining in villeinship to his lord. That he was legally tied to the soil did not worry him, for even as a free man he would still be tied to it, through farming necessity. The poor could never be really independent, whether free or villein.

Those early spring months of the year 1246 continued cold and very wet. The river rose alarmingly and many cottagers feared for their safety during the night for, their small dwellings being of mud and rough wood, could all too easily be inundated and float downstream.

"There's liars among us," an old woman said. "There's liars for sure! Rivers rise up to drown liars. Those waters spring out from a well in the centre of the earth and the beings who live down there can't abide a liar. So someone will drown, you'll see, and he'll be a liar – or she, for that matter. Womenfolk can be terrible at lying."

And so it turned out. Robert of Pydeham was a tenant of the Church Manor, and held one virgate of land at a rent of five shillings a year, along with all the usual services (but not the two hens at Christmas that his neighbour, Robert of Stepe, had to give). One of these services was the carting of timber with his own cart and horses. On the March day in question, he and his man, Geoffrey Bonde, whose very small holding was worth only sixpence a year and who owed so few services that he had time to work for Robert, were told by the Reeve to collect felled timber from the woods above Langrish. They were to take it to the Bishop's barn in East Meon for the repair of the Manor gatehouse. There it would be cut up by the Bishop's own servants while old John Miller, who kept the mill just below the village, would perform his service of mending the doors and walls of the barn.

Now it so happened that Robert of Pydeham was a greedy man, ever ready to enrich himself at the expense of others. He and Geoffrey devised a plan whereby some of the timber would be off-loaded from the cart and hidden in a thicket for Robert's own use later. Geoffrey was sworn to silence and when promised a sheaf of oats at harvest, gladly agreed.

The plan was carried out successfully and the theft unnoticed by the workers at the Manor House. As the next few cartloads carried the full quantity of timber, all would have been well if it had not been that the two lingered by the saw-pit, at which no one was working, the sawyer having been called away. As Robert and Geoffrey gleefully congratulated themselves on having succeeded in their plan, a voice from the pit spoke up.

"I hears you! I hears you! You dirty scoundrels! I hears what you done – thieves the pair of you!"

It seemed the under-sawyer had remained in the pit while his top dog was away. The guilty pair cast a startled look at the sawdust-covered head of the man and ran for their cart and horses. The incident was reported to the Reeve but the man was not sure of the identity of the two.

"I couldn't see them," he declared, "what with the wood-dust in my eyes and me being down the pit – you know what it's like when you're under dog – but I reckon I knows those voices and Robert of Pydeham was one, and it might be Geoffrey Bonde was the other."

For a few days it was the talk of the village and the two accused were summoned before the Beadle and told of the charges against them. They were questioned in turn but each swore they were innocent of theft, and definitely not the men whose voices the sawyer had heard. Without proper identification and not even proof that timber had indeed been stolen, the matter was dropped, for the case was too flimsy to report even at the next Court Leet. Nevertheless, the Steward was informed of the situation and a warning given to the suspected thieves.

But that night the old woman's prophecy came true for Robert drank too much at the ale-house and fell into the swollen river and drowned. Then everyone knew he had been guilty of lying, and when Geoffrey Bonde next came into the village, mud was thrown at him and his hovel set on fire. In much fear he confessed to the crime and returned the missing timber to the stack beside the barn.

With Robert dead, Richard immediately applied to the Bishop for permission to rent some of his land. "Much better than trying to assart some of the wood's edge," he told Christina. "Robert was a rogue, but a good farmer and his strips well kept." When permission was granted, he gathered together all the money he could – including that gained from a lamb he sold especially at Petersfield market – and paid the Bishop's Steward the necessary fine for entry into his new landholding. Now, with his work and responsibilities increased yet again, and because Christina was now with child, he hired John Carter of Oxenbourne to help him, for he, like the disgraced Geoffrey Bonde, held so little land he paid no more than twelve pence a year, with only one hen at Christmas, and did no services. To him Richard offered four pence for ploughing over two days, two pence for harrowing an acre at sowing time, four days of haymaking at two pence a day, four days at harvest at a three-halfpence a day and, in the autumn and winter, one penny a day for four days when threshing. Such terms the young man was very willing to accept for, with money in hand, he would be able to pay his rent without anxiety and have a little over to eke out what he gained from his own inadequate two half-acre plots.

Richard felt himself becoming increasingly important in the village. Alexander Bigendon, who, being old and having no sons, was excused some of the ploughing and paid no more than a penny in place of mowing the meadow, was likely to die soon. Richard hoped that he would be chosen to replace him as one of the Bishop's Jurymen. These, he knew, concerned themselves at the Court with cases regarding services and customs owed to the lord Bishop by the tenants of Meon Church Manor. The work would be tedious and without pay, but the Courts were not held very often and he would be associating with such men as Adam Patrike, John le Palmere, John Miller, William Detileston, Radulf of Tyleston and Robert of Stepe. The last was a particularly well-thought-of tenant, whose service-work was virtually the same as that of the ill-fated Robert of Pydeham, and who was very much favoured by the Bailiff. Surely, with these as associates, and his work at the Fishponds satisfactory, he might even be elected by his fellows as Reeve. That was truly arduous work but well-rewarded, for he would receive a stipend of three shillings each year in precious coins. In addition, he would be allowed wheat from one of the better acres of the lord's demesne, and food during the harvesting period from the first day of August until Michaelmas. If he worked in the lord's service during the afternoons also, he could claim his midday meal throughout the year. His ambitious dreams ran strongly and high.

On a day in early June when the weather was hot and sultry he went into the church, for there the stonework kept the temperature cool and even. Passing up the new south aisle into the Lady Chapel he knelt for a few minutes in thanksgiving for his increasingly successful life. Unwilling yet to face the heat outside, he looked idly about him. He could not remember much of what the church had looked like before it was enlarged in the year 1230, because he had been only a child then, but he wondered about the need there had been to extend, for it was seldom that all the people of the village attended the same service. Even though the population was now larger than it had been the hundred years before, when it was first built, there was still plenty of space. Vaguely he remembered words of Father Mylo about the new importance of the altar in religion and the extra ritual that now had to be performed. Perhaps it was for this reason that the chancel had been extended and made lighter by larger windows, for the drama of the Eucharist at the altar was thus newly emphasised. Not only that, he remembered, but the veneration granted to the Holy Virgin had increased also, and it had become necessary to erect a whole new chapel in her honour. But the south aisle? Why was that built? Was it because of more people being in the village, or was it just to accommodate an extra side altar now that there was a second curate, or because of the size of the Bishop's party when he was in residence?

Slowly he wandered westwards and through the south transept. That the builders had knocked holes through the previous outer walls, he knew. He could just remember the mess there had been when the south wall of the nave had been taken down, so that new pillars could make an open arcade to the south aisle. Dust everywhere. He could remember that.

With these memories Richard wandered out into the sunshine and turned to climb the tall hill behind the church. There might be a breeze up there.

Strictly speaking, he was not allowed in the Bishop's Deer Park but village people had climbed that hill since time out of mind, and it was only after Bishop Peter des Roche had enclosed it, twenty years ago, that they had been prevented from doing so. Many of the village tenants still owed service for maintaining the enclosure banks and fences, their fathers having erected them, and all built to keep in the deer. He climbed slowly through the tangled thicket and then out onto the clearer grass, knowing there was small chance of meeting anyone. In June there was no hunting, as the deer were fawning, and John Steil, the Bishop's huntsman, with his twenty three greyhounds (those large animals who hunted by sight) and the eighteen running-dogs who worked by scent, were all lodged at the great residence at Waltham and would not be around now. The only person he might meet was the Parker, who lived in a small two-roomed lodge known as Parker's Piece on top of the hill, from where he could watch for poachers. But he was not in sight.

Richard sat down on the chalky turf, enjoying the shade from an overhanging thorn bush. Life was very good. And he need not check on the Fish Ponds just yet.

Based on:

The Bishop of Winchester's Fishponds in Hampshire, 1150 – 1400 by Edward Roberts.
Proceedings of the Hampshire Field Club & Archaeological Society, Volume 42 for 1986.

The Bishop of Winchester's Deer Parks in Hampshire, 1200 – 1400 by Edwards Roberts.
Proceedings of the Hampshire Field Club & Archaeological Society, Volume 44 for 1988.

The Bishop of Winchester's Fishponds & Deer Parks by Edward Roberts.
Proceedings of the Hampshire Field Club & Archaeological Society, Volume 49 for 1994.

13c Custumals of East Meon. Hampshire Records Office. (M405, 163M84).
Translated privately by Mrs. Una Rees.

English Society in the Early Middle Ages by Doris Mary Stenton. Pelican History, 1991.

Life on the English Manor, 1150 – 1400 by H. S. Bennett. Alan Sutton, 1987.

The English: A Social History, 1066 – 1945 by Christopher Hibbert. Paladin, 1988.

The Medieval Village by G. G. Coulton. Dover Publications, 1989.

Life in a Medieval Village by Gwyneth Morgan. Cambridge University Press, 1975.

Chapter Nine

The Great Plague, 1348

MARIA had been born in the year 1303 at Westbury where her father, Geoffrey Pilat, was a successful tenant of the Bishop of Winchester. So successful, in fact, that in the year 1327 he had been called upon to pay that iniquitous tax known as the Lay Subsidy to the amount of twelve pence a year, which represented one fifteenth of the value of his movable belongings, including growing crops.

Not, of course, that his twelve pence was the highest payment from their village, for that dubious honour was held by John de Lauynton, who was assessed at thirteen shillings and four pence a year, while Thomas le Parays had to find five shillings. The only comfort was that the liability of a taxable town-dweller was based on one-tenth of the value of his moveable assets, which was much worse.

The King's Treasury had been lucky to receive as much as it did that year, for the weather had been appalling and thus income low. The first really bad harvest had been in 1310 and Maria could just remember the cold rains which swept the fields in late spring, rotting the corn seeds before they could germinate and allowing all manner of weeds to spread across the ploughlands. In the summer that followed she had been given the task of lifting up flattened and sodden wheat stalks so that the men could harvest them by sickle and, later still, she had shared her father's despair as the cut sheaves blackened and rotted where they stood. The final yield was pitifully small and of negligible quality. Summer after summer was like that and Geoffrey Pilat, along with some of his neighbours, gradually reduced corn growing and turned instead to keeping more livestock. For that reason, wheat, barley and even rye increased to prohibitive prices, being in short supply, and the poor starved, for flour was too expensive to buy.

The Pilat family starved, too. It was a bad year on every count, for Maria had nearly drowned in the June floods that spread either side of the Meon, while trying to rescue a young calf from the swollen river. Her mother and younger sister died from pneumonia. Her father broke his leg when he slipped in the mud and fell under a cartwheel. The Curate from East Meon, who had care of the Chapel of St. Nicholas at Westbury, announced that the rain was surely to be seen as God's punishment for their sins. In 1318 sheep suffered badly from murrains of different kinds including infestations of liver-fluke, foot rot and then blowfly strike, the last particularly affecting lambs up to twelve months old. Some animals died of pneumonia, especially after being shorn of their fleeces. These were often worthless in any case, as the wool had begun to rot on the sheeps' backs, and even the pelts from dead animals were often spoilt by maggot holes.

The next year their cattle caught foot-and-mouth disease, followed by rinderpest, and the herd became reduced by nearly half. Plough-oxen were now hard to find. Geoffrey Pilat, like other farmers, burned his dead and infected animals and placed their heads on posts at the field-entrances to warn passers-by to keep away, for the diseases were highly infectious. Such precautions were of no use, however, because carrion crows fed on the heads and spread the disease themselves.

Some cattle and sheep survived, of course, but it was nearly impossible to preserve their meat when killed as usual in the Autumn for, with the weather so cold and wet in Summer, there was insufficient sun to evaporate sea-water from the salterns, leading to a shortage of curing-salt.

Farmers had been accustomed to buying their salt from Hayling Island or the Portsmouth area during the Summer when it was at its cheapest, the salterns being unable to store their surplus and glad to dispose of it locally. Now, however, even Summer salt was too expensive for most, and preserving became nearly impossible.

There was also much grumbling that the King did not dip his hand into his own treasure and buy supplies from overseas to keep his people from death. The knowledge that the whole of northern Europe was also suffering famine and millions were dying there, did not assuage the complaints. When a small hen's egg cost a penny – the price of half a day's labour – deep depression filled the villagers and some just died of despair.

There was one Summer, though, which was exceptionally hot. In 1333 the heat caused fearful drought all down the Meon valley and the river became a trickle. The grass did not grow and crops withered but, as the following winter was nearly normal, hope began to revive that climatic instability might be at an end. This hope was cruelly shattered by the winter of 1334 which was the coldest anyone could remember. Ice and snow lay over the land for months, rivers froze and word came that in London people were walking on the Thames. Humans died in their hundreds of chest infections and influenza, and where the water supply was foul and inadequate, of typhoid, dysentery and diphtheria. Villages became bleak and empty places. Surviving wild animals even came out of the woods and invaded farmsteads in search of fodder. Pauperization and hunger lay over the land but, despite this, in 1340 there was a new tax, and because it exceeded that imposed in 1290, caused much bitterness and increased the poverty.

At least the Meon area was spared the horror which struck villages further north, for there the rye from which the poor made their bread became infected with ergot-blight. Whole communities were said to suffer hallucinations, often leading to convulsions, seeming madness and then to gangrene and finally death.

It was through all this terrible time that Maria managed to live. By the year 1344 and the worst famine of all, she was aged forty-one and still unmarried. Her father had died, the landholding was virtually derelict and she had become thin, wrinkled and exhausted. Her hair was grey, her hands ruined by chilblains and her often bare feet so deadened by cold that they bled without her knowing. Animal prices had risen to such heights that few could afford to restock and, to add to all the difficulties, there was a great gale locally. This brought down many trees and blew over some of the more ruinous shacks and barns, leaving the poorest without their dwellings or shelter for their animals. The gale also damaged the roof of the hay-barn at East Meon Manor.

Maria knew of this only because Thomas de Overton, the Bailiff there, sent the Reeve to ask if Will the Thatcher would repair it, as the regular thatcher and his son had died. When the Reeve had reined in his horse near where Maria was working, he called across to ask where Will lived. As she stumbled over to him, the tattered rags round her feet making her clumsy, she offered to show him, for the hovel was hidden somewhat in the woods. While they went he questioned her about the state of affairs since the gale.

"At least we have firewood a'plenty," she said, "with all the branches down." Then she smiled somewhat ruefully. "And no fear of being accused of cutting the underwood."

The Reeve made no reply but when she lagged a little behind the horse, he said, "Come on, woman! Catch hold of my stirrup if you can't keep up. I've a lot to do today." Even with that help she could not maintain the pace and finally gasped out, "Can't go no further,Master. I'm done. It's the hunger-weakness, see."

"Tell me where I go from here, then," he replied.

She pointed out the wood paths as best she could and then leant against a tree for support. When he was out of sight she sank to the ground and, huddled between its roots, remained there dizzy, exhausted and gasping for breath. She was roused after a time by the Reeve's voice telling her to go home or she would freeze to death. Only then did she realise that time had passed and he had returned from his mission, but she could do no more than nod her head. When he had gone, she struggled to her feet and began to stagger toward the hamlet, thankful that the path was now downhill. When she came to her cold and leaking cot, she managed to reach the pile of straw which did duty as a bed and there collapsed.

She came to herself again much later with the realisation that she was lying in a cart and seemingly covered with a blanket. She neither knew nor cared how she had come there, nor where she was going. Even so she was somewhat ashamed, for to ride in a cart was a despised sign of weakness and seldom indulged in by man or woman. Later still she was aware of being bundled onto a hurdle and carried into a great barn and laid on a bed of straw. Then a woman came to her holding a bowl of steaming broth. Gradually sense came back, along with a little warmth to her body and she saw that, far from being alone, there were three other women alongside her, two of them holding babies. She knew then that the Reeve had reported her condition to the Bailiff and he had sent men to bring her here to East Meon. After a while she heard a new voice – that of Father Roger. He spoke to the other women but not to her, perhaps not wanting to tax her strength, but through half-closed eyelids she could sense him studying her face. When he had said a prayer over her, she did manage to mumble "Amen" and heard him give her a blessing.

As the days passed much of her strength returned, and although still weak, she was able to help a little with the feeding of the other women and with nursing one baby, the other having died. One day the Bailiff sent for her in his chamber and she was intimidated to see the parchments, account books and ink-horns lying on the tables. He seemed such a learned man, obviously able to read and write.

"Maria Pilat", he began, "I have looked at the affairs of your land and have concluded that it is too derelict to be worth its rent. Moreover, now that you are so aged and still weak, I feel it should be surrendered to another tenant. As you have no husband or kin alive, I have arranged for you to be housekeeper to Father Roger, for his previous woman succumbed to disease and has been dead this three-month. Are you willing?"

"Yes, Master", she replied, torn between fear of this new situation and thankfulness that she would have no more farming to do, and yet receive food and lodging. "Yes, I accept, and that gladly, thanking you, Master. And thanking you, too, for the bringing of me here. I was near unto death back home".

He sent her, then, straightaway to the Priest's House which stood near the church and in which the Curate lived, for the Vicar, Father John Ace of Southampton, being the Public Notary, worked almost exclusively in Winchester for the new Bishop, William Edington. Father Roger was not at home when she arrived, but as the door was open, she entered, and finding the kitchen vessels in need of a wash, filled the cauldron hanging on its hook inside the chimney piece, and waited for the water to heat. Life certainly became easier for her and she gradually regained much of her former health. The Curate was a pleasant man and his house more easily cleaned than the tumbledown shack in which she had lived for so long. She received no payment for her work, of course, having been rescued from penury, but she found she could make a little money for herself by taking on additional spinning for those households lacking a spinster.

On the occasions when the Bishop and his entourage visited East Meon, they stayed in the Manor House and she saw little of them, but whenever Prior Alexander Heriard of the Convent of St. Swithin in Winchester, who was in charge of that great Cathedral, arrived on business, she was proud to be able to provide some of his men with warm and comfortable lodgings. The Vicarage floor had been cobbled after the rise in rainfall of recent years, and although this made the place much warmer and drier, Maria did find it harder to sweep than the previous beaten earth. Several years earlier the Manor House had also had stone paving laid on its floors and main passageways for the same reason, and this new innovation had been the Kitchen Clerk's great pride. Perhaps it had been the overnight stay of the Archbishop of Canterbury back in 1305 that had exposed the lack of comfort.

In more recent years several Bishops had commented on the poverty of the East Meon priests and their own dwelling house. Much of this poverty was caused by tenants retaining many of the Small Tithes illegally, instead of paying them to their priest, and this had led to a tiresome and expensive case being presented in January, 1325, to the Consistory Court in Winchester before Bishop John de Sandale. The Bishop finally declared that the parishioners should most certainly pay their dues whether in milk, wool, cheese, calves, foals, pigs, piglets, geese, eggs, honey, hay, flax, hemp, apples or other such Small Tithes. He had reminded them that the Vicar was dependent on Altar Fees and the receipt of those same Tithes in order to live. In addition, he had the care of two Curates and the Chaplains of the chapels of Froxfield, Steep, Westbury and St.-Mary-in-the-Field. The Bishop found that one of the problems of having allowed such abuse of Tithes to continue over the years was that they had seemingly acquired the force of law, and were thus harder to eradicate. For this reason he threatened excommunication against any who contravened his ruling, and stressed the need for what he called 'a spirit of mutual love' between those who had been at variance. Maria had heard that there was little of this 'love' and that the holders of larger properties (such as Richard de Medelynton, William de la Strode,

John Attehath, John Palmere, Roger atte Sole and Thomas Compe) were particularly angered. They pointed out that in 1317 the Church had been allocated five extra quarters of wheat (to be given by the Bishop himself) as well as the income from ten acres of arable land, and the tithe of wool due to the Chapel at Westbury, which had previously been wrongly paid to the Bishopric. They did not see why the Small Tithes should be insisted upon. However, it was through their eventual payment that the Vicar of East Meon had been able to improve his Priest House.

The Church itself had not been forgotten, either. Seven years before, in 1341, new lecterns had been made for the chancel at a cost of one pound, thirteen shillings and nine pence. Twenty shillings of this had gone to the carpenter, eight shillings and ten pence had been paid for the wood, twenty-two pence for moving the chancel benches to accommodate the new lecterns, and five pence for colouring these with ochre. In addition, the lead of the chancel roof had been repaired (two shillings and eight pence) and three shillings and four pence had been paid for binding books in the church and supplying tasselled bookmarks in silk. Altogether, the Church and Vicarage were much improved and more worthy of belonging to the Bishop, and Maria was proud to be associated with such splendour.

Gradually she came to know the people of East Meon. She realised that her age and grey hair meant she was no threat to the women of the parish, who might fear for the faithfulness of their husbands if she was younger. In particular she formed a friendship with a lively widow, Johanna la Naing, of Coombe, who had a relative living in Langrish called Alice de Ouetone and two more in Riplington, Walter and Richard Ouetone. All four of them had been assessed for Lay Subsidies and so had sizeable landholdings. Occasionally Johanna would walk over to Langrish to visit Alice, calling to see Maria on the way, although when she went to Riplington her route was by way of Halnaker Lane and Drayton, and not by the East Meon lanes. As the Chapel of Our-Lady-in-the-Field was as near to Coombe as the parish church, she would go to either one or the other on Sundays, but always to East Meon for a marriage or a burial, a field chapel not being licensed for those services. It was thus that she came to know Maria.

On one occasion she arrived at the Vicarage in a state of pleasureable fluster. "It's Bartholomew Smith", she blurted out. "Him at the forge. He wants to marry me. It's ridiculous – I'm all of twenty-eight and lost all my three children."

Maria sat her down and poured her a mug of small-ale. "This Bartholomew", she asked. "What age is he that he's still interested in marriage?".

It then transpired that he was a year younger than Johanna, already had two children and wished for no more. "You've discussed it then?" Maria queried. "You must like him a bit."

"Course I like him! That's no problem – it's Father Roger. I went to confession on Saturday, and blushing a bit, I will admit, mentioned having – well, impure thoughts. And he was shocked! Seems a widow like me shouldn't be thinking such things. Then he gave me a great talking to about sins of the body, and how sinful thoughts could be as bad as sinful deeds. I didn't listen to the half of it. He's taken vows of celibacy – but I haven't! And what's wrong with looking forward to a bit of married fun? The good God gave us bodies, didn't he? And natural desires?"

She took a deep drink of the ale while Maria pondered what to answer. Her loyalties were immediately with the Curate, for it was he whom she looked after, but she also understood Johanna's feelings and could see no harm in them – provided she waited for the wedding before they were indulged.

"It's not easy for him," she said at last. "Being a priest means he has to look on bodily desire as being sinful. Having children's all right. But taking pleasure in one's body without intent to re-produce – well that's another thing."

"But that's so old-fashioned!" Johanna exclaimed. "My grandam told me she could remember when priests thought virginity within marriage was the holiest thing of all! Can you imagine it? Thank goodness most of them have changed – now see bodily union as a sacrament or something. Or so Bartholomew says. I don't know for myself. But if Father Roger is going to marry us I don't want him looking at me askance. And, oh, Maria, he's a good man – Bartholomew I mean, not the Father! I'll marry him whatever the Church says, for nobody pays much attention to the clergy nowadays."

"Calm yourself, Johanna! Don't fret! Just keep hold of those thoughts and get wed as soon as you can."

The other woman jumped up and cried excitedly, "I will! I will! And now I must be off to see Alice." She hurried to the door and then turned beseechingly to Maria. "You'll tell the Father I'm a good woman, won't you? And chaste? It's just my thoughts, see. Things jump into my head when I'm not looking. That's all." Then she was gone.

Her banns were called in church within a few weeks, and when the marriage day arrived Father Roger waited for the couple at the church door, where he asked them each in turn whether they gave their consent to the union. Before their witnesses each declared they did and then a pile of pennies was set aside to distribute to the poor. The ring was blessed and laid on three fingers of Johanna's right hand with the words "In the name of the Father and of the Son and of the Holy Ghost". Then Bartholomew slipped the ring onto the third finger of her left hand and, after more prayers and blessings, they entered the church followed by their friends. There, after more prayers, the couple prostrated themselves before the altar until at the 'Peace' they rose and Father Roger gave Bartholomew the 'Pax' and he gave it to his wife with a kiss. Then they received the sacrament and the Mass was over. The only item omitted (and that by unspoken agreement) was the rite of blessing the bridal chamber. As this was a second marriage for each of them, and because neither was young or desired children, they chose not to mention the matter to Father Roger and he did not mention it to them.

A few weeks later, Johanna went with Bartholomew to the Tuesday market at Hambledon, that village having been granted a Market Charter many years earlier by King Henry III in 1256. She came home full of delight for she had sold all her eggs and most of the butter and had bought a length of good cloth for a tunic for her husband.

"They had shops, Maria, as well as market stalls!" she had exclaimed. "We can't have shops here, it seems, because we don't have a proper market – only the fair in Chapel Field in August – and a shop is wonderful! Much better than just stalls out in the rain. I felt really grand going into one – that's really why I bought the cloth!"

It was not long after the Hambledon excursion that Johanna fell ill. She seemed in great pain and her breathing was difficult and then, to the horror of all, she began to develop nodules under the skin of her legs and these turned to ulcers. When the surrounding skin began to thicken and to lose all feeling it was realised she had leprosy, that most dreaded of diseases.

Maria was appalled. And filled with shame, for leprosy was thought to be easily caught at that stage and she dare not go to her friend for she had Father Roger to

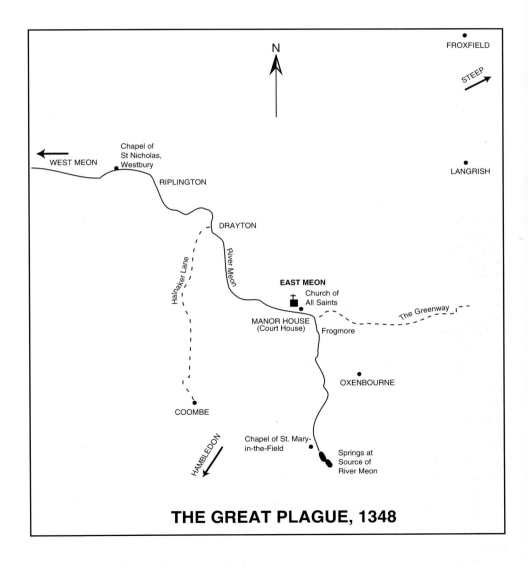

THE GREAT PLAGUE, 1348

consider and look after. The most she dared do was stand outside the hut and talk through the doorway. Bartholomew had already fled, leaving the forge and all his tools behind, for he was very scared. The disease was quite incurable. It was thus left to Maria to bring food and ale to the sick woman and leave them outside the opening, but it was not many days before she became aware of the gangrenous smell and learned to stand upwind of the doorway.

Then Johanna was taken away. When that happened Maria knew that she would never be seen again in the village for she would have been sent to a leper hospital – perhaps in Portsmouth, for it was from there that an outbreak had arrived in Hambledon, or to that on Magdalen Hill, Winchester. Father Roger tried to comfort Maria by insisting he had performed all the rites he could for Johanna. He had even sprinkled a shovelful of earth over her feet as she hobbled towards the waiting cart. This was a necessary, but symbolic gesture, to show she was already counted among the dead and so separated from the mainstream of society. When the cart had left, he went on to explain, he had returned to the church and said the special version of a requiem Mass for her soul.

"An unclean woman," he told Maria sadly, "and Divine judgement fell upon her. I should not have been party to the marriage. I knew it at the time but I thought her intentions were chaste. God clearly knew better. She is dead to Him – as to us."

Maria was deeply saddened and thought often of Johanna, praying for her many times. She knew that leprosy gave only a lingering and painful death, unlike the various plagues and smallpox which killed quickly. Even if Johanna did recover she would never return, for there was no one to fend for her. Lepers were truly outcasts, forbidden to touch anything except with a stick or while wearing gloves, and it was compulsory to wear shoes at all times. They could not wash nor drink from any common source of water, were banned from churches, markets and other gatherings and were counted as dead. Maria's prayers were more for her speedy death than for a quick recovery.

As there was no other case of leprosy in the village, Bartholomew returned and continued as if Johanna had never existed. But because she was not dead there was not even a grave to visit, nor any other memorial to show that she had ever lived. She was truly dead while still alive.

The next year the weather was bad again and the harvest ruined. By Christmas-tide food was in short supply and despair returned to the village. Two years of normal weather had lulled people into false hope that famine and hunger were things of the past, but clearly they were not. Memories of her own hardship and near-starvation led Maria to save her own food to give to those she saw in most need and she, in turn, became weakened and thin. She knew it was impossible to keep everyone in health and saw that children must be sacrificed to keep their parents alive. Orphans would most likely die anyhow, while adults without children might just survive and eventually be capable of producing more children. So she saved her scraps for the young adults and if, among those, the women fed their children, that was nothing to do with her. She could only give, and pray, and wait for better seasons.

In the warmer summer of 1348 news came of a great pestilence in the country. It came up the Meon valley, hitting East Meon in August, and so sudden was its onslaught, the people were totally bewildered and did not know how to save themselves.

John Wylde was the first to die. He developed painful swellings in his armpits and groin, then a high fever, acquired blotches on his skin and died before nightfall. People said it was leprosy again, caught in some way from poor Johanna. Then widow Edith Hackere developed the same symptoms and died alone in her hovel, then the four children of the Kyno family, then the wife of Richard Penystronge, then Walter Ponte, Walter Kuku and Anne and Richard Brekehus. The villagers were very frightened and overcome with horror, for the disease was foul-smelling and those infected died in agony, their supturating sores being left undressed, for none would go near them except the clergy.

Father Roger and the curates worked ceaselessly among the dying, giving them the last rites and trying to ease their passage to the next world, but after a few days Father Adam caught the infection and Father Lawrence ran away, none knew to where. More and more people sickened. Richard Puchel died while tending his sheep and lay undiscovered all day. Robert Scut left for work in the morning and by evening discovered his wife and baby dead. The whole Bul family was wiped out. Altogether over one hundred people died in that outbreak alone.

In terror, people besought Father Roger to absolve them from their sins, for this plague was surely a punishment from God like the one that befell Pharaoh in Egypt in the time of Moses. But he, exhausted, could do no more than urge them to pray and repent, giving absolution to as many as he could. When, after two days, Father Adam died, there was even greater bewilderment for a priest, although fully mortal, also had something superhuman and holy attached to him at his ordination. If God could take His own in this way, what hope was there for ordinary people?

One early September morning a fog lay over the village and there was much fear of this. Somebody called it a 'miasmic cloud' and cried out it was dropping down disease upon them. As if to prove this, Alys Illeston began to scream from terrible headaches and ran about the village clutching her head. She seemed to have gone mad and when finally she collapsed on the riverbank, vomiting blood, nobody went to her. Nobody dared. When two more adults and a child had died, Richard Patriche stood outside his house and cursed the fog. He shouted at it, waving his arms about in a vain attempt to move it on, and others joined him with cloths and sheets which they flapped continuously in the air – anything to dispel this evil cloud. Children copied them, shouting until they were hoarse, and then somebody had the idea of ringing the church bell for that had always been a precaution against the Devil and his works. By noon the mist was seen to be gradually lifting and there was sober rejoicing, particularly as no further people were found dead or dying.

News came from Winchester that the disease had reached there and, after Christmas, they heard that the churchyard cemeteries were so full that new ground had to be consecrated. When even that failed to suffice, the townsfolk took to tipping their dead into a common pit outside the city walls. This dismayed the Prior and other clergy for no service was said over them. Later still, a part of the city near the High Street was consecrated as a burial ground, for the deaths in Winchester were very high. All work on the building of new west towers of the Cathedral had to be halted for lack of skilled craftsmen, although the two earlier towers were already demolished in readiness for their replacements. These were never built.

In East Meon life was taken up again by the survivors, albeit with nervous caution. Many landholdings had become vacant owing to deaths and the Bishop's Steward at the Manor sought new tenants, often without success. The realisation came slowly to people that there was now more land available but fewer to work it and thus the labourers could, in some instances, name their own terms and refuse to submit to the old imposition of labour-services. Fewer were willing now to see themselves as mere villeins, tending the Bishop's land, for they saw they could increase their own holdings by taking up those of the dead. Many offered to commute their old week-works for direct money rents, for each knew the assessment of his land's worth, the week-works being based on this.

In a small way village life began to change and a new mood of independence spread among the menfolk. They began to buy their freedom from servitude to the Bishop, and when the relevant entry was made on the Manorial Rolls, they obtained a copy of the deed. This made them copyholders and thus free tenants, even able to move from one manor to another in a way impossible before. In return the Bishop, who now received money as rent instead of labour, was be able to hire men to work solely for himself. As more and more achieved this new status of copyholder, Maria saw that the poorer villagers, unable to buy themselves out of servitude, would gradually become nothing more than landless labourers, working for low money-wages. She was very concerned for them.

She had survived the epidemic of plague without illness and now knew most of the remaining villagers by name, for she had helped to nurse those few who had sickened but not died. She began to be spoken of in terms of awe, and it was said that the road to Heaven ran through the house where she dwelt. She refused any praise for herself, saying simply that her inspiration was the Good Lord and His servant, Father Roger, who had also survived.

There was still confusion among the people that God's own priests could die of the plague in the same way as common folk. They had been taught that He would protect and take care of those who fulfilled His commandments and had faith in His love. Yet they saw that Father Adam, a good and holy man, had died, while Robert Tybalde, a noted rogue, still flourished. Murmuring began to be heard that the teachings of the Church might not be always correct, that God did not always answer the prayers submitted through the Saints or His clergy. They wondered whether prayers could be submitted directly to God or His Son, with no priestly intermediary at all. Nothing of this was mentioned to Father Roger but there was a notable falling off in attendance at Mass.

Later in 1349 the pestilence struck again and, as the death toll mounted, so the old fears and panic returned. People's resistance to the disease had been greatly weakened by the previous years of bad harvests and when Maria looked at their already emaciated bodies she wondered how any could survive. Besides this physical ill health she saw a new pessimism and total weariness of mind. What was the point, people felt, in ploughing, sowing or even harvesting if death was at one's shoulder, ready to take one off in a totally unpredictable manner? None knew what carried this plague and so no precautions could be taken against it, although some thought that if an infected person looked directly at you at the point of death, then surely you would die too. Such looks could kill. Because of this, people became increasingly fearful of each other, for who knew which neighbour, friend or family member was about to die? Inevitably this led to a certain withdrawal from community life among some, and to a wildness of behaviour among others. Drinking strong ale to excess became common, as did the gorging on food, promiscuity and flagrant sexual misbehaviour. In towns there were reports of such wildness that men and women were seen coupling openly in the streets. What did such things matter when their days were numbered? It was a case of taking one's pleasures where one could, for there might not be a second chance. This led to the abandonment of responsibility for the welfare of families. Theft became common, with people tramping in and out of other's houses, stealing what pleased them.

There was no new Curate to replace the dead Father Adam nor the absconded Robert – too many clergy had died in the plague and fewer young men were willing to enter the priesthood. It seemed to those who still clung to their religious faith that the world had gone mad, that now what people thought mattered was worldly success, money and, above all, pleasure. Some, it is true, turned more and more to the Church, believing that their salvation depended on good actions, rather than just on faith. Allowing for the uncertain brevity of earthly life, the good of their soul was of paramount importance. Some, seeking spiritual comfort from Holy Church, were disappointed. Even Father Roger could not explain the workings of God. Nevertheless, through this longing for the soul's salvation, acts of benevolence increased in the village and pious charity blossomed.

And so it was that the village became divided between the religious and the wanton, and it did not pass unnoticed that several of the libertines prospered while as many of the pious died in the pestilences. The ways of God were surely inscrutable. One of those who died was Elizabeth Lampet, and she left behind an infant born prematurely from the agonies of the plague. She died alone in her small cot and it was only the crying of the baby that drew people's attention. No one knew what to do with the small boy until someone thought of Maria. "She'll take him," they said.

The tiny bundle was carried to the Vicarage and pressed into Maria's arms. "Son of Joseph and Elizabeth Lampet. Two days old. Mother's dead. Joseph's sickening." Then they left.

Maria looked at the wizened little face and was filled with alarm. She was aged forty-six and never had children of her own. Still, she had seen enough small babies nursed through infancy to know some of the things she must do, so she carried him into the house and bathed him in lukewarm water to cleanse him. Laying him down on her bed, well wrapped in her blanket, she fetched Father Roger to perform the baptismal service, for none knew how long the child might live. It was essential that he be absolved from any sinfulness that had lain in the sexual act that produced him and thus to have Satan driven out. She judged it unwise to wait for a ceremony in church, for he was very frail and, as all knew, baptised children had a better chance of survival – besides, a baptised child could not be stolen away by the fairies and a changeling left in his place.

"What are we to call him?" Father Roger asked. "He has to have a name to be received into the fellowship of Christ."

"Call him Geoffrey", Maria said. "After my father".

A problem then arose as to his feeding. A wet-nurse was needed, for infants reared on sheep's or cow's milk seldom thrived. Surely, she thought, there must be women who were still feeding their young and had milk to spare? One woman came to mind immediately, for she had given birth only three days before and her child had died. He could be taken there. She wrapped up the baby well and walked towards where the mother lived but met a woman dragging along a bundle of firing-faggots.

When she had explained her errand she was told, "Don't you go there! That babe never died, it was murdered! That Edith never wanted it, what with all this plague and her being so poor, so she just baptized it with river water and smothered it. So don't go there! Her milk would be evil-tainted."

"Where then?" Maria asked "Who still has milk?"

"Try Margaret Ando. She might have."

So Maria took the tiny child there, and thankfully, Margaret was willing. "But I'll need to be paid," she said, looking sideways at Maria. "Wet-nurses is paid, as you very well know. Besides, I'm only taking him to oblige, you being the priest's housekeeper and all."

Maria had not thought of payment. She had so little money herself and had no idea what a wet-nurse could ask. Finally she asked, "Could you just feed him? Then I'll take him back again. That way I could manage, I think."

"Oh yes?" Margaret replied. "But what'll you do when he yells his little head off for a drink? Babies is very greedy, you know. Always yelling for more. The only way to quieten them is to feed them again and again. Better to leave him here."

Finally, however, Maria persuaded the woman to feed him only. "And I'll stay with you while he gets it", she added, not trusting the woman.

When she had him back in her care she thought about swaddling-bands. She had no good linen to tear up but she remembered a surplice that Father Lawrence had left behind. When she had laid a small pad of rags on the child's lower parts, she wrapped the swaddling strips around him so that he was comfortable but not too restricted. He would be as happy like that as in the womb, she thought, for he was certainly warmer than she was in her draughty and unheated room. Secure, he would be, and his little soft limbs would not become dislocated or misformed.

Twice more that day she bathed him, each time before taking him to Margaret for his feed, for she knew that to bathe him afterwards would hamper his digestion. She tried to be as careful as possible in keeping the linen bands clean, for with the weather being so wet they would take a long time to dry when she washed them. As she did not have even the roughest cradle, she laid him in her own bed, wondering how she would sleep for the fear of overlying him. That night as she crept under the blanket, shivering in her nakedness, she held the sleeping child in her arms both for her own comfort and for his.

He lived for only three days more and then quietly died. The few pence that she had paid to Margaret still left her with enough to pay the burial fee and for a Mass for his soul's repose. "I'll do all I can for him," she thought "for his father is too ill to see to such things, being near to death himself."

But the father survived, for the buboes had burst quickly, giving him more chance of recovery. Maria went to his home and told the story of his small son's death.

"He's better off out of it", the man said roughly. "Anyway, what'd I do with a child? Better dead."

Periodically over the next year the plague returned and more died. Those so inclined still sought help in prayer, and Bishop Edington even granted a licence to Joan de Middleton for an oratory in her home at Oxenbourne, for the parish church was some way off and she was elderly. Elsewhere in the Manor loose living continued among a few. Word came that the Bishop had been informed that a married couple of East Meon, John and Alice Damie, had separated and were both living dissolute lives. The Vicar (under whose jurisdiction they came) was told that he must exhort them to amend their ways and resume married life.

Gradually, however, the pestilence abated and life resumed a more even course. The revenues owed to the Bishop varied very little from before, as what he lost in rents through deaths was made up through the tax paid as heriots by the bereaved families. More people were copyholders now and fewer villeins, but this did not affect the day-to-day life of the village, except that copyholders were more content for they were working entirely for themselves and not part-time for the Bishop.

Father Roger remained in the Priest House with Maria as his housekeeper, and in the year 1351, a new Curate was appointed to aid him in the work. It was only in the winter of 1354 that Maria succumbed to a chest infection and died, much mourned as a holy woman, and was buried in the churchyard.

Based On:

A History of East Meon by F. G. Standfield. Phillimore, 1984.

The Making of Britain: The High Middle Ages, 1200 – 1550 by Trevor Rowley. Paladin, 1988.

Victorian County History of Hampshire', Vol. III. Edited by William Page, 1908.
(Reprinted by the University of London, Institute of Historical Research, 1973.)

The Register of Bishops John de Sandale and Rigaud de Asserio, 1326 – 27.
Edited by Francis Joseph Baigent. Hampshire Record Society, 1897.

The Register of the Common Seal of the Priory of St. Swithun. 1345 – 1497. Edited by Joan Greatrex.
Hampshire Record Series, Vol II. H.C.C., 1978.

The Black Death by Philip Ziegler. Collins, 1969.

The Black Death by Robert S. Gottfried. Macmillan, 1986.

The Effect of the Black Death on the Estates of the See of Winchester
by Elizabeth Levett and A. Ballard. Oxford Studies in Social and Legal History, Vol V.
Oxford University Press, 1916.

The Medieval Idea of Marriage by Christopher Brooke. Oxford University Press, 1991.

Childhood in the Middle Ages by Shulamith Shahar. Routledge, 1992.

Chapter Ten

Richard Stympe's Story, 1499

I still say it should have been properly written down – and that years ago. This present rumpus would then never have happened and we would all have been saved a deal of fuss and bother. Written down and signed by the Pope – that's what should have happened – and nothing is going to change my mind because it would have been so easy to do. Just think of all those learned clerks and Latin-speaking lawyers that the Pope had, so eager and ready to put quill to parchment, and they weren't used in time. What stupidity!

But, then, I suppose we were not to know what kind of Archbishop of Canterbury we were going to have. John Morton may be a Cardinal Archbishop and high in the estimation of the Pope, but the Pope doesn't know how ruthless, unjust and greedy he can be. Here in England we do, and Archbishop of Canterbury or no, he is not a good man.

We have suffered under bad bishops, of course, and the story is still told that when King Edward IV went on a royal progress through Hampshire he was at one point met by a crowd of men complaining about Bishop Wayneflete of Winchester. In one account I heard, the tenants seized the Bishop and threatened his life and he had to be rescued by the King, who then arrested the ringleaders, many from the Meon region. I believe they were all tried in the House of Peers in 1461 when judgement (naturally) was given for the Bishop. But what happened to them I do not know.

The present trouble began with the death in 1492 of Peter Courtenay, Bishop of Winchester, and the resulting vacancy of his see. The trouble was not that a new bishop of our diocese was yet to be appointed – we were used to temporary vacant sees – but of who was to take the Bishop's revenues from the parishes during that vacancy. In most places, you see, they would have gone to the Archbishop, but from time beyond mind just two of the parishes in the diocese of Winchester had, during an interregnum, passed on those revenues to the Prior and Convent of the cathedral church of Winchester and not, as in other parishes, to the Archbishop. This was traditional. And those two parishes were East Meon and Hambledon where, whenever there was no bishop, the Prior of St. Swithun's in Winchester arranged to have the tithes either delivered to him in kind or sold for cash and the money given to him. It had always happened that way and we thought it always would.

But that wasn't so in this vacancy, oh, no! Instead of the usual monk coming out from Winchester, the Archbishop sent his own man, Robert Sherborne, with his servant, John Gossage, down to East Meon and Hambledon demanding the lot, in cash or goods. And the farmers, scared out of their wits for fear of the Archbishop and of his threat to excommunicate them, paid up.

Well, that's not justice for Prior Thomas Hunton or the Convent, look at it how you will. (Intimidation not being a Christian virtue.) So Prior Hunton, who is not as soft as you would expect, complained direct to the Pope in Rome for he knew he'd get no justice from the Cardinal Archbishop in Canterbury. And he complained more than once, for the Archbishop (bully that he is) tried to impose silence on the Prior and forbid him to seek his rights on threat of excommunication. The Prior considered these to be very tyrannical actions and refused to accept them.

Mind you, I don't think the Prior was truly fussed about one or two years' loss of tithes and the money they represented, but he would have minded very much about the loss of rights. If he gave in this time it would be all neatly documented and filed away at Canterbury for use against him or the next prior when another bishop died or moved away.

So, as I've said, the Prior decided to fight and to challenge the Archbishop before the Pope in Rome. The Prior is a very brave man because a Cardinal Archbishop has a mighty lot of power in the Church and the threat of excommunication for disobedience is of most awful seriousness. But the Prior sends off to Rome, just the same, to try to stop the Archbishop from inventing new rules in this or any other matter whenever he thought fit. Bullies have to be stopped somehow.

Now the Pope (who is Alexander VI) was in a bit of a quandary because this East Meon case should not really have been submitted to him at all as there was no legal need for it to be heard in the court at Rome. So in May, 1494, he passed the whole matter over to Anthony Flores, now the Bishop of Castellimare, who is an Auditor of the Sacred Palace and so trained in legal matters.

The case began all right but as there were few of the relevant documents or other evidence in Rome it proved a slow-moving affair. So this Anthony Flores told the Archbishop in Canterbury to send his proctors and all the papers that he thought would prove his argument over to Rome for him to study – a real mass of papers from the Lambeth Registry those proctors took – but not one of them could actually prove the case against the Prior where East Meon and Hambledon were concerned. There was plenty of proof that in other parishes in the diocese of Winchester the tithes and revenues went to the Archbishop during an interregnum, but not even one that said those from East Meon or Hambledon did, despite some confusion over 'spiritualities' and 'temporalities' in the two parishes. It seemed to me that the great and mighty Cardinal John Morton had not a leg to stand on! And was I pleased!

Because Rome was such a long way off, Bishop Anthony Flores delegated the case to senior churchmen in England to save both sides from further expense and inconvenience. To begin with these judges were to be chosen from the Bishop of Durham, the Bishop of Bath and Wells, the Abbot of Westminster, the Abbot of Waltham Holy Cross and the Abbot of Bermondsey. These men could either hear the case jointly or singly but were asked to sort out the matter and end the case once and for all. The Pope wanted it over and done with and I don't blame him, either.

The Abbot of Bermondsey was the judge who first heard the evidence and he, without more ado, declared in favour of the Archbishop and, in addition, awarded him all the expenses occasioned by the case and said that these were to be paid by the Prior and Convent of Winchester.

The Prior refused to accept this ridiculous ruling and appealed once more to Rome, claiming to be wrongfully oppressed by the judgement and asking for justice. The Pope (no doubt in some irritation) said he would hand the whole matter back to Bishop Anthony Flores to sort out – but Flores was away from the curia at the time so it was eventually passed to John, the Cardinal Priest of Santa Maria Transtiber, who then took over all the correspondence and documents. This included the Prior's last letter to the Pope, which I later discovered fulminated against the Archbishop, Cardinal John Morton, using phrases such as he had "falsely asserted" (that is to say, lied); "daily added injury to injury"; threatened "spiritual and temporal penalties" and had tried to impose upon the Convent "perpetual silence under threat of the most dire penalties", and so on and so on (the remainder of which I cannot now remember).

I do remember, however, that the letter closed with: "It is notorious that the Archbishop is Primate in the kingdom, and mighty in word and deed, and that nobody can be found who would dare proceed and pronounce against him". (Except our Prior and his monks, that is! Brave men, all.)

Finally it was ordered that all relevant documents and evidence should be produced at a meeting of the aggrieved parties, and a notice to this effect to be posted on the doors of East Meon and Hambledon churches and on those of the Cathedral at Canterbury. If the leading litigants could not go to the meeting themselves they were to appoint proctors to act for them.

On Prior Hunton's side one of the proctors was Bartholomew de Perusio but for some reason (perhaps playing for time?) he failed to attend the meeting. So a new demand for a meeting was sent out and this time a copy was affixed to the door of the monks' Chapter House in Winchester as well as to that of their Cathedral church. This notice was sealed most grandly with the seal and authorisation of the Archdeacon of Middlesex. The Prior had seemingly kept out of sight during this affixing – which took place on a November afternoon in 1495 – but as the man nailing it up saw that it was being read by some of the monks he later said he felt justified in assuming that the Prior would be informed by them in due course (which he was).

Finally, then, there was this meeting just before Christmas in the Long Chapel of St. Paul's Cathedral in London. Brother William Manwood, monk of Winchester, came bearing a letter of proxy from the Prior and Convent and the business was able to begin.

When transcripts were produced of all the documents offered as evidence (which had been written out by the Notaries Public) they were read aloud while the monk and others very wisely checked their accuracy against the original registers from Lambeth. (Very wise, I thought.) When the documents were finally approved, yet another meeting was called for mid-January, 1496, to be held in the Long Chapel at St. Paul's. You'll notice that these meetings were mostly called during the winter months when the roads were bad. The Archbishop must have hoped he'd so inconvenience the Prior that he would give in the sooner and it's certainly true that for whatever reason, when that meeting was held, nobody appeared on behalf of the Prior and the Convent and it had to continue without them.

Nevertheless matters did proceed even if somewhat slowly, and the next meeting was convened eighteen months later in August, 1497, in the parish church of Holy Cross, Southampton. Here Manwood again presented his letter of proxy from the

Prior and Convent but little business was done – except, I gather, for agreeing to the angry and persistent claims by the Abbot of St. Augustine's, Canterbury, for his expenses to be paid in full to recompense him for his time and inconvenience in travelling to the meeting. However, at the next meeting (in late October and in the same place) the monks' proctors were able to produce witnesses on the Prior's behalf.

And I was one of those witnesses – which is how I know so much of this affair. We witnesses were seven parishioners of East Meon and two of Hambledon. We should also have had the witness of Warden Michael Clefe of the College in Winchester but, because of old age and ill health, it was felt that a journey to Southampton would endanger his life, so his testimony was to be heard either in the Cathedral or in Fromond's Chapel at the Winchester College.

Inevitably we had to listen to all the documents from both sides being read out, and it seemed to me that the Prior's case rested on a grant made by King Edward III in 1331 when he gave to the Prior and Convent the custody of the churches of East Meon and Hambledon during the vacancy of the see and it was confirmed by Pope John XXII. (It was signed in Avignon, France, I must admit, after the Vatican had moved there, but the signing was well before the split in the Church when we had two Popes so I could not see that its validity could be questioned.)

There were one or two more documents of a like nature which were helpful to us, especially an earlier one of 1172 from Bishop Henry de Blois of Winchester to the Prior and Convent which spoke of dignities, liberties, customs, fees and services of the manorial tenants of East Meon and Hambledon being theirs in a vacancy. Which seemed to me to be proof enough, although our own priest, Vicar William Chippenham asked to be sworn in to testify on behalf of the parish. The judges (who were the Abbots of Waltham Holy Cross, Hyde and Titchfield) agreed that he could but, in fact, he added very little to the evidence and did not really help the Prior's case at all.

Then it was our turn. All we witnesses were asked the same questions in the same order, some of them relating to our names, parentage, birthplace, means of livelihood and a few others, such as how we knew anything of this matter of tithes during the vacancy of the see. None of the questions was difficult, though, and we had no trouble in answering. It was just somewhat tedious.

First to be questioned was old Richard Hether, now well over eighty years old. He said he had been born in East Meon, moved to Privett when he was twenty-two and stayed there for three years. Then he lived for thirty more at Woodlands and after that returned here to East Meon, where he has been for the last thirty or so years, and now lives with his son-in-law, Thomas Pynk. He is not literate but has known the Priory of St. Swithun's in Winchester since his youth and knows the Treasurer there but none of the monks. He also knows Hambledon church and has seen the late Bishops Beaufort and Wayneflete and Bishop Peter Courtenay (whose death caused this pother) when they came to East Meon three or four times a year, as they did. But he had never seen the Archbishop – to whom he had no hostility and hoped to gain nothing from a victory by the Prior and Convent. Nevertheless, he maintained that it is common knowledge among the parishioners that during a vacancy of the see the Prior and Convent received all the tithes that would normally go to the Bishop. In addition, he remembered seeing a man with tithed sheaves which he said he was taking to the church barn of East Meon for the use of the Prior and Convent. But no, he could not remember the man's name nor from whose corn the sheaves came.

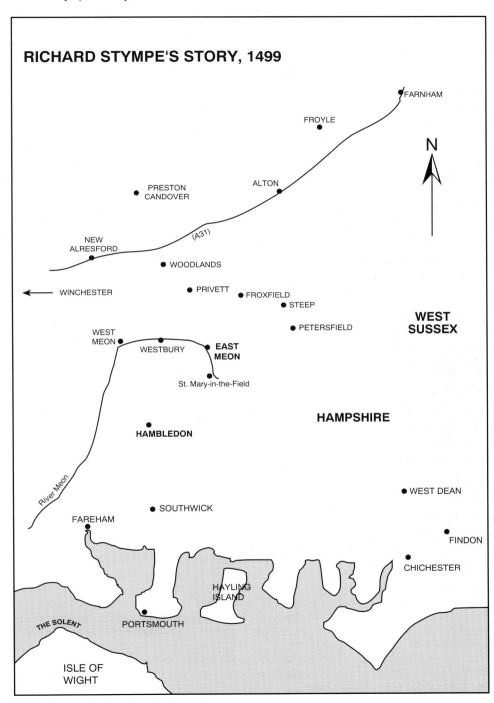

RICHARD STYMPE'S STORY, 1499

N

FARNHAM

FROYLE

PRESTON
CANDOVER

ALTON

NEW
ALRESFORD

(A31)

WOODLANDS

WINCHESTER

PRIVETT

FROXFIELD

STEEP

PETERSFIELD

WEST
SUSSEX

WEST
MEON

WESTBURY

EAST
MEON

St. Mary-in-the-Field

HAMPSHIRE

HAMBLEDON

River Meon

WEST DEAN

SOUTHWICK

FINDON

FAREHAM

CHICHESTER

HAYLING
ISLAND

THE SOLENT

PORTSMOUTH

ISLE OF
WIGHT

Shaking a little, the old man was allowed to sit down and another elderly parishioner, with an equally long memory, took his place.

John Raustowe has also worked the land and has lived in the parish of East Meon for more than seventy-two years and before that he lived in Hambledon, where he was born. (Although he is now over eighty and illiterate, he still has his wits very much about him – as I know well because he has a cot on the edge of the village close to mine.) He said he had not known any of the Priors of Winchester but he has known four of the Bishops from the times when they came out to East Meon for the hunting or for business. He declared that he knew the tithes and the other items normally went to the Bishop because it was once his own job to collect the sheaves from the farmers of both East Meon and Hambledon and to take them to the Bishop's barns in both parishes. He had done this for years but he also knew that when a bishop died and a new one was not yet appointed the tithes went to the Prior and Convent in Winchester. That, he said, was common knowledge among the parishioners but no, he had not actually seen them being handed over nor known whether they were in kind or in cash.

Then we had crabby old Thomas att Hasill – well, not old really, compared to the other two as he was only aged sixty-something and so much younger. His memory is just as good, though, and memory is what counts in a case like this. Thomas has lived here in East Meon since his youth and is of free-birth like the other two but, unlike them, is really on the edge of poverty. (His father, Richard att Hasill, was also an East Meon man who never made much of himself either.) Thomas said he had known the Prior of Winchester for six years and one of the monks for a month or more while, like John Raustowe, he had known the four Bishops (Beaufort, Wayneflete, Courtenay and now our new Bishop, Thomas Langton) but he had not paid much attention to what went on during the vacancies that fell between them as (and this rather sourly) such things were not matters to concern him. Nevertheless (with a sly smile and some triumph) he did know that after the deaths of Bishops Beaufort and Wayneflete the Prior and Convent received all the Bishop's tithes from the churches of East Meon and Hambledon as well as from their chapels of Froxfield, Steep and Westbury during the whole of the vacancies. He believed this to be true because he had never heard to the contrary, and if it had been the Archbishop or his officials who had collected the tithes he would have known, since he has been in the parish sixty years or more and had never heard of such things and (as if to clinch the matter) neither had his father, who had known the parish for just as long before that.

After this they brought forward William Weston, our butcher, who had been born in East Meon and lived here since his youth, about sixty years ago. He is literate, of free status (not, mind you, that there are many villeins left now) and is the natural son of John Weston, also of East Meon (who, we all suspect, set him up in the butchery trade). His testimony is much the same as that of the others, but he did remember that after the death of Bishop Wayneflete the tithe of sheaves from East Meon was placed as usual in our big barn. A monk, of whose name he was not now sure, came from Winchester and in the name of the Prior and Convent sealed the doors of the barn, not only at East Meon but of those at Froxfield and Steep, in which the grain was stored. This he saw himself. Later he saw the same monk reach an agreement with Simon Bee of East Meon for the sale of those sheaves on behalf of the Prior and Convent, and believed that later Simon gave the money to the same monk, although he did not know how much that money was. Moreover, he said, during that self-same vacancy the monk held a Court (which he could not have done if the Prior had not held the jurisdiction) at which his own father, John Weston, had to pay the Prior 10 shillings for a cottage which he held from East Meon Church, and John Goss had to pay 3s.4d. for ten acres, as did John Bull for another ten acres.

William Bulbeck followed William Weston. He was born at Froyle over sixty years ago and was the natural son of John Bulbeck and had been in East Meon for more than forty years, working the land. He has done pretty well for himself, it seems, and I was somewhat surprised that he had goods and chattels worth at least £40 as that is more than I have and he never struck me as being rich. However, he said he was a tenant of the Prior and Convent for lands at an annual rent of 10 shillings and knew the Prior and some of the monks. Furthermore, he could add to the testimony of William Weston as the monk of whom William had spoken was now the Sub-Prior, and when he came out to East Meon following the death of Bishop Wayneflete, he had to admonish the parishioners for not keeping the sheaves to be tithed separate from their own. Well, what with the bishop dead, it was only natural to hope that if the two lots were well mixed no one would be able to tell how much was due to the Prior. You can't blame the cottagers. Wheat is food, after all. It seems, though, that the monk had railed at them a bit and William said that many of the parishioners did take them to the barn, after all. (Some parishioners, mind you, but not all! I guess there were households which ate rather better than usual that winter but I'm sure the monks never starved.)

Then came Thomas Holden, another farming man, who has lived at East Meon for more than fifty years and is now over sixty-nine. He was born in Farnham, Surrey, the natural son of William Holden, and is literate and of free status. His goods are worth £20. He bore out the testimony of the others, adding a bit here and a bit there, but he did reveal that just after the death of our last Bishop (that is to say, Bishop Peter Courtenay) the tithes and revenues of the two churches and the chapels were collected by Richard Cager of East Meon, not for the monks but to be paid to a Mr. Robert Sherborne, the Archbishop's commissary. It seems that Richard Cager only handed over the money after this Sherborne had promised that if they should indeed have gone to the Prior and Convent of St. Swithun's then he would repay their value to the Prior. I don't think Richard altogether trusted Mr. Sherborne but as he is a very fearsome man and full of power Richard felt helpless against him.

I was the next witness and declared I was the natural son of Thomas Stympe, deceased, of West Dean, Sussex, although I was born at Findon, also in Sussex. I have lived now in East Meon for more than thirty years, am over fifty-five, am literate and of free status, holding goods worth about £20. I am a tenant of the Prior and Convent for a rent of 12 shillings a year, but as I am also their collector of rents (which amount to £40 a year) I am paid back 40s. a year. In addition, I am a tenant of the Bishop of Winchester for other land and also manage for my own advantage ('farm', they call it) certain matters of the Church here in East Meon, for which privilege I pay the bishop £8.8s.4d. per annum.

I continued with my testimony and told the judges that I knew the present Prior and some of the monks and knew the Archbishop well by sight. I confirmed all that the other witnesses had said. I did add, however, that the tithe money was not paid direct to Mr. Robert Sherborne, the Archbishop's man, as was suggested by the previous witness, but to John Gossage, Mr. Sherborne's servant. I had seen for myself how this Gossage had frightened poor Richard Cager, the tithe and rent collector, by waving about a citation that seemingly declared that if the revenues were not paid over, Cager would find himself face to face with the Archbishop. It was after this threat that Cager meekly agreed to follow Gossage to Alton (where he had to go on business) and pay over the money there.

As it happened, a lot of other people had to go to Alton to hand over their dues to Gossage and I went with them. They went in fear, but I went to prove that I had already paid the £8.8s.4d that I owed the Bishop and held the receipt.

However, I went on to tell the judges that I was in Taunton in Somerset (our Bishop has land there) while the see of Bath and Wells was vacant, and this same Mr. Sherborne was Vicar General in Spirituals for the Archbishop. Now, in Taunton in a vacancy, all the tithes and revenues are paid by tradition direct to the Archbishop. As I knew this, I thought it politic to suggest that perhaps Mr. Sherborne had confused the normal run of things in a vacancy throughout the province of Canterbury with the abnormal arrangements for East Meon and Hambledon. An easy mistake to make, I said, and it should not be held against Mr. Sherborne.

(This sounded somewhat as if I was trying to protect Sherborne and I was blamed for it afterwards in the village but, as a travelled man and one somewhat educated, it seemed to me to be both a judicious and an unprejudiced attitude to take and one that could do me no harm in the future. It was strictly hypocritical, of course, as I am still strongly and whole-heartedly on the side of Prior Hunton and the Convent but a man has to protect his own interests even while fighting for justice.)

We then had to sit through the testimonies of the two Hambledon witnesses – John Flesshmonger and John Wyndar, both farming men. John Flesshmonger began life sixty years ago in Preston Candover before moving to Southwick and then to Hambledon, where he has been for the last twenty-five years or so. A good farmer and normally not easily cowed. Although his evidence was entirely in favour of the Prior and Convent, he had nevertheless paid over the money from the tithe of sheaves to Mr. Sherborne. Admittedly, that was only after he had been summoned to the Hospital of St. Cross at Winchester where he was threatened (like Cager) with having to face the Cardinal Archbishop himself. That was quite enough to take the courage from him.

The last witness, John Wyndar, added nothing to what had already been said and we waited to hear that justice was now to be done and that the Prior and Convent of St. Swithun's would re-establish their rights.

But, of course, it did not happen that way.

While this seven-year case had been going on (and our new Bishop Langton of Winchester had been appointed) the Archbishop, crafty man that he is, had persuaded the Pope to issue several new Bulls, Mandates and Indults in his own favour, including one that gave him the sole right over all the revenues from the parishes within every diocese under his jurisdiction during a vacancy of a see – which would now include East Meon and Hambledon, of course. Against this the Prior's defence became worthless and he was clearly the loser although he refused to admit that he was.

Then, on 7th January, 1499, the Abbot of Bermondsey (who seems to have been the judge in charge of most of the proceedings) decided to excommunicate our Prior of St. Swithun's for not admitting that the Archbishop had won the case. What a thing to be excommunicated for! I have never heard of anything so shameful in all my life. It is one thing to threaten and bully in order to get one's own way but quite another to put those threats into practice. We, in the village and frightened though we might be, were wholly on the side of the Prior, for the excommunication would cut him off from all the rights and privileges of the church and, worst of all, from the sacraments. We mourned for him.

It was during July of that same year that the Pope declared the formal closing of the case – giving some sort of victory to Archbishop Morton, I suppose – and stated that the final costs were to be borne by the Prior and Convent at Winchester. The sum was very high for it was announced that they had to pay 400 marks to the Archbishop, not all at once I am glad to say, but in three instalments, the last by Easter, 1501.

One very important victory did go to Prior Hunton, though, for the Pope withdrew the penalties imposed by the Abbot of Bermondsey on him and absolved from excommunication both he, the Convent, their advocates, proctors and all those involved in the affair on their behalf – but on pain of being re-excommunicated if the Convent failed to pay up as required! The poor Prior had to agree to this and to sign his name on the document setting it all forth. Then a new Prior was appointed, Thomas Silkstede, and he is burdened with finding the remainder of the debt and where he'll get the money from, I don't know.

And so the notorious affair of the Pope, the Cardinal, the Prior and the rights to East Meon's tithes came to an end. But we, here in the village, are left with the very sad feeling that the Church has become too powerful and too self-seeking. Where now, we ask, is the humility of Christ's representatives who serve God only with justice and mercy? We can see that a change will have to come – there are too many grumbles, complaints and criticisms of church policy and practice. Power goes to people's heads, be they common folk or bishops, and bishops, like kings, are ever greedy.

John Morton, Cardinal Archbishop of Canterbury, is an evil man and may he repent his wickedness before the Day of Judgement arrives. He has served the Church ill but, nevertheless, may he be forgiven. If he repents.

God save all our souls. Amen.

Based on: work by Christopher Harper-Bill in *The Register of John Morton, Archbishop of Canterbury 1486-1500, Vol. I (Canterbury and York Society, LXXV 1987)* and in *Archbishop John Morton and the Province of Canterbury 1486-1500 (Journal of Ecclesiastical History, XXIX, 1978.)*

Hambledon by John Goldsmith. Phillimore, 1994.

Chapter Eleven

The Reformation and the Curate of East Meon, 1556

"I do not agree with you, sir. That I do not." Edward Wryte, newly returned to East Meon on vacation from the University of Cambridge, spoke with great firmness. "I cannot agree on this matter. Your argument does not hold."

His father, Robert Wryte, sighed, clearly deploring his son's attitude. "Very well", he said, "we shall leave the matter there, but I tell you, Edward, that I cannot – and will not – tolerate Protestantism being preached in my house."

"Sir", the young man replied formally, making a small bow. He picked up his book of sermons by Hugh Latimer and the slimmer volume by Thomas Bilney, and left the room. At least he had tried to explain his thinking to his father – he had not condemned him without first trying to gain his understanding.

Moodily he wandered out of the house and into the orchard. What a pity that people closed their minds to all that was going on in Europe now. The practice of religion really was changing. The Christian faith itself was not debatable, but the practice of it certainly was. The group of reformers and modernists in Cambridge had made that clear at their meetings in the White Horse Tavern. That inn was called 'Little Germany' now, for many of its patrons not only discussed the New Learning that was sweeping the Continent, but the theological teachings of Martin Luther and the works of the Swiss Protestant minister, Ulrich Swingli. The topic of the moment was reform of the Catholic Church, as envisaged by Erasmus, and Edward found those evenings in the tavern inspirational. If only his father could hear those learned and upright men discussing such things, then surely he would have greater sympathy for his son's beliefs.

Desiderus Erasmus of Rotterdam, for instance – his father had hardly heard of him, while to Edward he was the greatest of all Humanists. Look at the men Erasmus had associated with in London, Cambridge and Oxford: John Colet, late Dean of St. Paul's; Sir Thomas More, the Lord Chancellor now that Cardinal Wolsey was dead,

Richard Fox, until recently Bishop of Winchester, and the present Bishop, Stephen Gardiner; Bishop John Fisher of Rochester; Hugh Latimer, and William Warham, who until his recent death was Archbishop of Canterbury. (It was Warham, Edward knew, who had bought Peak Farm, outside East Meon, for £200 from the Tygall family in 1505 and left it to his nephew, William Warham, and his wife Elizabeth, who lived there now.)

What men these Humanists were! And how right that they esteemed Erasmus so highly for he was, after all, a truly international figure and the greatest thinker of the time. People were looking to him for inspiration and adopting his championship of Liberty of Thought, and the idea that reason and moderation were the best solvers of problems. He was clearly not a heretic, ready to denounce Catholicism, for both the leaders of the Reforming Movement and those still entrenched in the Catholic faith looked to him for guidance. A truly great man.

Edward was not a theologian, for he was studying Law, but he could not help but be involved in the controversies of his time. In a way it was of only small importance that King Henry was seeking a divorce from Catherine of Aragon, for it was held by many people to be reasonable for him to do so. With the all-important matter of the Royal Succession in mind, and the Queen having produced only one living child, the Princess Mary, it was seen as natural for the King to want to re-marry in the hope of a male heir. The recent wars between the Yorkist and Lancastrian branches of the Plantagenets had been to decide that very matter, and England now longed for a settled male succession, decided without war.

What interested Edward more than the divorce was the subject of Royal Supremacy over the Church in England. He knew that anti-clerical feeling was rife in the country, for the abuses of the Church and its clergy were considerable, and many felt its government should be taken out of Papal control and given to the King and Parliament. This was quite a separate issue from the divorce, but there was as much controversy over this as over the other for, if ecclesiastical authority were to be transferred to the Crown, who was to tell if it would be better managed and with fewer abuses?

But it was the New Learning that engaged most of Edward's attention. The New Learning – that Erasmus-inspired rebirth of the study of Ancient Greek and Latin writers, their teachings and philosophies. Education was now seen as all-important, and even Bishops no longer founded monasteries but schools and university colleges. As long ago as 1382 Bishop William of Wykeham had founded in Winchester the College of St. Mary to educate boys for the priesthood, and, in 1379, New College in Oxford for undergraduates. William Wayneflete, a later Bishop of Winchester, had founded Magdalen College in Oxford in 1458 and to fund it had closed Selborne Priory and many other monastic foundations, and even given it the income from his lands at Hilhampton, just outside East Meon. It was the same story in Cambridge, as Edward knew well. King's College had been founded by King Henry VI in 1445, in connection with his Eton College of 1440. Jesus College was on the site of a suppressed nunnery. Christ's College and St John's were both founded by Lady Margaret Beaufort, mother of King Henry VII. Education was now of huge importance to the country, and nobles and young men were no longer limited to military life, where excellence in feats of arms and courage in battle were all that mattered. To be 'cultured' was now the fashion.

So Edward Wryte sat in his father's orchard, wishing himself back at Cambridge among men who thought in modern ways and had minds open to the critical appraisal of new ideas and the renaissance of old. He had recently learnt to play the lute and tried his hand at sonnet-writing. He had read Plato and some of Aristotle, had dabbled a little in alchemy and astrology. He saw himself becoming one of the multi-talented young, and a veritable 'Universal Man', able to discourse on any subject from the writings of Plutarch and the correct notation for a madrigal, to reasons for the growth of Protestantism.

There he paused. Was he, indeed, a Protestant? His father seemed to think he was, but his father did not know the complexities of that subject. Did he, Edward, really believe, as a Protestant, in the superiority of the Bible as a source of Christian teaching over that of the Catholic Church? And where did he feel his individual responsibility lay – directly to God or to the Papal authority under whose rule he had been brought up? Did he, like Martin Luther, condemn the public sale of indulgences to raise funds for church-building, and especially that of St Peter's in Rome? Did he really want to read the Bible in English and whenever he wished, rather than just hear it read in Church on a Sunday? Did he uphold the principle of permitting private judgement in interpreting Holy Scripture? Did he agree with the Papal Declaration of 1529, prohibiting any innovation at all in Church practice or doctrine? Or did he side with those German princes and cities who strongly disagreed, and who issued in that same year their 'Protestatio' against such a ruling, thus giving their name to the whole movement?

Restlessly he reached for fallen apples, shed by the over-burdened trees in the June drop, and tossed them one by one over the hedge. The whole problem of religious faith was too difficult to solve alone. If only he were back in Cambridge he could test his thinking against that of his friends. There was nobody here who could help him. East Meon was not exactly a haven for philosophers or the politically advanced! Even Father Rychard was not much use. He might be young and with a lively mind, but Edward could not see him having an aptitude for critical thinking. He was, after all, a priest of the Catholic Church and curate here. Yet he might be better than nobody. Perhaps he would wander up to the Church to see if he was about, or, if not, seek out William Bren or John Leffe. No one else he could think of had either the inclination or ability to discuss matters other than farming or market prices. What a waste of time these vacations were!

He found Father Rychard Alyn in the Lady Chapel and waited until his prayers were finished. Then, when the Curate had risen to his feet and made his genuflection, he addressed him.

"Can I talk?" he asked rather brusquely, a little uncertain of what to say. "I'm confused about – well, whether I'm a Protestant or not."

The Curate looked at him in silence for a moment. "Come out into the litten. We can talk there undisturbed."

In the churchyard they found a patch in the sun, and seated themselves among the wild flowers and the grave mounds of the village dead. "Now", said the priest. "Tell me your problem."

So Edward did, talking at some length, surprised by the quiet attention given to him. "I really want to know", he finished. "Do you think I'm a Protestant – or not?"

"That is a matter you must decide for yourself. No man can lean on another's opinion over such a fundamental issue. Pray for guidance from Almighty God that His Word may enter in and lead you to the right decision."

"Yes", Edward mumbled awkwardly, disconcerted by the formality of the reply. "Yes. But prayer – ". He broke off and turned to pull at grass stalks in a somewhat distracted manner. "Prayer never seems to be answered."

"Have patience. And try to empty your mind and heart of all preconceived ideas. At present, I think, you want God to give His assent and His blessing to your Protestant leanings. You would – am I not right? – be very seriously disappointed if He pointed you towards a full return to the Catholic Church? Pray for true guidance, and be unfettered by superficial interest in the present fashion for Protestantism." Then he paused. "Now I can say no more."

Edward, too, fell silent. He knew the advice was sound but was inexplicably reluctant to take it. What he needed was more talk, more debate about the situation, more thrashing out of the points both in favour and against the changes proposed. He was aware that reform within the Church had long been sought, and he knew of groups such as the Lollards, led by John Wycliffe in the fourteenth century; the Hussites, followers of John Hus of Bohemia, who had been burned at the stake for heresy in 1415; even, much earlier, the protests made by the Waldensians and the dualist Cathars.

"But I'm not a heretic!" he burst out. "I believe in God – the Christian God – and in Christ. It's just that some of the practises of the Church feel wrong. And I protest at the lack of reform."

"I know", Father Rychard replied strongly. "I – "

Edward looked at him quickly but the priest was rising to his feet. "I must go now", he said hastily. "Think about what I've said."

"But – you're a Protestant yourself!" the younger man declared in astonishment. "You're one of us!"

For a long moment neither said anything. Then Father Rychard sank to the ground again. "Keep your voice down, I beseech you. My position is hard enough without the village hearing."

Edward said nothing further, too surprised to assimilate this information fully. After a short while, the priest said in a low, sad voice, "I don't know how to act. Any more than you do. I long for the decision to be taken out of my hands." Then he smiled ruefully. "In a clap of thunder, perhaps? Or an ordinance from God writ in letters of fire in the sky?"

"But the Bishop?" Edward queried. "Bishop Gardiner? Have you told him?"

"Not yet. Nor my Vicar, John Heliar, whom I seldom see but to whom my loyalty is due as his Curate. I haven't told him either."

"But the Bishop is on the side of reform, surely? He's been on diplomatic missions to Rome, trying to get the King's divorce, so he's not one of the Pope's men. But – well, I suppose that doesn't make him an active Protestant, either."

"No, it doesn't", Father Rychard replied. "And John Heliar certainly isn't one. He's a very, very convinced and orthodox Catholic. And that's my problem. He's not only my Vicar but also the Rector of Warblington and Domestic Chaplain to the Countess of Salisbury at the Castle there. In addition he's a friend of her three sons, the Poles, and especially of the second son, Reginald, who is strongly against Protestantism. I'm never going to convince Heliar of the need for reform, so I don't know what to do. I just don't know. I could resign, I suppose", he concluded.

"No! No! That won't help anybody! Just stay here and see what happens. The King might decide to remain a true Catholic – which he seems to be at heart – or we get the reforms we need. The Act of Supremacy may never be passed and then you could go on owing allegiance to the Pope and your Vicar while working for reform. You're still young and things may change."

The curate shook his head. "John Heliar will never change. Nor will the Poles – or their mother, the Countess – they're Yorkist, you see. Plantagenets of the House of York, of the White Rose, and cousins of the King. They're important people, and that's why Henry wants them on his side over this divorce. They're extremely influential abroad, being royal, and should England ever rise up against the King, the Poles are very real contenders for the throne. The eldest son is Henry, Lord Montagu, as you probably know, and the youngest is Sir Geoffrey, a rather weak man, I think, and not at all like Reginald, the middle son, who's brilliant and a favourite of the King. In fact, I believe Pole has left for Rome because he fears the King's wrath over his disapproval of a divorce. He even turned down the King's offer to be Bishop of Winchester or Archbishop of York when Cardinal Wolsey died in 1530, provided he agreed over a new marriage to Anne Boleyn. But he wouldn't accept. He gave up great honours for his principles."

Then he smiled sadly. " I wish I knew where my principles lay. When I became a priest I took vows to uphold the Catholic Church's teaching and I've done that throughout my time here. But now? Who knows! I am not, I think, a vow-breaker and yet I yearn so earnestly to restrain the abuses of the Church and to help men to reach God more directly. And I can only see this happening if we abandon the inflexible rule and authority of the Pope. So I'm in great pain and mental turmoil."

Edward did not know what to say so he returned to pulling at grass-stalks. "I shan't tell anyone of what you've said. And I feel, well, honoured that you've spoken to me so openly."

When he had left the curate he returned home, feeling strangely comforted. Even here, in rural Hampshire, he was not alone. Confusion and heart-searching were not confined to universities.

Edward was back in Cambridge when the news broke towards the end of January, 1533, that the King had secretly married the now pregnant Anne Boleyn. Having tried for many years to obtain a legal divorce through representations to Rome, Henry had waited no longer and re-married, many thought bigamously. With the King's friend, Thomas Cranmer, now Archbishop of Canterbury, and Thomas Cromwell his chief adviser, Henry had no trouble in arranging the desired divorce. By May, 1533, the marriage to Catherine of Aragon was declared void and that to Anne Boleyn valid. This, at least, would protect the legitimacy of the new child, expected in September. It would also settle the matter of the Royal Succession, for the King was convinced his new queen would produce the longed for son. Both he and the country groaned when the child was a girl, to be named Elizabeth.

In the following year of 1534, the Act of Supremacy was issued, making Henry the Supreme Head of the Church of England. The monastic foundations were then threatened with dissolution, for not only would they have been Catholic centres of unrest but Henry needed the money their sale would bring. It soon became clear, though, that Thomas Cromwell was moving very cautiously in this matter, closing at first only those smaller and least efficient houses which had incomes of less than £200 a year. When Newark Priory, near Ripley in Surrey, was dissolved, the land it held at Rothercombe in the parish of East Meon, was granted by the King to Thomas Knight, who also gained the lands and rents the Priory had held in East Meon itself. (Edward heard, however, that this Knight did not hold them for long, selling them to Thomas Uvedale for £126.) More local lands changed hands in 1536 when Durford Abbey, just over the Sussex border from Petersfield, was suppressed. Its small properties in Langrish and East Meon (each worth no more than two shillings a year in rent) passed to Sir William Fitzwilliam, of Cowdray Castle, once the King's whipping-boy. Shortly afterwards he acquired the suppressed Easeborne Priory at Midhurst, and other lands in Ditcham, Buriton, Petersfield, Liss, Winchester and elsewhere.

During the Christmas festivities of 1536, Edward again sought out Father Rychard. "We have just heard the Pope has made Reginald Pole a Cardinal! The man isn't even a priest! How can he be a Cardinal?"

"A reward, perhaps?" the Curate suggested. "For his treatise *'De Unitate Ecclesiastica'*? It's in support of the Papal primacy and against the King having taken over the Church in England. Any hope Henry had of a reconciliation with Pole must be finished."

"But it's so extraordinary!" Edward burst out. "Everything seems to be happening this year – Erasmus has died, so has William Tyndale (and how grateful I am for his New Testament in English) and now this Cardinal business. Then there are religious uprisings in the North under Robert Aske – what does he call it? – the 'Pilgrimage of Grace'? And I've heard that Pole is to be made a Legate, as well as everything else, and told to back the Northern Rebels and to persuade France and the Emperor Charles V to invade England. To get rid of Henry and bring back the Pope! I mean, that's treason! That's treason, surely? The man's a traitor to his country, advocating invasion!"

During his last summer at Cambridge, Edward heard that the rebellious Robert Aske and his followers had been hanged and the uprising suppressed with much slaughter. He heard, too, that the King was now implacably against the Pole family. Henry, Lord Montagu, the eldest brother, was imprisoned, as was his cousin, Henry Courtenay, Marquess of Exeter, who had estates at Halnaker near Chichester. Sir Geoffrey Pole was arrested and questioned about his brother Reginald's plans for invasion, and their mother, Margaret, Countess of Salisbury, had her Warblington Castle searched for incriminating documents.

By this time it was clear that John Heliar, Vicar of East Meon, had left England secretly – easy enough to do from the little fishing port of Emsworth, near Warblington – and with his servant, Henry Penning, was now thought to be in Paris. Because of his close connection with the Pole family it had become no longer safe to remain in England. Indeed, he was charged with treason in his absence and forfeited his benefices of Warblington and East Meon, where new clergy were installed. That forfeiture occurred despite the efforts of Sir William Paulet, perhaps the greatest landowner in the county and later to become Marquess of Winchester, who had offered Heliar his protection. He had even sent Heliar's brother-in-law, John Fowle, to Louvain for a false certificate purporting to show the priest was studying there, in a vain attempt to prevent the two parishes being lost to him.

Edward's mother told him how distressed she was by the new Vicar. "He's called Father John. Father John Simpson. But he doesn't feel like a priest to me – he's trying to make Protestants of us all. I don't know what Bishop Gardiner was thinking of to appoint him."

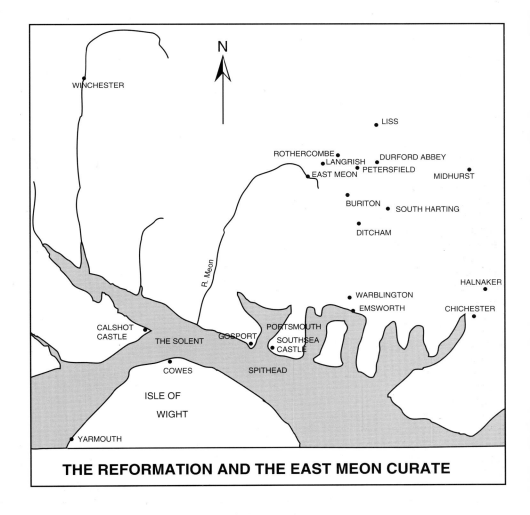

THE REFORMATION AND THE EAST MEON CURATE

Edward smiled. His mother, Margaret, would never be anything but a good Catholic, wedded to the old ways and the old securities. His younger brother, Nycholas, had no such scruples. Being a farmer by inclination as well as occupation, he was more interested in the recent rise in the price of wool, and was clearing ground on the farm for extra sheep-walks to exploit the boom. Edward did not know about his father. Robert Wryte was a man of few words, wrapped up in managing his ever-increasing landholdings, and since he had forbidden talk of Protestantism in his house, Edward had not discussed the matter with him.

One day in 1538, however, his father entered the parlour in obvious distress. "It's shocking!" he declared. "Cruel and shocking! England is becoming barbaric!" Red in the face with anger, he stumped round the room until his wife bade him explain the trouble.

"It's the cruelty of it! Taking an old woman like that! Monstrous! Monstrous!"

"Which old woman?" Edward asked.

"The Countess, of course! That lovely, saintly lady. He's put her in Cowdray Castle under house-arrest. And treating her very badly. She's sixty-nine. She shouldn't be treated like that."

It seemed that not only was Margaret, the Countess of Salisbury, now imprisoned by her questioner, Sir William Fitzwilliam, soon to be the first Earl of Southampton, but her eldest son, Lord Montagu, and his cousin, the Marquess of Exeter, had both been executed. The youngest son, Sir Geoffrey Pole, was detained but gained his life by revealing all he knew about the plots to overthrow the King, even though that meant implicating his friends and family. The King was justified in his fear of invasion, for the Catholic countries of France, under Francis I (he who had been so jovial with Henry on the Field of the Cloth of Gold in 1520) and the Emperor, Charles V, the Hapsburg ruler of Germany, Spain and the Spanish Netherlands, were indeed plotting to attack England.

"But Emperor Charles was in Winchester only a few years back!" Edward exclaimed. "The King showed him the Round Table in the Castle, which he'd had re-painted especially, as well as Winchester College. How can people turn on their friends like that?"

"My dear boy", his mother answered mildly. "Religion. Most quarrels nowadays are about money or religion. Human nature doesn't improve."

Edward was working hard in a lawyer's office in Winchester at this time and had taken lodgings not far from the Cathedral. When he could, and the weather was fair, he rode back to East Meon, partly out of filial duty and partly because he had become attracted to Elizabeth Maunfield, the daughter of a neighbouring farmer. He was at home when he heard that the Countess had been moved to the Tower in London, and that her son, the Cardinal, was now in Liège in Flanders, where he was trying to organise both King Francis and the Emperor Charles to cross the Channel and attack England.

The position of the Catholic Princess Mary, elder daughter of the King, now became crucial for, if an invasion succeeded, she would be placed on the throne. In view of this, the King moved her from palace to palace and castle to castle, hoping always to keep these moves secret from his enemies for fear of their seizing her. Spies, scouts and informers from both sides became very active. Reports were sent from England across the Channel by members of the Catholic faction and likewise messages would come from the Continent, brought by those working for the King and the Protestant cause. One such man was the poet, Sir Thomas Wyatt, who had received orders from Henry to send agents to assassinate Reginald Pole, but the Cardinal managed to escape and take refuge in Italy.

Another informant was Gervase Tyndall, once employed in the household of the Countess but who, now working for the King, revealed not only how John Heliar had made his escape from Warblington, but the ways in which messages were being sent overseas to the Cardinal. He revealed also that Heliar and Penning had been transported to France by Hugh Holland, who was a seaman and able to traverse the Channel without hindrance, coming and going as often as required. (Later it was heard that Holland, amongst others, had been captured and executed).

A brilliant double-agent, who provided sufficiently accurate information to bluff both sides (including the very astute Thomas Cromwell) was Michael Throckmorton who, on one occasion, was captured in Picardy but survived. Pole naturally had his own informants in England, many of them sympathetic clerics, one of whom was George Crofts, Chancellor of Chichester Cathedral. (Pole's benefice of South Harting, where he was Rector, lay in the Diocese of Chichester.) To add to all these complexities and double-dealing, the two great Catholic monarchs had their own spy systems, that of the Emperor being headed by the Swiss schemer, Eustace Chapuys, who had done so much to bring down Lord Montagu and the Marquess of Exeter.

Through all this period of religious uncertainty, Father Rychard remained Curate of East Meon. Occasionally he would discuss the state of affairs with Edward, one day revealing he no longer had the heart for life. "I am a man in great distress", he explained.

"But why?" Edward asked in surprise. "Surely now that you've actually taken the Oath of Supremacy to the King and his Church, and are an open Protestant, life is much easier?"

"I wish it were." There was a long pause and then, "I broke my vows, you see. I ceased to be a Catholic. I am a man whose word is thus worth nothing. As I've said to you before, when I first became a priest I vowed to uphold the Catholic Church's teaching and now I'm not doing so." He went on in a weary voice, "I preach the new faith as laid down by Archbishop Cranmer; I have erased the Pope's name from the mass-books; I have agreed to the removal of the stoup. I have handed over to the King's Commissioners – oh, so much of our lovely plate. Our silver cruets, our little chalice (now that Communion is in wine as well as bread, the old chalice was not large enough), the Pyx and even the golden monstrance."

"But there are good things, now", Edward insisted, anxiety tingeing his voice. "We can read the Bible ourselves, can't we? And in English. And all the services are in English, too. Think how that helps the common people! We don't even have to believe in Purgatory any more. And – and –"

He came to a halt when he saw tears running down his friend's face. Awkwardly he put his arm round the other's shoulder and held him tightly. "It's all right!" he said. "It's all right!"

But the priest shook his head. "It's not all right! I've broken my vows! God forgive me! God forgive me!"

Roughly he broke away and half ran into the church. Edward followed him in great concern, but when he saw the other prostrated before the altar of the Lady Chapel, banging one fist again and again on the step, he hesitated to intrude and crept away. Back in his parents' home, he sought out his mother. "Tell me," he said. "Are you all right? About religion, I mean. And is Father?"

Margaret Wryte laid down the chicken she had been plucking. "Why do you ask?" she enquired cautiously.

"Oh, I don't know," Edward replied. "Just wondered." Then he went to stare out of the window, so recently glazed at considerable cost, and now his mother's pride. "I've been talking to Father Rychard. He seems upset."

"Yes", his mother said, picking up the bird again.

When she said no more, he turned back to her. "Are you really distressed?"

Once more she replied, "Yes", and went on with her work.

There was silence between them for a while and then she said slowly, "It's all right for you young people. You can accept new ideas. But we've grown up with the Catholic Church and didn't look for change. We've had to adapt, because that's the ruling, but we aren't Protestants. Never will be. I still have my rosary and the crucifix over my bed. I still say the old Latin prayers and my Hail Marys. I won't change now. But Daughter Kateryne – I do worry about her. Her latest infant should be baptised soon but she's very uncertain what he'd be baptised into. Parnell and Johanne, they're only little girls and too young to understand. But I'm hoping they'll grow up as Catholics, even if they have to attend these new services."

Then she smiled up at him. "Don't you worry about your father and me. We're old. And we're not alone in our beliefs. There's many a good Catholic still living in this village, and although we don't hear Mass very often, we do when it matters most. There are priests from the monasteries, you see, who have taken pensions from the Government but who still practise the old ways, although not, of course, in church."

The next day he rode back to Winchester and his work, still concerned for his parents. Religion had become a matter of dispute and, it seemed, of greed and the spoilation of holy places. He had been horrified to hear that Thomas Cromwell had ordered the destruction of shrines, including that of St. Swithun in the Cathedral, taking even the great cross of emeralds. Word came that although Chichester Cathedral had lost three caskets of jewels, the greatest haul was said to have been from the pilgrimage shrine of St. Thomas à Becket in Canterbury. This had yielded for the King two great chests of jewels and twenty-four wagon-loads of other treasure. From every corner of England the story was the same. And now the greater Abbeys were being closed and their lands sold at the standard price of twenty years' rent. Property speculation was becoming rife, and although Edward welcomed the additional legal work this gave him, he was appalled by the rapidity of the changes taking place. Fortunes were being made by cornering the market in wheat, or by enclosing arable land for sheep-walks (thus throwing many labourers out of work) or by racking-up the rents on tenanted properties.

Robert Wryte, who had an increasing number of landholdings himself, refused to behave in this way and made sure that Nycholas followed suit. He would rail against the King's 'New Men' – those who were more businessmen than farmers and had few religious scruples or social consciences. Edward used to bring him from Winchester the latest pamphlets circulating there, for these described such men as idle, self-seeking, uneducated and without courtesy. Nobody liked them. They were naturally unpopular with the poor and were shunned by the established families, were preached against in Church and seemingly not altogether trusted by the King and his Council. East Meon was not greatly affected by these changes, although smaller properties did change owners, for the Bishop continued to hold most of the land, even though it was now largely tenanted. Local feeling had run very high over Cromwell's shrine-breaking

Commissioners, and many villagers were deeply shocked, even those who were not overly religious. They were confused too. All their lives they had been taught that the Church held the keys to Heaven, and that only through submission to its teaching and to the Pope could salvation be gained. Now they were worried, for they did not know if the King, who had replaced the Pope, could save their souls or not, although many were glad to have been freed from the tyranny and oppression of Cardinal Wolsey. They had rejoiced when the King's legitimate son, Edward, had been born, but would have rejoiced still further if the burden of taxes had been lightened. It was true that the compulsory payment of 'Peter's Pence' to Rome had been abolished, but the King's new Church had issued various statutes from 1534 onwards which exacted even larger sums than those previously paid to the Papacy.

When, in 1538, Francis I returned to the Pope's earlier proposals to invade England, Henry reacted by drastically improving his navy and initiating a long line of defensive forts on the South coast. They ran from Deal in Kent to Pendennis and St. Mawes in Cornwall. Edward Wryte, on one of his journeys on legal business, went to watch Southsea Castle going up. It not only added to the earlier defences at Portsmouth and protected the new dockyards, but was built to a revolutionary design to take account of the new use of cannon. Edward was deeply interested in this, and over the next few years also managed to visit Hurst and Calshot Castles, although not the Isle of Wight and the sites of proposed forts at Sandown, Yarmouth and Cowes. With the addition of the nightly raising of the great chain of iron links that stretched between the Round Tower at Portsmouth and a similar one at Gosport, the Harbour and Dockyards were considered well-defended.

As by this time Edward's career had begun to advance, he felt able to court Elizabeth Maunfield more assiduously. To this end he would walk from his parents' home in East Meon to her father's prosperous farm beneath the downs and, more often than not, be invited to join them for dinner at noon.

On one occasion Elizabeth's grandmother told Edward about her own courting days, and then added, "Now, don't you go about marriage like some in high places I could mention. We've had another divorce, I hear, and yet another new marriage – and that to a very flighty piece, I believe. You'd think he'd know better at forty-nine. And poor Thomas Cromwell, with his head chopped off, on the same day as the wedding. For treason, I understand, though what he'd done wrong none can tell – save getting the King married to Anne of Cleves." She paused a moment and then declared, "I didn't really care for Cromwell myself, but no man deserves a blunt axe."

That was in July, 1540, and by February , 1542, Catherine Howard, Henry's fifth wife, had indeed been tried, found guilty of adultery, and beheaded. Between those two dates Margaret, Countess of Salisbury, was taken from her prison in the Tower and also beheaded. The King was clearly still nervous about the 'White Rose' faction, and it was after his mother's death that Sir Geoffrey Pole escaped overseas to join his brother, the Cardinal. By this time Edward and Elizabeth were married and living in Winchester, with their first child expected in a few months' time. Edward was still working towards promotion and now had a number of personal clients, whose affairs his senior partners did not wish to handle. It was while on business for one of these that he happened to be in Portsmouth on 20th July, 1545. On that day, the French fleet sailed into the Solent, determined to punish King Henry for his recent capture of Boulogne and to prevent him from sending reinforcements to his army in France. The King had travelled to Hampshire and, while overlooking Spithead, watched the battle.

The pride of the navy, 'Mary Rose', had been built to a new concept as a floating gun-platform and on that day had sailed out of harbour with her gunports open, ready for battle. To the horror of all, she turned too sharply, keeled over, the sea flooded in and she sank almost immediately. Portsmouth was distraught and the King devastated but, despite this catastrophic loss, the French were driven out of the Solent and Boulogne did not fall.

News began to reach Winchester during the next year that the King's health was failing. An upsurge in plots and counter-plots followed and it became an uneasy time. The heir to the throne, Prince Edward, was only nine years old and there was much scrambling for power among the courtiers, politicians and leading churchmen.

Finally it was decided that Thomas Seymour, uncle of the prince and later Duke of Somerset, should be the Lord Protector. By the time the King died at the end of January, 1547, the leading men in power were all fervent Protestants, for they had gained immeasurably from the dissolution of the monasteries and the new land enclosures. But the people were restless.

Even in East Meon several of the larger property owners became worried. Robert Wryte and his son, Nycholas, became even more careful and conciliatory in their dealings with the labourers. Revolt was in the air again, not only over the denial of papal authority, for Henry's reforms of the Church were still not fully accepted, but because of hardship among the common people. So many were now dispossessed of their lands. Wealth seemed to be reserved for the already rich. No one was surprised when, in 1549 Robert Ket led an uprising near Norwich, which ended in a massacre by the Protector's troops. Nor at the revolt of Catholics in the Western counties against the new Book of Common Prayer, introduced by Archbishop Cranmer and enforced by the 'Act of Uniformity', which also made the hearing of Mass illegal. Edward feared for his parents at this news.

A few years later, when he came back to East Meon to see his parents, he met Father Rychard. After exchanging the usual courtesies, the Curate said bitterly, "They're at it again. King Edward's Commissioners. They're going round every county making inventories of remaining plate and vestments – they're not needed, it seems, with the new services." He laughed shortly. "I hear that in some places the copes and other vestments are being cut up to make ladies' robes. Sacrilege! All sacrilege! Nothing of the old holiness and beauty is left. Did you know that we can't say prayers for the dead any more? That the old stone altars are thrown out to act as flooring to be trodden underfoot? Our Rood screen has gone, and the great Rood over it. And I've heard that Bishops are taking the sacraments sitting at a table – kneeling is no longer a sign of worship!"

He turned restlessly away and then burst out, "They have even taken the statue of Our Lady! They dropped it and it smashed. Oh, Edward, to see her lovely, holy image in pieces and her face trodden on was terrible. Terrible! And I hate it! I hate it all! I truly wish I'd never entered the Church." He turned again to Edward. "I have to teach people what I no longer believe. Trying to lead them to God, when God seems an impossible concept. I'm acting a lie – I don't believe in this new Church. But, oh Edward", he cried out "What went wrong? What went wrong? We began, you and I, with such high aspirations and deep faith. And now there's nothing. Humanism is dead. Sensible reforms are abandoned. Now it's all Acts of Parliament and Royal Decrees. Enforced by threats. Where's the holiness in that?"

This conversation disturbed Edward profoundly and, during the ride back to Winchester, he worried. He also worried at the news that the young King was dying of tuberculosis. The nobles were now plotting to put an unknown Protestant girl on the throne who had little claim to royal blood. If Lady Jane Grey were made Queen, and not the Princess Mary, elder daughter of Henry VIII, there would be very serious trouble in the country. Mary was deeply Catholic, as had been her mother, Catherine of Aragon, but at least she was the true claimant to the throne and of deep piety. England would prefer her to anyone else.

Edward VI died in July, 1553, and Lady Jane Grey was Queen for nine days before being arrested for treason. When Mary Tudor entered London she was cheered thankfully by the populace.

"Now we shall have peace", Edward told his wife. "Now we can go back to the old ways and begin again to make the Catholic Church more holy and more in keeping with the times. More truly reformed."

A few days later he received a joyful letter from Rychard Alyn in East Meon. "They have returned our Church treasures!" he wrote. "Queen Mary's Commissioners have brought them all back, and delivered them into the hands of John Pyne and John Carlins, the church wardens! So our two chalices are back, with their patens! Four bells are now in the steeple. We have the vestments again – the purple velvet suit and the red one, the white damask, the green silk and blue satin sets, even the blue and white silk one! The altar cloths are back, too, and the two pairs of latten candlesticks. We have the six surcopes and, last but not least, our pair of organs! Thanks be to God! Now we have the semblance of a church again. I can't tell you how excited I am! I had to sign their inventory, of course, along with John Posted, and the Commissioners kept one copy and the churchwardens the other. And, believe it or not, we all have strict instructions not to embezzle! But, oh, Edward, God is very good!"

Edward was truly delighted at the news and, in particular, he thought of the happiness his parents would feel. To be openly Catholic again and to be able to celebrate Mass in church would fill them with elation. A few days later, though, he received another letter, this time from his mother to say that his father was ill with the fever that was rampant in the village. Rychard Alyn had died from the same cause but it was thought his father would recover. The Curate's death was a great sadness, for he had been a good friend of many years' standing. Edward was thankful, though, that he had died so full of joy. If he had departed only a few months earlier, before Queen Mary's accession, he would have died in a state of depression and disillusionment.

Yet, as the weeks went by Edward himself became disillusioned. With an avidly Catholic queen on the throne, the political scene was returning to plots and schemes and betrayals. The suppression of Protestantism was even fiercer than Henry VIII's suppression of Catholicism.

Archbishop Cranmer was arrested for heresy, as were Bishop John Hooper, the elderly Bishop Hugh Latimer and Nicholas Ridley, Bishop of London. Sir Thomas Wyatt, son of the poet, was executed for rebellion, while Lady Jane Grey and her husband were also beheaded. It was said that in London scores of bodies could be seen hanging from gibbets. That year of 1553 was not peaceful. There was talk now of Queen Mary marrying Philip of Spain, the Catholic son of Emperor Charles V. The marriage ceremony would be held in Winchester Cathedral and Edward dreaded the day. He could see that from then on the monarchy would be so strictly orthodox that there would be no room for the 'sensible reforms' of the Church of which Rychard Alyn had written. All would be bigotry again. And cruelty. And hate.

Some time later he heard that Cardinal Reginald Pole had returned to England and, having been no more than a Deacon all these years, was finally ordained Priest in 1556. He became the Archbishop of Canterbury immediately afterwards, celebrating Mass for the very first time. Edward enquired about Pole's friend, the absent East Meon Vicar, John Heliar, and heard that he had retired to Rome where he had died in 1541. In Winchester the clergy changed back to being Catholics, with the Protestant Bishop, John Ponet, dismissed as a married priest, and Stephen Gardiner returning to the post. Although the Prior of St. Swithun's, William Basyng, had become the first Dean of the Cathedral under Henry VIII (and his Convent the first Chapter) he had long retired and been replaced by a Catholic priest.

Despite these upheavals in the country, Edward was now making good progress in his legal career and was earning well. His father explained that because of this, when the time came for him to make his will, he intended to leave the main land holdings to Nycholas, although he was the second son. The leasehold of one of the other East Meon farms, he would leave to Edward.

"So that my son's son has a place here", he said. "But I would like you to pay an annuity from the income to your mother while she lives."

"Of course, Father", he replied. "Of course." And they smiled at each other, a new warmth between them.

Based on:

Who's Who in History, Vol II. England 1485 – 1603 by C R N Routh. Blackwell, 1964.

Reform and Reformation by G R Elton.
Edward Arnold, 1981.

A Diet for Henry VIII: The Failure of Reginald Pole's 1537 Legation by Thomas F Mayer. Article in 'Journal of the North American Conference on British Studies', 1987.

England Under The Tudors by G R Elton. Routledge, 1991.

Tudor England by John Guy. O U P, 1990.

The Life and Times of Henry VIII by Robert Lacey. Weidenfield and Nicholson, 1992.

The Tudors by Christopher Morris.Fontana/Collins, 1990.

A History of East Meon by F G Standfield. Phillimore, 1984.

Warblington Church Leaflet by Norman Simmonds, 1979.

DYERS'
WOAD

Chapter Twelve

The Hampshire Beacon Plot, 1586

MICHAEL Dunnett knew something was afoot the moment he entered the ale-house. Being early June and blessedly warm after the bitter Spring, the door stood open, giving the men inside no warning of his arrival.

"Good day!" he greeted them "Day, Betsy!" he added to the ale-wife. "A mug of your best, please." Then he glanced at the five men already there. He wondered what they were planning, for they looked both sheepish and guilty. Poaching on Park Hill, maybe, and yet neither Jonathan Stye nor Richard Potts was an adventurous man. In some amusement he watched each in turn hastily finish his ale and, mumbling about having to get home else the wife would be after him, leave the small front room of Betsy's ramshackle house which did duty as a tavern.

Michael sipped his drink and turned conversationally to the brewster. "Fine day, Betsy. Let's hope it lasts." Then he turned to gaze through the open door. He knew quite well she was waiting for him to enquire about the secretive conversation so obviously having just taken place, but he also knew he would gain more information by remaining silent.

"Hope the day lasts for hay making," Betsy said finally. "Us don't want it cold and wet like last year. Lost too much good fodder, we did."

Michael grunted in reply. And waited.

"Not seen you here for a day or so. Too busy, I 'spect? Being Parish Constable keeps you busy?"

"Middling, middling," he answered.

"That Peter Striker, who was here just now. Talk by the hour, he will. You'd think he had nothing better to do."

Oh, yes?" he said. "I know Peter usually has some scheme to set the world to rights. But one man by himself can't alter much."

"And that's a true word! That's why he needs a group of them. To act all together, like."

"Not poaching again, is it?" Michael encouraged her. "But he wouldn't need a gang for that? Not unless they were netting. And June's the wrong month for deer – with does feeding their young, the meat flavour's no good. But how like Peter to plan a raid in a close-month!" He sipped his ale again. "I don't think I need be interested – it'll never come off."

"Oh, it's not poaching they was on about! Indeed not. Something much grander."

"With Jonathan and Richard in on it? Those two? Too frit, they'd be. I think it's nothing at all, Betsy. Maybe you heard wrong."

"That I did not!" she retorted. "There's a lot of them in it. Not just from East Meon, like, but all over. And it's to happen in June. I heard that much. And it's to do with the price of corn and woad."

"Woad?" he queried. "We don't grow a deal of that round here. Only where sheep-walks are being ploughed up again, now that wool prices have dropped so low. What has woad to do with it? Doesn't sound likely to me."

"Well," she said, put out by his scornful tone. "'Oad is what I heard. That, and corn shortages. I don't know no more. But I tell you, Michael Dunnett, they're up to something."

"I dare say, I dare say. No doubt someone'll tell me about it. Hannah Ryde, now. She usually has the news. I'll ask her."

"No need for that!" Betsy replied crossly. "It's my ale-house that lot comes to – not hers. I'll tell 'ee if I hears more."

"Why, Betsy! That's very civil of you. I'll drop in every now and again to hear the latest – and enjoy your good ale."

With that he left, still puzzling over their conversation. Being a Constable was not easy. For the one year of his appointment he was avoided by some of his friends and even his family could become cautious in his presence. Still, it had not been worth refusing the post, for the fine for doing so was six shillings and eight pence as well as a period in the stocks, and that humiliation was definitely to be avoided. Unpopular though the job was, he had felt obliged to take his turn with other householders. Law and order had to be maintained in these unruly times and, at least, he knew he had the physical stature and presence to enforce them. He regretted, though, the amount of time his duties occupied – and all for no pay. It was as well, he thought, that Zacharias Stick was a reasonably conscientious farm-servant, able to run the tenement without him.

As he walked along the High Street, Michael thought it might be as well to call on young Harper at the wheelwright's. The next payment was due from him for the maintenance of his illegitimate child. Since the Bastardy Act of 1576 it was possible for magistrates to imprison the erring parents, but in this case the Justices had decided against doing so. Michael approved their decision, finding money payments more appropriate. Seeing to the apprenticing of youths was another of the constable's jobs, and with young Harper's family being not only feckless but lazy, the youth had been as disinclined to learn the wheelwright's trade as his father had been to put him to it. But, Michael thought, prison for either parent of the bastard infant would inevitably have thrown the upkeep of the babe onto the Parish charity, now under the supervision of the Overseers of the Poor. It was a pity, though, that the lad and girl were both of this parish, making East Meon obliged to grant the infant Settlement Rights of legal residence. What a pity, also, he had not received orders to cut off the girl's waist-long hair to show she was no longer a virgin. Nor, because she herself was born here, was he able to drive her over the boundary into another parish as he would have liked. Certificates of Settlement were a great disadvantage when trying to rid a village of its undesirables!

After collecting the maintenance money and handing it over to the infant's mother, Michael leant over the wooden fence to inspect the parish bull. The animal was also his responsibility, and he was glad to see it grazing peacefully in the close among the village heifers. No trouble there, at least. Turning to retrace his steps, he caught a glimpse of John Tribe, who had been one of the men in Betsy's ale-house. This brought back his earlier puzzlement over their furtive behaviour and he wondered what John was doing here. Was he so leisured these days that he could afford to neglect the fine mill he had set up in Ramsdean, on Criddell Stream? Or was there really some mischief brewing, as Betsy insisted? The Constable was responsible for catching and detaining suspected criminals, and for executing whatever punishment the Justices ordered, but he was aware as yet of no crime having been committed, no riot in need of suppression, nor the holding of any unlawful assembly. He had no evidence of ill-doing at all. Only his own unease.

A few days later he was called to a brawl. The longer evenings of June meant more opportunity for the village ruffians to gather on the river bridge and cause a disturbance. Michael quickly realized that this was a truly rough fight, with not only angry shouting and bad language, but fists cracking on heads and bodies thrown down. Quite an audience had already gathered, watching in delight, for a good brawl was fine entertainment, whatever the initial quarrel. Seeing it was something he could not quell by himself, he hurried to the house of Josiah Pringle, the Parish Beadle, who was, among other things, his deputy when need arose.

Michael banged on Pringle's door and shouted for the man to come out. "Quick!" he said. "They're brawling on the bridge. I need help." The Beadle opened the door but then turned back into the house. "For Heaven's sake! Just come! Don't bother with the coat or wand of office! This is urgent."

Reluctantly, Pringle emerged in his shirt sleeves. Michael knew how unwilling the Beadle was to appear on parish business without the official insignia of his position, so he was grateful that he had come so promptly. They hurried to the bridge where the fight was continuing, with even more participants joining in the fray, and Michael regretted he was not carrying the heavy Constable's staff. He could really have laid about him with that. It was, perhaps, the very presence of the two parish officers that reduced the ferocity of the fight. Finally, except for the odd scuffle or two, order was restored. No one seemed seriously injured, although several were bleeding from the nose or mouth. Clearly it had been a good fight, but not more severe than normal, and it appeared that this time no knives or daggers had been used. But Michael needed to know how it began. The explanation was not long in coming.

"It's him what began it," shouted Simon Cowley, pointing to a running figure disappearing down the street, clutching a laden sack. "Broke open me mother's flour chest. Took a gallon or so of meal, he did. So I chased him, and me friends joined in. Then his own friends came and we had a fight. And a good 'un it was, too!" In pride he held up his hands to display bleeding knuckles. "I knocked three of 'em down!" he boasted.

Ada Cowley, Simon's mother, was the wife of a builder, busy these days in erecting village houses using some of the new-fangled brick. As a consequence the family was a little better off than most of the villagers and could probably afford to buy corn, even at current high prices.

"So you're naming William Sharp as a thief, are you?"

"Well, no. Not exactly. He's running off now to put it back. My Mam hasn't lost no flour after all, Master. It'll all be back in the chest by now."

Michael grunted. "No theft: no crime. But he'd better not try it again."

The boy laughed. "That he won't! Reckon he's lost a tooth or two. I landed him a real wallop!"

The Constable waited until the crowd had dispersed, thankful the matter had been settled so quickly. Fisticuffs he did not mind, but anything more serious would have had to be reported to the Justices. And for him that meant a lot of paper work, followed by time wasted in Court. But he'd have to watch the young ones. Getting out of hand, they were. Not that he really blamed William Sharp for stealing – his family was very poor. It was the price and the shortage of corn that was to blame. That, and people having more children and old people living longer and there being too many mouths to feed. Health was better in a general way, it seemed, but the authorities had recently been buying up a lot of grain to supply the army in the Netherlands and a real shortage was resulting. He sighed, remembering the old days when the village had been more or less self-sufficient and everyone in employment. Hard, those days had been. But safer. Now robbery and violence were everywhere and it was no longer wise to travel alone. The government was trying to cure immorality, violence and poverty with more and yet more regulations, but the truth was no one could cure poverty by inflicting punishment on the unemployed. That was the Puritan influence due to Calvinist teaching. Puritans saw poverty as an inherent wickedness and evil that could only be driven out of the poor by punishment.

Michael looked up the river and at the cottages on its either side. Peaceful and contented the village seemed, now the brawling was over, but he was well aware that the biggest trade the pedlars and chapmen did when passing through was in locks, bolts, chains and padlocks of every size. There was no respect for property nowadays and it was no longer safe to leave the house-door open. He sighed again and turned his thoughts to vagabonds. They were now a real problem in the parish, and it was his responsibility to keep them in order and move them on. Vagrants were becoming a plague although they were not allowed to beg unless they had a Licence from the Justices to do so. Whole gangs of vagrants there were now, terrifying to meet, of men, women and children, all preying on villagers and travellers. It was quite common for there to be robbery with violence, for goods being taken to market to be seized, or for purses to be cut from men's belts and the victims assaulted. In addition, houses were often broken into and ransacked for food and saleable goods; horses, sheep and cattle were stolen. But, worst of all, barns, cornstacks and even house-thatch were frequently set alight. Even more difficult to detect than the vagabonds were the smartly dressed "conners", who tricked people out of their wealth, and those who held forged Licences to Beg.

Yes, it was a rough and disorderly age and he had almost had his fill of putting people in the stocks. Sometimes, with a rogue who would not desist from wickedness, he had been ordered to tie him to the rear of a cart and whip him through the village until the blood ran down his bare back. Such men were undeserving of pity – they were scum, and dirty, verminous and foul mouthed. There was nothing to be done with such vagabonds and masterless men but punish them, give them the certificate to show the punishment received, and then drive them away, over the parish boundary. And yet – and yet some were truly pitiful.

He remembered one woman who was heavy with child and had two small children at her skirt. "Mercy!" she had called out. "Food, for the love of God! I can go no further". And she had sunk to the ground, too weak to walk on.

"Where's your man?" Michael had asked roughly. "Where are you from? Where's your place of settlement?"

He studied her shape as he spoke, trying to decide whether the bulge of her belly was real or only a bundle of rags under her tattered gown to simulate pregnancy. Vagrants were up to all sorts of tricks. Some even tied arsenic to their arms or legs to bring up running sores. Others dressed in filthy rags, daubed their face with blood and pretended to have the falling sickness, foaming at the mouth with the aid of a piece of soap. (Michael had heard this could earn over fourteen shillings a day at a town market.) Or an 'Abraham Man', who pretended to be mad. 'Poor Tom' or 'Tom a' Bedlam' he would be called, and would roam the countryside half-naked, and with shouts and lunatic behaviour would terrify women and servants into giving him money. Others pretended to be shipwrecked sailors, or to be collecting for a new hospital now the monasteries were closed. Some acted as deaf mutes, while all of them, given the chance, were hookers and anglers who would steal clothing from open windows by means of hooked poles. Michael was thankful that a few years before, in 1578, a House of Correction had been set up in Winchester. This was for the training and supervision of all those in the county who refused to take up work when it was offered to them. He thought the place must be overflowing by now.

He continued to study the woman before him and decided she was genuine and in real need. And yet, legally, he could not help her. Since the Act of 1572, a fine of twenty shillings was imposed on anyone helping a beggar with food or alms or lodging. This clearly did not succeed in either suppressing begging, or the charity of ordinary people, and yet he was legally bound by it – and especially so as the Constable.

"Stay here", he had commanded her. Crossing the bridge to an inn, he remarked to the ale-wife, "That were two very good tankards of your best ale you've just given me. I thank you. Chalk the price of them up on the slate."

When the woman had stared at him in astonishment he added, "The price would feed a starving woman and two children, don't you think? Even with the price of bread so high?"

With that he had tipped his head to indicate the street. and having thanked her, left the inn, hoping she would understand his unspoken message. A little later he had passed that way again and been relieved to see the beggarwoman gone. Of all his many tasks, punishing women was the one he disliked most and he avoided it whenever he could but, women or men, punished they had to be. There were just too many vagrants and wandering-folk. The law declared that anyone over fourteen years of age who was convicted of begging without a licence, or who was living in a 'roguish way', had to be whipped by the constable. If they then refused any work offered them he had to burn through the lobe of the right ear with a hot iron of an inch in circumference. For a second and similar offence, one ear could be cut off, while a third occasion meant the loss of the other. No one knew what to do with the multitude of unemployed and the only remedy was to scare them into work. And yet there was no work. That was the root cause of the trouble.

During the first thirty years of Elizabeth's reign there had been serious disruptions in overseas trade, due to her wars on the Continent and various expeditions on the high seas. When returning soldiers and seamen were discharged at the ports they were left to fend for themselves, workless and often homeless, and it was no wonder they formed themselves into gangs of 'Sturdy Beggars'. In the main they were fit and healthy young men, let loose to wander the countryside to steal what they could. It was said that when a town saw such a gang approaching, the great gates were shut against them for, when the beggars were coming to town, it was best to hide the valuables and bolt and bar the house doors.

Many agricultural workers were also unemployed. Since the period thirty or so years ago when the price of wool had risen, causing good arable land to be put down to pasture and the number of sheep flocks to multiply, fewer men were needed on the land. Workers had been turned out of their hovels, their small vegetable plots ploughed over and sown with grass. Often the hovels themselves had been knocked down to make way for sheep. Then the price of wool had dropped as the Continental markets ceased to trade with England. It fell from twenty shillings and eight pence a tod in 1546 to only sixteen shillings in 1561, causing farmers to think again of wheat, only to find that there was now insufficient ploughland, so much being down to grass. With a constantly growing population there was now a lack of grain – especially after a bad harvest such as that of last year. Naturally the price of corn rose. And rose again, with the cost of a loaf of bread rising with it, until in 1576 the Queen's Council had been forced to prohibit the export of all grain, even to the army. If wages had risen at the same rate as a loaf of bread, all might have been well, but they did not, and hunger resulted. With so many agricultural workers unemployed, labour was cheap and work scarce. Their standard of living fell disastrously and many, unable to afford corn, were reduced to mixing ground acorns, tree-bark, grass seeds, dandelion roots or even earth with their flour to make it go further.

In many places Charities were set up by individuals to help the old, the sick, the crippled and the widowed, but there was no such Charity in East Meon – only the small bequests made to the poor in the wills of the better off. Here, since 1572, impoverished villagers had to rely on the two Overseers of the Poor and the Poor Rate they raised from the wealthier residents. Although most of the deserving but indigent households obtained this relief, it was not a satisfactory arrangement, and funds could certainly not extend to helping the poor or vagrants from other parishes. This was why Michael, as Constable, had to whip or stock such people and hand them over to the Constable of the next parish. Poverty was proving unconquerable. If only humans could live on moonbeams as partridges did!

He straightened up from the bridge and moved towards the church, having checked on the village pound as he passed. No animals happened to be there but he did not know whether that was because none had strayed or because John Hutt was a lazy Pinder. He knew it was usually the Hayward, Peter Simonson, who caught the animals and brought them in, for being in charge of the repair of the manor and parish fences, he was keenest to see wandering and destructive animals placed where they could do no more harm. Still, care of the pound was one responsibility a Constable did not have, so he walked on, turned left by the church and then left again. It was time to call on Betsy.

"I'll have a mug of the cheap stuff, please," he said on entering the low, gloomy room. "I'm short of coins again." He did have plenty of money in the leather purse on his belt, but as one of his jobs was to keep an eye on ale-houses, he felt he should sample the ale from the cheaper barrel. He was not the parish Ale-taster but was concerned about quality – in some places it was said there was more water in the ale than there was in the river. "Any more news of our plotting and secretive friends?" he asked.

"Now, Master, you know better than to ask me like that – straight out. I have a business to run, and if my customers thought I went in for passing on their tattle, they wouldn't come again."

"No, of course not. I beg pardon. Let me put this to you, then – we know the price of wheat has gone up but how about woad? Heard any news of that lately?"

"Not a thing," she replied. "Not a thing. There doesn't seem to be much interest in 'oad. Not hereabouts, anyways. But I tell you what, Master, this fine weather'd be good for bonfires. Big bonfires would burn a treat." She looked at him quizzically from under her mop of dirty hair. "Would you agree, then?"

"Aye, I would," he said, puzzled but seeking to keep the conversation going. "And would we be burning these big fires too close to barns and such?"

"Lord love us, no! Nowhere near a barn! Out in the open, more likely."

Michael tried to work out where her hints should take him. Then he said, "There's bonfires at Midsummer, somewhere. With dancing round and worship. Do you favour that, Betsy? The old ways of worship? In times gone by?"

"That I don't," she replied crossly. "And don't you go making me out to be a heathen."

He soothed her down as best he could and then resorted to his previous stratagem of appearing indifferent. Draining his tankard quickly he remarked he had to be off, the Vicar was expecting him. He had to collect the list of those who did not attend church regularly, and who it was the Constable's job to chastise and bully into conformity. It was by this means that recusant Catholics were often discovered.

"Well, if you're going by the church I expect you'll be checking the parish armour."

Startled, Michael halted. Turning back to her he said slowly, "I will, I think. It's about time I had another look at it. And thank you, Betsy. Your kindness is appreciated."

A little worried now he entered the litten and walked up to the church. Was there going to be an armed uprising? Is that what Betsy meant? But against whom, and why? He entered the building and, pulling the key-chain from the neck of his shirt, he unlocked the great chest that held the parish weaponry. At least the gun which belonged to the whole village was there. And the helmets. And the three corselets. Satisfied, he closed and relocked the coffer and crossed to where the halberds, pikes and unstrung longbows were stored. They were all there, too. So what had Betsy meant? He could not, of course, check the armour held by law in private hands, for he had no right of enquiry there. Since the first year of the Queen's reign, weapons were held according to a man's wealth – if his income was between £5 and £10 a year then he had to keep a corselet, a bill, a halberd, a longbow and a steel helmet. If he was richer, then he had to keep a greater number of weapons in proportion to his wealth. Not, Michael knew, that the owner himself was required to fight, but it was his legal duty to provide arms for others to use in defence of the peace, according to his financial or landholding status.

There were a number of such big men in the parish – John Baker, for instance, who had bought the Bereleigh lands four years ago for £200; the Fawconers of Westbury, who also held Greatham; John Love of Basing in the Tithing of Longhurst; various members of the Wryte family (all of whom were now classed as gentlemen) including Nycholas, who rented South Mill; John Pynke of Oxenbourne; the two Strouders, John and Richard; many of the Langrishe family of Bordean, Ramsdean and Langrish itself, and various others in Coombe and East Meon. He supposed he must also include John Stockman, for he had been assigned the lease of East Meon Park by Queen Elizabeth, who had been granted it by the Bishop. However, he had heard that Stockman had since re-assigned it to William Neale of Warnford, so who was responsible for that armour he did not know. (Neale must be very rich, though, for it was said he was trying to buy Peak Tygall Farm to add to his holdings.) Perhaps it was as well that the High Constable of the Hundred was charged with inspecting all armour twice a year. Michael himself had only to see that the men turned up for the musters, and as they were only held once every three years, this was not an onerous task. The men quite enjoyed these general musters as the village belonged to the Alton division and, with so many parading, they were quite lively and enjoyable. What were not so popular were the local musters, for these were used for training in the use of the newly introduced guns and pikes, which were now replacing bows and halberds. He was in charge of a Trained Band and had found some of the locals very slow to learn the new skills. Slow and reluctant.

As the day was sultry, with a hint of thunder, Michael decided to ride over to Petersfield to see if he could hear of any talk of uprisings there. He might take Margrit, too. His wife did not often have the chance to visit the town, except on market days when she was too busy selling her butter, eggs and cheeses to enjoy herself. When asked, she said she was happy to accompany him.

"No use taking my dough down to the baker's today," she told him, "for it wouldn't rise in this thundery weather. So I'll save my labour and come with you. It'll do me good to catch a bit of air – this heat's straight out of Hell's mouth."

Michael bridled the horse and put on him the double saddle so that his wife could ride pillion. When both were mounted he turned round to ask if she were comfortable.

"Aye," she replied, "my seat is at ease but I'm not at ease about the beer on your breath. The Devil sings in ale-houses, you know, and I've heard you've been seeing a lot of that Betsy."

"In line of business, my dear. In line of business. Checking up on village rumours, that's all, and an ale-house is the best place to catch them. We're off to Petersfield now to do the same thing. Just say if you'd rather not come."

Margrit sniffed. "Oh, I'll come all right. If only to keep an eye on you." Then she laughed. "I can't see old Betsy to your liking, somehow! Nevertheless, Master Constable, just remember that the Devil can be hidden in a cup of liquor as easy as he can in a woman's eye!"

The green lanes were very pleasant on that hot morning. Trees gave shade where they hung over the track and the spring grass smelt sweetly beneath the horse's hooves. When they reached The Square of the small town they tied the animal to the fence, which on market days was a stock pen. A great many cattle were sold in Petersfield each week, though cloth-weaving was the main industry. Much cloth was in the form of kersey, a coarse material used for doublets, breeches and, when ribbed, for hose. Local sheep were ideal for kersey as they produced a short-staple wool, and this was carded and spun locally as a cottage industry, giving much work to poorer families. The woven cloth was then sold to London merchants or exported, principally to the Low Countries. When the boom in wool prices had occurred a few years before and sheep had been increasingly bred to keep up with the demand, it was realised there were insufficient fulling mills to treat the woven cloth. It was then that Henry Mervyn had converted part of Durford Mill for fulling – as was Hurst Mill, which had previously ground only corn for Ditcham, West Harting and Nursted. The Mervyn family had done well for themselves over the years and now Sir Edmund, who lived in Castle House, fronting the Square, was the richest man in town and its Member of Parliament. Other local clothiers who had prospered from the cloth trade were William Bagyn and Will Shorter and, as Michael had done business with both, he planned to seek them out to test for rumours of an armed uprising. He began his search, however, at the White Hart in the High Street.

He and Margrit seated themselves on a bench, their ale being brought to them by the tavern-keeper. It was no trouble to persuade him to talk and the conversation began with a discussion on the present slump in wool prices. "All due," the man said, "to the ruining of the coinage. And the Queen's foreign policy. That Council of hers is no good for trade. It's all interference and new regulations. Can't leave well alone so we can get on with buying and selling. Look at the inspectors that come round now, measuring the cloth! Drives the clothiers mad, it does!" He then gave a sly wink and a grin. "As if they'd sell cloth too short or too narrow! Insulting, it is!"

"It's a mercy the town has the leather trade to fall back on," Michael remarked.

"Aye, but the tanning is turning into a worry now. We're running short of oaks, see, what with all the ships a'building down in Portsmouth. And for tanning we need good bark, felled in April, May or June, when there's most sap in it. The ship-timber is most likely felled in winter, and that bark's no good to the leather trade. We're running out of trees, I tell you. Just as well more houses are being built with brick in them, otherwise we'd be in a real fix."

"I've heard that," Michael admitted. "But it's not just the oaks that are going – it's the beeches, too. Look at Anthony Uvedale's woods at Hambledon and Newlands, down near Southwick. Stripped, they are. England's losing trees faster than they can grow."

"That it is! And all those trees cut down for iron foundries in Sussex! And for glass-making, too. I heard they used to make glass at Ditcham, when William Overton was Rector of Buriton, and furnaces need a terrible amount of fuel."

"So I believe," Michael agreed. He drank deeply from his tankard, wiped his lips on the back of his hand and remarked, "Is there a lot of folks out of work, then? Here in the town? Disquiet, and that?"

"No, I can't say there is. As yet. Being on the Portsmouth road from London helps, you see, although Deptford, on the Thames, is taking some of the Navy trade. Even so, we get a lot of road traffic, with imports and exports passing through, and that means business for hostelries and inns." The tapster rubbed his chin and added, "And the tanneries are all right as yet – except for the bark. Down near the Forebridge they are, as you'll know. But what a stench when the wind's from the south! All the innards of the animals thrown in the stream to rot. And the skins steeping in the lime-pits – not nice, not nice." Then he grinned. "There's one thing about both tanning and cloth-working that does me a bit of good, though – they need urine, see, in the processes. Ammonia, it is, and with a good sized place like this I collect a fair amount during a day. Sell it to 'em, I do! First I sells the ale, then I sells the results!" He chuckled and the Dunnets joined in until Michael strove to return the conversation to uprisings.

"Oh, aye," the man agreed. "I suppose there's unrest. Course there is. Price of wheat's too high and there's a bad shortage, too. There'll be starvation soon, I shouldn't wonder, especially now Poor Boxes are not allowed in the churches. But I did hear tell of some men up Farringdon way who are plotting something, but I don't know what."

Trying to conceal his excitement, Michael pressed him for further details but clearly the man knew nothing more. When other customers entered the inn, Michael said they must leave. Taking Margrit by the arm he steered her into the street and back to the horse. "I'll have to go to Farringdon," he told her. "I need to get to the bottom of this. I think it may be yet another plot against the Queen by the Catholics. We've had too many of them, this last year or so."

As they returned to East Meon they discussed the Catholic families who lived in the locality and were known to be recusants, refusing to attend the Church of England services as they were bound to do by law. Since a Statute of Parliament in 1581, all those absent from church (unless hearing the English service at home) were fined £20 a month. This was a harsh enough penalty for the rich but was an impossible burden for the poor. There were tales from Winchester of those who were unable to pay being publicly whipped through the streets. Such treatment inevitably led to many Catholics simply pretending to be Protestant by attending the parish church and so avoiding the fine. It was expected that many of these would eventually end up by ceasing to be Catholic in all except inclination, giving up all hope of returning to the Papal fold. Later still had come the Act of 1584, which required all Jesuits and Catholic priests to leave the kingdom within forty days – or else be seen as traitors to the Crown. Equally fierce were the penalties imposed on those who knew of priests but did not report them. This led to terrible conflicts of loyalty among Catholics, with much self-saving betrayal but also many deeds of courage.

"I've heard," Michael remarked, "there are so many recusants at every Quarter Sessions in Winchester that the Clerks of the Peace are overrun by them. Can't keep up with the paper work! And Bishop Cooper wants to ship them all over to Flanders as labourers, to keep the prisons from overflowing!"

"It doesn't seem right," Margrit said slowly. "They're Christians, after all."

"True. But they keep plotting against the Queen. Look at the Babington Plot we're just hearing about – to free Mary, Queen of Scots, from prison and put her on the English throne. And there was the Throckmorton Plot, don't forget. And Philip of Spain, planning a holy crusade or some such nonsense, in order to take the throne himself. I even heard of a French plan to invade us by way of Sussex, and another through Wales. (That one was said to have been thought up by the Pole family.) Then there was something called the Rudolfi Plot, a bit earlier. It seems you can't trust a Catholic, and that's the beginning and the end of it. Even the Duke of Norfolk had to be beheaded ten years or so ago."

"But there are still Catholics round our village and I can't see them as wicked. They're just like us, really. No better and no worse. Why can't they be left in peace?"

"Because they'll cause civil war, that's why!" Michael answered firmly. "They won't be happy till we have Catholic Mary of Scotland on the throne, and popes and cardinals and such like, bossing us about. They'd put the church services back into Latin, and I wouldn't like that and nor would you."

There was silence for a while and then Michael said, "The Catholics are as harsh on Protestants as our Queen is on them, you know. It's not all one-sided. The

Catholics killed off William the Silent, Prince of Orange, for being a Protestant. And that massacre of the Protestant Huguenots in France on St. Bartholomew's Day, fourteen years ago. No wonder so many escaped to England. No, Margrit, one side's as bad as the other, I'm afraid."

"And as good as each other!" she retorted. "Look at Robert and Anthony Joy, for instance. Good men they've been in Rothercombe, and yet they've stuck Robert in that House of Correction at Winchester, as if he was a layabout vagabond! And that poor old widow, Elizabeth Tichborne of West Tisted, who couldn't go to church even if she'd wanted to because she is bed-bound. They make her pay over £13 a year – and that she can only manage with the help of friends – for her late husband's money was all tied up in a trust for their children. And Mr. William Fawconer at Westbury – they've taken two-thirds of the income from his estate, I've heard. Amounts to over £72 a year. Yet he's a good man, too."

"I know, I know," her husband conceded. "When you come down to putting names and faces to those caught up in the law, it seems a bit different. I've heard myself that Elizabeth Turner, a gentleman's wife of Steep, is in trouble. Her husband has to pay £20 a month for her, although he goes to Church of England services. And they've not only taken two-thirds of Stephen Vachell's income from Weston Farm and Heath House, but they've put him in gaol at Winchester. Along with Nicholas Tichborne and a couple of priests and two nuns, I believe. But Peter Tichborne's in the Southwark Prison in London, though, as is George Cotton of Warblington Castle and Henry Shelley of Buriton." Then he hesitated. "But I think Mr. Shelley died there, two years back. Anyway, there's still Mrs. Shelley, a daughter and three servants at Mapledurham House – and all Catholic. They'll be bankrupted soon. I suppose that's the idea – bankrupt Catholics out of existence.

"There's Mr. Anthony Uvedale, don't forget," Margrit added. "You know you mentioned him cutting down his woods, while we were talking to the inn-keeper in Petersfield? Well, I didn't like to say anything at the time, for it's too dangerous to mention religion nowadays, but I heard his woods were felled at Woodcote as well as Hambledon to pay his costs. He's one of those who has to pay two-thirds of his income to the Crown and he needed the money. Then there's the Goldsmiths of Exton. They're Catholics. As are the Dormers of Idsworth. None of them is bad. They shouldn't suffer."

"And I tell you who I think has to pay the £20 a month," Michael added thoughtfully, "That's Mr. William Edmonds, who lives up Holloway in the village. You never see him in church, do you? Even if he is a yeoman farmer, that's a lot of money to find, especially with the price of wool going down and him mostly in sheep. Then there's the rent of Punsholt House and sixty acres of land that Henry Knight leases. I think that goes to the Crown, too. I seem to remember that Mr. Anthony Norton allowed an old monk from the closed-down Westminster Abbey to live at Punsholt. When he died, friends carried his body to some ruins of an old chapel and buried it there. The Nortons are all recusant, from what I hear. Blendworth people."

"I think it's terrible, Catholics not being allowed proper burial in churchyards. As if they were heathens."

They rode again in silence until Michael said, "There's a priest's hiding place in Mapledurham House, you know. It used to be secret but I've heard there's a hollow space in the parlour, by the livery cupboard, which'll take two men. Fooled searchers many a time. And there's said to be a vault, the trapdoor of which is under a little table and it has iron grating for a window, which looks like a cellar light from outside. There's a rosemary bush growing by it, seemingly."

Later he asked, "So who of all the folk we've named do you think is stirring up people for an armed revolt? That Peter Striker, who goes to Betsy's for his drink, doesn't seem likely. Nor yet Jonathan Pike nor Richard Atwood. Wouldn't say boo to a goose, the pair of them. And then the business of the price of corn. And growing woad, and Betsy's bonfires and the weapons. Can't make head nor tail of it. Doesn't seem to have the taste of a Catholic plot, somehow. I'll just have to go to Farringdon to find out what I can."

Two days later he set off, but before he had reached even the church gate he met Richard Bunting, who he knew to be a weaver at Selborne. When the two had exchanged the customary greetings, Michael asked him who he was visiting in East Meon.

"No one, really." the man replied. "Just thought I'd look for custom. Times is hard in Selborne, with not many wanting new cloth, so I thought I'd try here. Tried in Farringdon yesterday, but no luck at all."

"Farringdon, eh?" Michael mused. "Well, I tell you what, why don't we drop into the ale-house for a yarn. I'm not going anywhere special."

The pair went to Betsy's and settled down with a tankard each of her best ale, paid for by Michael. For a while they chatted about the weather and of a cousin of Michael's who lived in Selborne. "All well there, is it?" he asked.

"No, it isn't, and that's the truth," Bunting declared. "Corn's too high. And I tell you this, until the next harvest's in, a lot of us is going to starve." He took a deep draught of ale and went on, "We can't continue long like this. Have to do something. It's all the fault of the Government and these licences and woad-quotas they've put out. They should have banned the stuff altogether. Good arable land is being put down to woad so farmers can make a bit of extra money – there's a real good price for woad nowadays. And us starving because of lack of wheat! We ought to do what they did in Romsey a few weeks back when more woad was sown than the quota allowed, and all of it without a licence."

He drank again, so Michael asked encouragingly, "What did they do? I've not heard."

"Why!" Bunting replied. "There was a riot! And the farmer near enough beaten out of his senses. Serve him right, for he'll have been one of them storing grain to keep the price high. Like a lot do round here, I'll be bound?" This last was spoken with a cock of the head and an enquiring glance at Michael. "I guess you have them here as well?"

"Certainly we do!" Michael lowered his voice to a tone sufficiently conspiratorial. "I could name a few names, myself."

"Could you, now? And would you like to put these men down? Same as they did at Romsey?"

"Aye! Why do you ask?"

After a moment's pause Bunting seemed to make up his mind. "Well, we've a plan afoot. And we need all the help we can get. If I tell you more, will you keep the secret?"

"Aye!" Michael said again, glad that Betsy was serving other customers and did not appear to be listening. "Surely I will!"

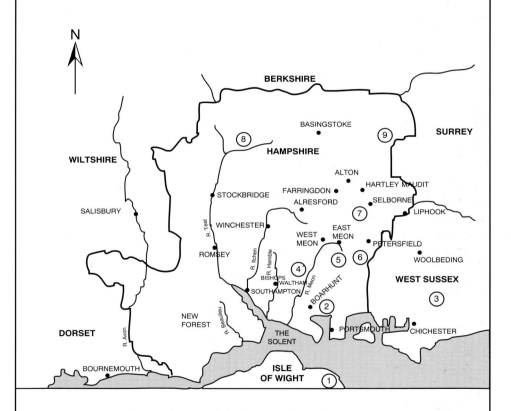

THE HAMPSHIRE BEACON PLOT, 1586

MAP OF BEACON SITES IN HAMPSHIRE
(Taken from the article by J. D. Jones of 1968)

1. West Forelands, I.o.W.
2. Portsdown.
3. The Trundle.
4. Exton.
5. "Barnett"

6. Butser Hill.
7. (Unnamed site).
8. Whitchurch.
9. Crondall.

"Well, it's the beacons, see. If we were to light them, then all the militia men would go running for their armour and guns and such, and we'd all go in great parties to the big barns and store-houses where the grain is. We'd get tons and tons of wheat out of them and everyone could have a share and we wouldn't starve. Nor our villages."

Michael hoped his eyes were glistening with excitement as he said eagerly. "I'd join you on that! I certainly would!" Then, "Here, let me get you another ale. Betsy! Serve this gentleman, if you please. On my slate."

When the tankard was refilled, Bunting said, "The sixth of June is the day. So there's not much time. But we've men all over the county ready to fire the beacons, and others ready and willing to gather the armed men to storm the barns. We need big gangs, see, otherwise the farmers and landowners would set their own guns on us, so we need to shoot them first."

"Well!" Michael said in admiration. "It all seems well enough thought out. But who are the leaders, then?"

Unexpectedly, Bunting became cagey. "Ah! Naming leaders is another matter. Don't know that I should."

"Quite right," Michael agreed. "Can't be too careful. You never know who is listening."

Both took their tankards and walked out of the door, Michael managing to wink at Betsy as he did so. "Since you spoke," he said "I've been remembering the rumpus a few years back when one of the Isle of Wight beacons was lit accidentally. So the Portsdown one was lit, too, and all the others, way inland, right into Berkshire. Real excitement that was, and no one could stop the militia from rushing to the coast to fight off the Spaniards!"

"That's what gave us the idea. That, and the house fire in Bath City that the beacon-watchers took for an alarm. All the weapons was handed out, see, and the militiamen marching in big groups. If we do the same, we'll break into those barns in no time. Easy! For the men'll all be on our side."

"And what of the leaders?" Michael asked again. "Who are they?"

"We haven't a proper captain because we're all in it together, like, but there's Zachary Mansell and William Mitchell, both of Hartley Maudit, along with William Stevens, who's a tailor in Farringdon. And Richard Noyse, who's a farm worker. Then there's William Musgrove, who works at tailoring in Selborne. And who else? Ah, yes. There's Geoffrey Carey, who's a weaver in Alton. I think that's all the top men – save Henry Lockyer of Woolbeding, near Midhurst, who's another tailor. Says he'll fire the Trundle beacon."

"There seems a lot in the cloth business," Michael remarked. "Why's that?"

"They're not all in cloth. There's a Farringdon man called Faithful, who's a smith, and another called Wolfe, who's a mason. And a farmworker from Sheet, Michael Hayward. But I suppose you're right, for there's yet another weaver called William Arthur, belonging to Alton." He mused for a moment and then said, "The cloth-workers, along with the sheep-farmers, did well until the trade with Antwerp stopped. The Queen's army is fighting the Spanish there now, and that means we've too much cloth piling up in this country. So those that live by spinning, carding and the working of wool are hard put to find the money to eat."

"And the woad?" Michael pressed. "Why is that a bother?"

" 'Cos we used to ship it in from the Azores for the dyers," Bunting replied. "And the Mediterranean. But now, being at war with Spain, we can't. So the farmers all over

England are seizing their chance to make a mint of money and are sowing woad themselves. Instead of wheat. So we'll rob them. Especially as a few seasons under woad is said to ruin the land. Makes it fit for nothing, neither wheat nor grass."

"I see," Michael nodded. "Tell me again when the beacons are to be lit."

"Sixth of June. And you'll join us, won't you? Light the Butser Hill beacon, mayhap? You know it?"

"I do. The wood for making it is given by East Meon Manor, out of Hyden Woods. Aye, I know it, all right."

"That's settled then," Bunting declared with satisfaction. "We'll be in touch. Meanwhile, I'll be on my way and thank you kindly for the ale."

They re-entered the ale-house to leave their tankards and Betsy came forward to take them. "Good day, to you, Master Bunting. Nice to see you again. With none of your friends here today it was good you came across the Constable."

"Constable?" the man queried in alarm. "Are you the ——- ? May Heaven preserve me! It was all a joke, sir. Not meant serious, like. Just a joke – and it took you in proper, didn't it? But I must away. Have to go."

The man hurried out and Michael turned to the grinning Betsy. "You're a wicked woman, Betsy!" he said, and they both laughed. Then he added seriously, "But I must stop this plot. I'll have to ride down to Beare at once and notify the Earl of Essex as he's Lord Lieutenant of the county. I must hurry. Not much time to lose, I think."

"Bless you, Master, don't fuss yourself! That's all been done long since. Richard Noyse, who's my uncle and one of the plotters, fell into a panic days ago and sent a message to the authorities to warn them. There'll be no beacons fired! The watchers are all prepared and the gangs will never get near them. It's all doomed to failure." She laughed and turned away. "It was a silly plan, anyway," she said. "Like small boys, they were. Spilling their secrets at every tavern they came to! You just go away home and look after your pretty wife."

"That I shall," he said. "But you're still a wicked woman!" Then he leant across and gave her a smacking kiss on the cheek. "And that's for making a fool out of me!"

Based on:

Elizabeth I by Christopher Haigh. Longmans, 1990.

The Life and Times of Elizabeth I by Neville Williams. Weidenfeld & Nicholson, 1992.

Sixteenth Century England by Joyce Youings. Penguin, 1991.

The Farmers of Old England by Eric Kerridge. Allen & Unwin, 1973.

A History of East Meon by F. G. Standfield. Phillimore, 1984.

The Reign of Elizabeth I edited by Christopher Haigh. Macmillan, 1984.

The Victoria County History of Hampshire, Vol. III. Edited by William Page, 1908.
Reprinted by University of London, Institute of Historical Research, 1973.

Elizabethan Life in Town and Country by M. St. Clare Byrne. Allan Sutton, 1987.

Hampshire Recusants by F. A. Gasquet. John Hodges, undated.

The Hampshire Beacon Plot of 1586 by J. D. Jones.
Proceedings of Hampshire Field Club and Archeological Society Volume 28, 1968.

Petersfield in Tudor Times by E. M. Yates. Petersfield Area Historical Society, 1979.
(*Petersfield Papers*, No. 5.)

Chapter Thirteen

The Civil War, 1644

MY name is Agnes Mulholland and I live in one of the newer brick and timber houses that lie in the High Street of East Meon, overlooking the river. I am now thirty-eight years old and have been widowed twice.

My first husband was Richard Smyther, a victualler and farmer, and we loved each other dearly. We rented our land in small plots around the village and we also had our several strips in the unenclosed open fields, giving us a total of near on 30 acres. Our main concerns were growing barley for ale and having enough cows for me to make extra cheeses for sale in the market in Petersfield – as well, of course, as keeping ourselves supplied with most of our daily needs.

I was a good brewster, saying it myself though I am, and became quite well-known locally. The row of ale-tubs sitting on their X-shaped horses in the brewhouse was witness to the demand, for I had gradually dropped into the habit of selling the occasional jugful to those as asked. However, we were careful not to develop that side of our activities to the extent that we became ale-house keepers, as neither Richard nor I wished to be tied to that trade. Most people brewed their ale at home, of course, and had no need of mine, but this was a wonderfully heady brew and many a passing farmer, drover or even labourer called in for refreshment. (The river water is dirty from cattle and the house-slops, and as not all the houses have their own well, ale is the only safe liquor.)

Beer was something I did not brew – and still don't, for I cannot like the bitter taste that hops give. My own strong ale is thick, sweet and keeps unusually well so I see no reason to spoil it. I know that beer is now fashionable, especially among the gentry, and that up at Court House Farm, which the Bishop has let to Sir John Pessall and his family, they have their own hopyard and drying kiln. As Richard did not like beer and neither did I, we left it alone. What I did take to doing, though, was to sell a few commodities that the villagers could not produce themselves such as rice, sugar, spices, foreign herbs and salt. These I bought in Petersfield market after I had sold my cheeses, and displayed them in my front room. From time to time I added a flitch of pork, salted on the big stone slab in the outhouse and then cured in the wooden trough, and an occasional truckle of cheese.

Gradually, however, and to the great distress of us both, Richard's health began to fail and he found the farming harder and harder to do. I've seen him come home in evening-time so white faced and exhausted that he could scarce eat his meal. I tried to help him by taking the plough while he led the horse, and by taking the sickle to cut the wheat or barley (leaving him to do the sheaf-tying). It was as hard for him to take the woman's work as it was for me to find the strength to do the man's. But we managed. We had to.

Finally I saw that even this was no use. When some of our rents fell due at Michaelmas Quarter Day (that is 29th of September) we gave up all our ploughland in the common fields and kept only the grass for the cows. This meant we would have no barley for my ale (I thought we could buy that in) but plenty enough milk for my cheeses. I also had ideas about my front room and the sales of produce I made there. I had the idea that I could entice the smaller villagers of East Meon, who had little stock or land, away from trying to brew, churn or cure at home in quantities that were of necessity very small. I argued that as we already had a butcher in the village why should we not have a grocer? Surely that would be a great boon to the poor?

To tell the truth I was so worried about Richard that such a scheme seemed a good way out of our difficulties, for I was determined not to apply to the Overseers for aid. That would be shame indeed, especially as I was still young and healthy. So the farming was much reduced and with it our modest prosperity. We made do with the rented pasture on which we kept our cows, heifers and the calves, and so were supplied with cheese-money at least. What with porkers always in the sty (fed and fattened on whey and skimmed milk from when I made butter and cheeses) and which were waiting to be turned into bacon and good salted pork for sale, we felt we could manage. With our old horse in the back bit of orchard for travel and carting we'd be pretty well independent.

The shop took a long time to make a profit, try as we might. People, I suppose, just weren't accustomed to not doing the work themselves and so felt guilty at being saved so much trouble. But I coaxed them and wheedled them and every now and again gave them a little bit of cheese free, "just to taste", or I would pop a sliver of tender salt pork into the hungry mouths of their children. In the end my shop no longer felt strange to them and they began to come of their own accord, often buying tiny amounts and always with long excuses as to why they had no cheese or bacon left of their own. Then they bought the salt and the spices and the rice, too, and the occasional trinket that I'd bring home on a market day. We did not prosper but neither did we starve. At least we were lucky in one sense for we had no babes to tend. I could not have managed the work alone if I had been carrying a child. And try as one will, a babe in arms takes a terrible lot of a mother's time.

Then, in the spring of 1626, when we were beginning to have difficulties in paying our bills and were fearful of falling into debt, King Charles announced that there was to be another General Muster of the county militia in July on Old Down, not two miles north of here. And Richard was again chosen to be one of the twenty victuallers. What a joy was that news! It did him no end of good to be chosen – lifted his depression a bit and made him feel less useless – for the contract would represent a goodly profit. But worry! I've never seen a man worry so much, knowing he couldn't do the work like he used to and not wanting to let me do it. Without telling him first, I hired a young lad from Coombe, called Thomas Drew. Only thirteen he was, but a big boy, sturdy and willing, and he came to work for us just for his keep, for we couldn't afford to pay him.

He lodged in the hay over the horse shed and boarded with us, eating his meals at our old trestle in the kitchen. His parents had died the year before in the outbreak of plague we had hereabouts.

So Thomas and I worked and worked for that Muster, making cheeses mostly, and brewing beer. Finally I sent the boy off on the horse with the pack-saddle behind him to Petersfield market to buy more cheeses. I had quite run out of rennet, as well as milk, and could make no more myself (besides which, there was no time for new cheeses to mature). We had a goodly few of flitches of bacon already salted or smoked and a good-sized tub full of fat pieces of pork soaking in brine, but I daren't kill another pig because, being spring, the weather was turning warm and the meat would soon go off. (If they had only let us know earlier about the Muster I could have killed more of our pigs instead of waiting until next winter-time. But that's governments for you! No understanding of these things.)

Anyway, the time for the Muster arrived, and what a Muster it was! Richard and Thomas took the horse and cart and carried some of the barrels of ale up to Old Down, coming back for the first load of cheeses, bacon, fat pork pieces and a big slab of butter. All were wrapped in huge dock leaves to keep them cool and fresh, as well as free from the chalky dust that's bound to be kicked up on a Muster site. I tried to keep Richard from working too hard, but you know how it is when a man's among other men – won't be seen as a weakling.

Mr. William Bolde was still the captain of our company and Richard said a better captain you never would see. Mind you, not all the armour could be found when the time came. It seems that sometimes a man on the muster-roll turned up but the householder, who was meant to furnish him with a musket or a corselet for his body-covering, had failed to do so and the poor fellow had to parade without looking like a soldier at all. Unless, in the opposite case, the furnishings arrived but the militiaman did not appear, and a temporary match could be made between the two. Richard said some of them looked uncomfortable beyond words in corselets that did not fit! At least the muskets were all of a size, being about four feet long. They were awful heavy, and the men said they were not as handy as the shorter ones, but those were now old-fashioned and no longer used. Of course, in the days of the old Queen Elizabeth, the Trained Bands had used bows and arrows as well as pikes and shoulder-guns, but when she died nobody bothered to train the Bands again until our late King James (whose coat of arms is over our church door) thought he'd better start them up again – by which time firearms had mostly changed in design.

So, as I say, when it came to our Muster and the drilling you can imagine the chaos! Nobody knew anything – and those that did had probably paid their £10 to buy themselves off the roll. The men grumbled and fussed, but we women felt they were quite proud in truth to be all dressed up as soldiers, with the drums and the pipes and the drill-sergeants shouting. We were proud of them, leastwise. I thought they looked lovely even though my Richard, being a victualler, was excused service, as was Thomas who was too young. My two wore just their working shirts (it was too warm for the doublets) and some old slops, open at the knee, instead of their usual trunk-hose. I saw no point in them showing off by dressing as if it was a Sunday, while they were doing no more than going backwards and forwards with the supplies in the cart.

Our company was a hundred and fifty strong and had truly hearty appetites. Still, it was all good profit for us, even though the road up the Hollow Way from the village was unpleasantly steep for our old horse, which did not do him any good. I think we were all disappointed that our victuals were not considered good enough to go for the officers, Commissioners and Justices of the Peace who were inspecting the Muster: it seems their provisions came from some grander place. Still, we did very well and were content.

Soon after the Muster Richard's health began to slip away again. It seemed as if he lost the will to improve – but, then, he had always suffered from an excess of the Melancholic Humour, perhaps due to his being in such close contact as a farmer with the element of Earth. Naturally I had the physician out from Petersfield but he could give little assistance, for he found that Richard had the Wasting Sickness and that even bleeding would not help. For this I was glad, he being so white faced already, even though it did mean that the doctor could not adjust the Body Fluids. I was told that his hope of continuing in life was very small but this I had guessed from the pain he suffered. I wept bitterly and in deep sorrow, for I loved him.

Long and terrible his illness was and I wore myself to a shadow, what with nursing him, running the shop, trying to replace the ale and victuals that had gone up to the Muster, seeing to the purchasing from market, the deliveries of goods to outlying customers and the keeping of the books. Luckily I was better educated than most females, my mother having taught me both my letters and numbers, so the figuring and accounting and the writing out of bills was no problem to me (providing that I could find the time to see to them). I was mightily glad, though, to have Thomas Drew to help me as else I do not know how I would have managed.

Richard finally slipped away from me on the sixteenth day of March, in the year of Our Lord, 1633, after over eight years of increasing pain. When he had been at the point of death the tolling bell was rung for him – nine strokes to tell he was a man and twenty-eight for his age. When he heard them he opened his eyes and smiled at me. He seemed at peace. I think hearing the bell did him good. At that moment I would have liked to have known that the old way of doing things still held and that the villagers, hearing the knell, would have knelt where they were and prayed for his departing soul. But such things are frowned on now, for we're not only Protestants but fast becoming Puritans.

We were to bury him at 2 o'clock in the afternoon, three days after his death. The parish coffin was brought down from the church by six of our neighbours and he was laid in it (for I could not afford a chest of our own). I had dressed him in his best shirt, laid a sprig of fresh rosemary dipped in rose water on his breast and folded round him the linen shroud that I had made from a sheet. Shortly before it was time to make our procession to the church, our vicar came and said some prayers beside him while we knelt. Richard had asked in his will that he should be "buried decently", with the old form of service, for he did not hold with the new way of doing things. He couldn't believe, any more than I could, that a funeral was no more than a mere disposal of the corpse – which people were now being taught to see as a loathsome and corrupt object. He felt the burial service was to assist the soul to Heaven, that the prayers of those remaining here on earth would help to make his path to the Almighty that much easier.

After the prayers, I provided the vicar, bearers and others in the house with a mug of ale each and some small flat cakes. Cakes and ale were ever the standby for the distressed and I felt it important that the old way of doing things should continue. Before the shroud was closed and tied above his head and below his feet, I did manage to sprinkle a little salt on his body. This, I admit, was purely superstition, but I hoped it would ward off evil spirits and stop his soul from wandering. I wanted him to lie in peace and not to be tied in any way to this base earth.

As the mourners left the house, I handed each a sprig of rosemary to carry in remembrance and so that they would have something to toss upon his shroud when he was laid in the open grave. With the vicar leading and the six bearers with the coffin following, we crossed the river by the Small Bridge and wended our way up the steep path to the church, the bell ringing the solemn forthfare the while, its knell sounding mournful in the wind.

When the soil had been sprinkled upon him and the final prayer said, we slowly dispersed. I was both saddened and embarrassed at not having a 'drinking' in the churchyard, as we always used to do and which I would have liked, but nowadays it was thought irreligious. It was only the chief mourners, therefore, who came back to the house with me for a small repast of cakes, buns and biscuits and a sup of cheap red wine, heated a little against the March winds.

Life was very strange over the next few days and I had little heart for anything. Thomas took over most things and even helped me to order a plaque to be set up in our Church of All Saints in memory of Richard, the vicar having granted permission for it to be put on the west wall of the south transept. It's not much of a memorial compared to the other grand ones, but I could afford no more. I would have liked a black marble surround to the tablet but I did not have the money, so I had a strip all round painted in black. From a distance it looks like marble and I think he would have been pleased. Many a grander man has a painted memorial. I've seen them in the Cathedral.

After his death, of course, we had to have the Probate Inventory taken and I chose the appraisers with care because I wanted all three to be able to actually sign their names at the page-end, rather than just make a mark. Richard deserved that much respect, I felt.

When our belongings were all listed they didn't amount to much, we having so little land or stock. For the first time I realised that, because of Richard's illness and our giving up real farming, we were almost poor. We had begun our married life as a go-ahead couple, aspiring for him to become a yeoman in the years to come. Now, as I looked at our property with the eyes of the appraisers, I saw that we had sunk quite low. Our horse seemed worth only £2; the pigs £1.9s.6d; a cock and five hens a mere 7s. while two cows, the heifer and two calves came to no more than £4.17s.6d. All the hay, the wood and what was in the woodpile, £1.13s.0d. And so on and so on. They even assessed the fodder of mixed hay and straw that was over the stalls in the stable and cowshed at a miserly 2d. Somehow, I don't know why, that last entry hurt me most. As if we had starved the animals. The most valuable of the farm equipment and other movables turned out to be the farm cart at £1, the cheese press at 2s. and the stone slab for salting meat, along with various tubs, troughs, vats and bowls at £1.17s.6d. Then they came into the house and went through every room. The ready money in Richard's purse was £2.10s.4d and they appraised all his wearing apparel at £1. When they had finished and had added it all up the Somma Totalis was only £28.13s.4d. I was deeply ashamed.

However, the days passed and work does not go away. If the truth be told, I was thankful for it. After eighteen months, during which time I had taught Thomas to read, I found myself courted by two men. (A healthy young widow with even a small house is a marketable commodity.) In the end I decided to marry the younger of the two,

Anthony Mulholland, I being in mind to have children. Anthony was quite personable and appeared to have no vices of which village gossip could tell me, and I did not dislike him. I considered that the sharing of the marriage bed would not be objectionable providing, that is, he did not pressure me to lie with him too often and was able to sire healthy children.

Anthony was a miller by trade but, as a younger son, stood little chance of inheriting the business and there was no longer room for him in the millhouse. So he married me. It was a convenience for us both. He and Thomas got on well so we decided to go back to farming. There was no real money in aught else. And if I was to have babies, Anthony declared that I should cease most of the heavy work I had been doing. He also said I must give up my little shop and my efforts to persuade the village into accepting a grocer in their midst. It had not worked. Not really, despite my self-pretence that I was building it up. And I was not to go on making ale for selling. Surely all this time, when I had been without a licence to sell, I had been acting against the laws, and it was a wonder that the ale-conners and those liable for licensing ale-houses had not taken me before the magistrates. The making of cheeses for Petersfield market he would allow. That and butter-making. I was now only to look after the household, tend the poultry, milk the cows, grow the herbs and vegetables (and he gave his consent to a few flowers, if I so wished), fill the stillroom with preserves for the winter, weave home-spun cloth for us all, salt the pork and smoke the bacon and brew just enough ale for our own consumption. It seemed enough but I smiled a little. It had been so long since decisions had not been of my own making. Quite early on we found that luck was with us in the matter of land. Several strips in the open fields became vacant and Anthony put in for them, and we found ourselves with quite a goodly-sized plot which made the cultivation easier. In a quiet way we began to prosper. Thomas, who had turned into a jovial young lad, was now paid a wage which pleased him greatly, even though it was very small, he being an in-servant with his board and lodging provided. He was willing and cheerful but this didn't stop me from giving him the occasional clout over the head when I felt it necessary. I didn't want him cocky. Within the first eight years of our marriage I bore three children: Alice, Lucilla and Richard (who was called after my first husband). Alice did not live beyond three years, sickening of the fever.

During this period Anthony reported hearing of trouble between the Parliament and King. Not that we had any full understanding of what he heard but it did distress us that our monarch, King Charles, had dismissed all those who helped him to govern and tried to rule by himself and that later, when those who sat in the Commons were recalled, he was in constant conflict with them. However royal affairs and governments were nothing to do with us – we just watched the price of wheat and sheep and listened to what the carriers had to say on their return from Petersfield Market. I believe, though, the men of the village argued the matter in the ale-house, some on the King's side and some on Parliament's, but to me it did not seem an urgent matter or one in which I needed to take sides. Taxes had always been with us and this new Ship Money the King wanted seemed just another burden to be borne, so I saw no good reason for fretting myself. Care of the children was fret enough.

Then a war broke out. I did not know about wars, save what little my mother had seen fit to tell me in between schooling me in the figuring, lettering and the way of needlework. Men got killed in wars, that much I did know, so when our vicar, the Reverend Mr. John Shrigley prayed for peace I said my Amens right well. Anthony must stay at home.

Months passed by and we were into the next year, 1643, and living on a diet of rumours which were all to do with places like London and Oxford. Then the King's men came marching down to recapture Winchester from Parliament in the October of that year, declaring the city was now on the royal side. I never heard of a battle there so I thought wars were maybe more to do with marching and galloping than with killing. I was wrong, of course, but I did not know that then. The King's army in this part had a general called Lord Hopton at its head and because fighting men need a permanent camp in winter they settled at Odiham, which is a good way north of Alton. Those who thought that the Parliament had the right of it were under General Waller, and he chose Farnham to be their winter base.

But the armies did not stay in their camps – oh no! Little groups of soldiery would go off to see if they could find little groups of soldiery from the other side. If they met, they would have somewhat of a battle called 'a skirmish' but not many got killed. Just a lot of shouting and clashing of swords and firing of muskets. Reminded me of the last Muster on Old Down all those years back! Only this was dangerous. I felt sorry for the farmers, though, for those skirmishes took place all over their land and must have made a terrible mess of the crops and the fields and the lanes, and even the farmyards themselves when they were galloped through. We heard that one of these skirmishes took place at Upper Bordean, but I gather it did not come to much. I expect the King's men (Royalists, they call them now) tangled with the men of Hercules Langrishe who lived thereabouts and those of Sir William Lewis, who had bought Bordean House from him. Strong Parliamentarians those two were, and powerful in that district.

Then, about the end of November, General Hopton of the King's army, seemingly tired of Odiham. He sent some of his men to settle in Alresford and some others in Alton, and worst of all (and this was really terrible) a goodly number to quarter in Petersfield. I had thought, you see, that the King's army would be all gentlemen and aristocrats with well-behaved followers, captained by such as Justices of the Peace and the like. But again I was wrong. The King had as many scallywags, rogues and ruffians in his army as had General Waller for the Parliament. Nothing at all to choose between them – and both sides treated us ordinary folk as if we were totally of no account.

One of the troubles was that there was no proper army camp near Petersfield so the men were just billeted in whatever houses they could find. None of the soldiers had much money – and what there was went on ale – and when it came to paying for their lodgings (and often board as well) the officers handed out 'Promissory Notes' that said the householder would be paid back later. Of course they never were, not that I heard of.

The Cavalry was the worst because of finding fodder for their horses. Many a cottager – and their own animals with them – were near to starvation because of the seizure of their goods and hay. Even the vital seed-corn, saved for the spring sowing of the crops, was fed to those horses. The infantry pikemen were bad to lodge, too, because they were all such big men and ate more. Their pikes, you see, were over sixteen feet long and very heavy. The smaller men couldn't handle them and they had to become musketeers. (This was the cause of a lot of brawling, for the pikers looked down on the smaller soldiers. Especially as their own job in battle was to defend the musketeers from the enemy cavalry while the long job of re-loading the muskets went on. There was a lot of resentment, I can tell you.)

The first army we had in Petersfield was part of the King's army, as I've said, and was both horse and foot soldiery, down from Odiham. A terrible amount of trouble went on in the town. I cannot say that the men looted the shops, exactly, but they did take what they wanted and, if they paid at all, it was only a penny or two. The Market was disrupted as well, with the army Quartermaster coming in and taking off the best of the sheep and cattle to feed the officers. Just take them, he would, and his Promissory Notes were never for the full market price but just for what he fancied to write down. Things became so bad that folk round here did not know whether to send their stock to market or not. As this was all in November when the farmers would normally be selling off those animals they could not feed over winter, it was a distressing time. Even young Thomas Drew no longer liked market days. He said that violence in the streets was increasing (especially after dark) and nobody felt safe anywhere.

After some time the troops moved out of Petersfield and we all breathed in relief. The violence and the pillage stopped overnight and we were heartily glad to see the end of the King's men, for all of us had lost market-trade, and many of the townsfolk goods as well. We heard, too, that many sheep and cattle had been stolen from the fields and horses had been openly taken. A wicked time it was and we were thankful it was over. Our peace was not to last, though. After a wet and dreary winter we heard that both armies were in the area again and we waited in apprehension.

In March (of 1644, that was) we found that West Meon held some of the King's men belonging to General Hopton's army. They were acting as a kind of outpost, protecting the route to Winchester which was still Royalist. Occasionally a few of them could be seen riding carefully along Park Hill above our own village, on the lookout for Parliament troops. When they saw that all was clear they would drop down into Frogmore, clatter along the High Street past our house, and back to their West Meon base. Then on the blustery late afternoon of 25th March more scouts appeared in East Meon. We took them to be Parliament men as they came from the Petersfield direction. None of us went into the streets and children were kept behind closed doors for, with two lots of soldiers so close to each other, we feared a battle. I remember Anthony muttering, "Please, Lord not here. Please no battle here." We were very frightened and I held Lucilla and Richard close to me while Anthony held the dog's jaws tight shut so that he should not bark. All soldiers were to be feared, of whichever side, and more than one farmer's dog had been used for target practice and was left to run wounded through the fields to die in some ditch. We were fond of our dog, so Anthony gripped him well.

But the scouts passed through without stopping and we relaxed a little. Too soon, though, for another group of mounted men rode by and those, Anthony said, were the Quartermasters heading for West Meon to take billets and livestock for their men and officers. As they and their small escort trotted along the river road to West Meon and entered that village, they must have met some of the King's men. We heard later that a skirmish had taken place and the Cavaliers' officer-in-charge had been captured, along with his fine horse and a goodly amount of money. I cannot believe that the folk of West Meon wanted a battle there, anymore than we did, and so maybe it was one of them who began the rumour that a great force of six hundred King's men were approaching from the Winchester side. Whoever began that tale must have been disappointed, because after the Parliament men had indeed retreated towards us

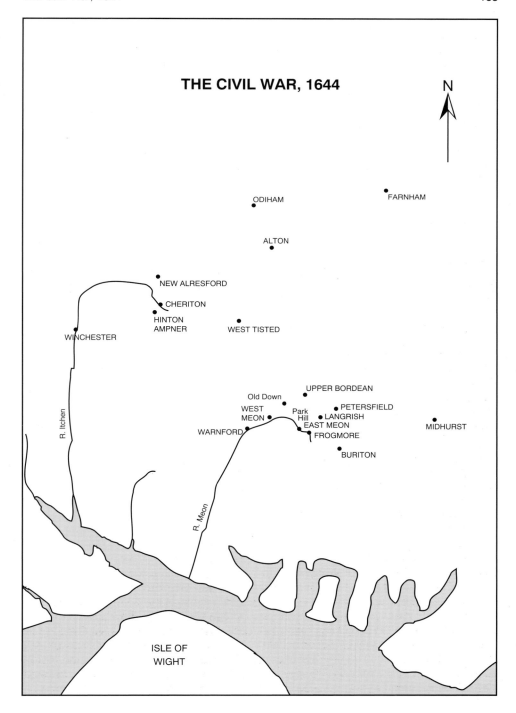

THE CIVIL WAR, 1644

N

FARNHAM

ODIHAM

ALTON

NEW ALRESFORD

CHERITON

HINTON
AMPNER

WEST TISTED

WINCHESTER

R. Itchen

UPPER BORDEAN

Old Down

WEST
MEON

PETERSFIELD

Park
Hill

LANGRISH

EAST MEON

WARNFORD

FROGMORE

MIDHURST

BURITON

R. Meon

ISLE OF
WIGHT

again, a party of their musketeers was rallied by a captain and led back to West Meon – which they then captured. They stayed there overnight, stabling their horses in the church, and seemingly because of being Puritans and not agreeing with such things, they knocked down the village cross which Cardinal Beaufort had put there years before. (Puritans call themselves religious but I can't see it myself. If they do not hold with the cross on which the Good Lord died, then how can they be Christians? And look at what they did in our Cathedral at Winchester – riding up the nave on their horses until they came to the altar, which they threw down, and broke the organ and attacked some of the monuments of the dead. Wicked, I call it.)

It was the next day after this that we were quite overrun by the Parliament troops. Foot and horse soldiers, they were, marching in with drums beating. You could not help but feel a little bit excited, along with feeling scared. There was a great number of them, too, and some were talking in a funny way (we found that those were all from London). Then another group rode past our house and we could see they were very important, with one man in particular who we reckoned a general, for the other officers all turned to him when they spoke.

After they had gone, a little time passed and then, with more clattering of horses' hooves and jangling of harness, more soldiers came by. And more. And more. "Dear Lord!" prayed Anthony again. "Keep the battle away from here. Somewhere else, Lord. Let the battle be somewhere else." But still the soldiers came, most on foot now, with muskets or pikes, past the church or over Park Hill or tramping down our street. One or two looked right in at our windows and I saw how tired they seemed. Really weary. Quite young, some of them were. I heard afterwards that although most had only travelled from Petersfield, the London Brigade had come from Midhurst with their general, Richard Browne, while others under Parliament's chief commander, Sir William Waller, had reached Petersfield from far away Arundel.

All those men had marched in the rain and seemed wet through despite their buff leather coats. Several went past barefoot and I guessed they had lost their shoes in the mud. Once I saw a soldier pick up a shoe that another man had discarded and, hopping, put it on his own naked foot. (Their shoes were of soft leather and had no special shoe for the right or left foot. They wore out very quickly, I'm told, and those infantry soldiers must have begrudged the horsemen their fine sturdy boots.) When the last had gone by we went on listening. They might come back, or another troop ride in, or a sergeant might bang on our door demanding food and lodging for his men and hay for his horses. It was the uncertainty that was so frightening. We did not know what was happening or what to expect.

"Where's Thomas?" Anthony asked, suddenly. "Where's the lad gone?" Calling out for him, he went into the back yard and across to the horse shed. When he returned, half angry, half laughing, he had Thomas by the ear. "He tried to hide the horse under a pile of hay!" he told me. "Scared the soldiers would have him!"

"And so they might have!" Thomas defended himself. "If not to ride, then to eat". He rubbed his scarlet ear and muttered "You'd have belted me if they'd found him!"

Then to our horror, we heard horses again. We listened and listened but they did not come our way. "Gone to the Court House?" Anthony wondered, and then, "Most likely the generals in search of dry beds". We never found out.

The next day, Wednesday, Thomas did not dare go to Petersfield market. He did slip out, though, to gather what news he could. (We felt it better that Anthony should not be seen in the street in case he was seized and forced into the army – on whichever side.) When he returned Thomas was very excited. "There's a big battle coming!" he cried "Out West Meon way! All those troops that came through here yestereve mustered on our Heath! Then there was a bit of a skirmish, it seems, and the King's men have fallen back and left three behind as prisoners. I'll just go out again and see what else there is to hear."

"What will happen?" I asked Anthony. "What will be the end of this? I don't understand why there's all this fighting and killing and anger against our King."

He came across to me and put his arm round my shoulders and held me close. Without speaking I leant my head against him and, as he stroked my hair, I knew that I loved him. After nine years of marriage I knew for the first time that I loved him. I turned my face into his hand and kissed the palm. "My love!" I murmured. When his hold on me tightened and his fingers caressed my cheek I knew it was the same for him. From a marriage based only on convenience and business necessity we had found happiness. So, in my turn, I touched his cheek and the war was momentarily forgotten.

Later, when Thomas returned, we learned that the King's men had made a counter-attack from the hill beyond West Meon and that the Parliamentarian, Major-General Browne, had had to move his London Brigade out of West Meon and further west. They were under threat all the time from the Royalists and some fighting did take place – on West Tisted Common, as we heard. Thomas then told us that General Browne had sent a messenger at the gallop to inform General Waller of the situation. Waller had then led his Brigade from their camp on our Heath and gone towards Cheriton – to which village the King's men were also moving in order to protect Winchester. Waller is said to have spent the night at Hinton Ampner House while his men were encamped in the open. The Royalists were grouped not far away, ready to defend Alresford, which lay behind them. The next day, on the 29th March, 1644, one of the worst battles of the war took place and the King's men were defeated. They left for Basing House, having retreated through Alresford (to which they set fire) and it seems that in that one battle they lost both control of Winchester and all the King's hopes for final victory. It must have been a terrible fight, that at Cheriton. I have heard tell that even now and after several years, the local folk will not go into the woods there because they can still hear the clashing of swords, the screams of horses and the groans of wounded men. Haunted, it is. And will be for many a year, I guess.

That spring, here in East Meon, we saw many army stragglers passing through from the west and heading back to London. Some were near to death from illness and we villagers hesitated to take them in or to succour them in any way. 'Army Fever' was a bad disease and we had heard that many people, in and out of the armies, had died from it. Born of dirt, it was. That and wet clothes and bad food, and if you took a fevered soldier into your house it was near enough the death-knell for you and yours. So we closed our doors to the sick, and it was a terrible thing to hear them whimpering from house to house and nobody offering them help. The purely wounded we did help, though, and merely prayed that the fever would not come on them whilst they were under our roofs.

After Cheriton our stragglers were all from the Parliament side and we heard much about army life from them. We took in one lad who had a badly slashed forearm, and he told us that their General Waller was a great one for discipline. If a soldier was found guilty of a serious offence he would be tied to a tree and shot. We also heard that many soldiers on both sides were unwilling to kill their own countrymen and tried to keep deaths in battle to as few as they could. Some even tried to desert but, if they were caught, they were hanged. We were told of one deserter in General Waller's own regiment who died this way, and another who was hanged for levelling his musket at his captain while he tried to rescue a comrade from detention. I asked, somewhat nervously, whether these things had happened while they were camped on East Meon Heath, but it seems they all occurred near Midhurst and before they came here.

By the end of that year (1644, that is) we were deeply tired of war. Cavalry troops from Parliament were back in Petersfield and now they were worse than before. Even unpaid soldiers need food, so they plundered and looted and were very violent towards us country folk. A hungry and undisciplined mob, they were, roaming the fields and countryside looking for things to eat. They hid in thick undergrowth beside the pathways and sprang out to sieze whoever or whatever happened to pass. The womenfolk dared not leave the village at all for fear of violence and because we had heard tales of rape and bodily assault. Produce for market was often stolen and carried away, and without being able to sell our cheeses and butter, geese or hens or eggs, we women had little or no money coming in. And the men could make no sale of livestock or new-threshed corn. So bad did the fear become that our children were scared to see a stranger walking by and we dreaded the sound of horse-harness jangling in the street. Prayers were said in church for peace but nobody believed it would come. The Good Lord was deaf to our pleas and the plundering and molesting and looting went on. Our vicar, the Reverend Mr Shrigley, did not know how to keep us in the faith of the Lord's loving care. Almighty God seemed to have forgotten us.

It was a terrible time. And not least because the Parliament army taxed us to sustain their troops whereas we had already been taxed (forcibly, I may say) by the King's army when that had been in the area. Taxed we were by both sides – and twice or more in one year. Householders no longer had a little store of silver laid by for their old age or to provide for their daughters at their wedding. All was taken. Promissory notes abounded but they were so much scrap paper. We even had to sell our horse to pay the last tax.

Perhaps a petition was drawn up in Petersfield and submitted to General Waller, the Parliament chief, or perhaps the officers in the area became disgusted with the rabble they could no longer control but, however it was, the General heard of our plight and of the unhappy people of Petersfield. He then issued a very strong Order to his army prohibiting all the things from which we had suffered, and said that any soldier found guilty of continuing such offences would be put to death. But plunder, I think, gets into a soldier's brain and he cannot stop. Even after that Order was given, I heard of several houses being broken into, marketing goods being taken from carts and quite young girls suffering violation. And then the 'Army Fever' began again. Soldiers died in their billets and gave the disease to their unwilling hosts. Often these died, too, and their children with them. In the market-place at Petersfield (and I daresay elsewhere,) country folk wore scarves about their faces and the taverns were deserted and the churches empty. Fear was all about us.

Anthony died. He sickened, and lay abed all one week, but he died just the same. The fever raged within him and would not be gainsaid. So he died. The second husband I had loved – just gone. We buried him in the churchyard with scant ceremony and without even a wooden headboard. I had no money left for a memorial such as I had given my Richard. I know where he lies but there is no mark to show his grave, and I daresay in a few years' time no one will recollect who is beneath his mound. A good man gone – and all to no purpose.

Then we were taxed again but this time we could not pay, no matter how much we were threatened with being left to the mercy of the soldiers if we did not find the money within thirty days. We could not pay. So they took the last goods from our house – our last pieces of pewter, a feather bed, the cheeses, one pig, and all the hens. When we were cleaned clear out, they left us alone. Just me, and Thomas Drew, Lucilla and little Richard. We relied for our sustenance on the charity of our neighbours and, together with them, we starved. In the New Year (a time of no merriment) we heard that the Commons had ordered that the burden of billeting soldiers in Hampshire should be lessened. The county forces under General Waller should receive regular pay and must cease to plunder the countryside. We were grateful – but this mercy had come too late. We began to hear of another general, called Oliver Cromwell, who was creating a New Army with proper uniforms and pay and discipline and I wished him well of it – but hoped it would pass us by. I wanted no more of armies.

Thomas left us to seek employment in Winchester – and he went with my blessing for he was a good lad and loyal – but the two children and I lingered on in the village. At least we had a roof over our heads, even if we were mainly hungry. All we had to look forward to was spring, when our bare feet would be less cold and the herbs would grow again in the hedgerows for us to eat.

We still had no means of livelihood for, with the horse gone and no draught oxen in the shed to put to the plough, I could not farm even if I was able to rent a bit of land. With no cows I could make no cheese or butter, and with no money to buy barley I could not brew ale, so I had nothing to take to the market or sell to my neighbours.

All I could think of to do was to go into schooling. I could, after all, read, write, do figuring and use my needle. I let it be known in the village that I would take any child under ten years old. If money for a fee was not available – and mostly it was not – then an egg or two, a half loaf of bread, or a mite of cheese would do as well for the few hours a week the children came. Like my failed shop, my school began small and for a long time it stayed small, but at least I could feed my two children. We struggled by somehow but the news that the King had been captured and was on the Isle of Wight hardly moved me at all. When, in 1649, they cut off his head, I was too tired and dispirited even to care. By that time I was labouring in the fields – a hired hand – and teaching in my little school in the evenings when the village children were no longer working at whatever small jobs were available. I had very little energy left for thinking about kings and such, especially as I was taking in washing for anyone unable to do their own. The washing was hard, hard work and by the time darkness came down I was often weeping with exhaustion.

But life went on and my children grew. Lucilla was set to work on a neighbour's farm for the pennies she could earn scaring birds from the crops with a clapper. It was boy's work, really, but Richard was still too young to be out in the fields all day and he was put to pot-washing in the ale-house (standing on a little stool to reach the water bowl). One of our troubles was that during these latter years the harvests were all very bad and food prices rose in a terrible way because of the shortages, with most people near to starvation for lack of bread. They spent money neither in the ale-houses nor on schooling nor in having an outside woman to do the washing.

Things were so different from what they had been, and even the one steady rock of our lives – the Church – was being changed. Under that General Cromwell (who later called himself our Lord Protector) and his Parliament, we were no longer allowed to worship in the old way that had been our habit since the Protestant King Henry the Eighth had taken us out of the clutches of the Pope and Rome. But it seemed that King Henry's way of doing things was still not Protestant enough and only the Puritan way could be favoured. I understood little of the matter and, like the rest of the village, was confused and distressed. Our good Mr Shrigley had looked after our spiritual needs for ten years or so and we had watched his children grow up and had benefitted from the kindness of his wife. We had attended his services and paid him our tithes and we could not understand why he was in trouble. All we could find out was that he was seen as being too 'Popish' and not enough of a Puritan. Admittedly he did not preach to us much but instead read Homilies and Texts from the Bible. This meant he was not in the new fashion for preaching. The Puritans, it seems, saw a minister's explanations of Holy Writ to be just as important as the ritual and ceremonies of the Church, and so preaching had become all the passion. Mr Shrigley did try more preaching but he stumbled over his words and hesitated for so long over the ideas he was trying to express that, in the main, his congregation stopped listening.

Then we heard that he had been turned out of the vicarage – he and his family with him – and put in prison. He had done no wrong that we could see but we were told he was a follower of Archbishop Laud, and like our Bishop Curle of Winchester, too fond of all things "Catholic". This, it seemed, was a crime. We waited in apprehension for what would come next and watched from the safety of Church Street when men came to move the things about in All Saints. Later that day a horse and cart drew up at the Parsonage House and furniture and belongings were carried inside. Later still we saw our new parson ride up, with his wife and children in a cart behind him. His name we discovered was the Reverend Richard Downes. We waited with alarm for Sunday service.

When the day came there was no bell to summon us to church. We entered nervously, in little groups, and found that the altar had been moved from under the east window and was put further into the body of the church. (It had not been many years since our Communion Table had been moved from the body of the church to under that window.) This was on Archbishop Laud's orders, and not everybody liked them, but he, poor man, was put in prison for taking King Charles' side, and in 1645 they beheaded him.) We were to go back now to calling it the Holy Table or the Lord's Table and not the Altar. When we took communion we were told not to kneel humbly at the altar rails – they had been taken away, in any case – but to stand. We were not even allowed to bend the knee in reverence as that was seen as a Romish trick. There were no candles on the Holy Table and Mr Downes did not wear the fine vestments that Mr Shrigley had worn. A great deal of the Communion silver had gone, too.

Everything, Mr Downes explained, was to be simple and plain. He would tell us all we needed to know in words we could understand. Despite this, we all made mistakes during the services. For instance, it took a long time for us not to sit for the reading of the Old Testament but to stand as we did for the Gospel. Both were now seen as deserving of equal reverence as both were the word of God. Very disrupted those first services were. We would forget when to stand and when to sit; we would make our normal genuflections only to remember half way down that these were now forbidden. People were covered with confusion and embarrassment and we felt abandoned by religion.

Gradually, though, as the weeks went by we became used to things, mainly I believe because of the sermons. Mr Downes was certainly an excellent Lecturer for he had been taught the meaning of those things in religion that had been a mystery before – certainly to me – and he stressed the importance of education and of the private reading of the Holy Book at home. Discussion of religion was now encouraged and Mr Downes held mid-week meetings with a Lecture, as well as the Sunday afternoon Lectures. The thing that amazed me was that people flocked to those Lectures, myself included. In the impoverished and uncertain world in which I lived, my Christian faith began to have some personal relevance again and I obtained great relief from it. If this was being a Puritan, then I was one.

The only thing I disagreed with was that Almighty God had ordained from the beginning of the world which of us should be saved and which damned. This seemed to me a cruel thing for a loving Father to do, for repentance and seeking of forgiveness for sin would now be futile. I never did agree with Mr Downes over that point. Other people disagreed with the new thinking, too, and some refused to abandon the old way of worship, which was Puritan enough for them. We heard that the Reverend Mr Bludworth, vicar of West Meon, had been turned out of house and living, as had the Reverend Dr Cox, vicar of Warnford, much earlier. Word came through that at Buriton the Reverend Benjamin Laney (who, it was said, had been a good and loving chaplain to the late King Charles) was dismissed, and that he had gone into hiding, none knew where. He was a scholar and a gentleman and never did anyone any harm, even if he was not very often at the Rectory, being engaged on King's business.

It wasn't seemly, somehow, to turn out all those reverend gentlemen. I knew from my own experience what it was like to be without any money coming in, but at least I had always had a house to live in, whereas they had neither. I was truly sorry for them, especially as some were old men. We even heard of one clergyman who had been turned out of his living and whose private estates had been plundered by the Parliament. He was seen in Winchester totally destitute and begging in the streets. When a passer-by casually threw away a crust of stale bread, the clergyman dropped his cloak over it and picking it up discreetly, went round a corner to eat it in the shadow of a building. I could not see how that was right or Christian. We are told in Holy Scripture to take care of the poor and sick and distressed and nobody was taking care of that old clergyman. I read in later years that our Bishop of Winchester at that time, Bishop Curle, had once described a Puritan as "such a one as loves God with all his soul and hates his neighbour with all his heart". But I don't know – I find it best not to take sides or get in a fluster about these things. I loved our church as it was and I have learnt to love it as it is now. Life never stands still and changes of one kind or another will always come.

One change that has come and has done me a wonder of good is education. Now that discussions and Lectures and Sermons are all in fashion, and book-reading a normal pastime, my little school is doing marvellously well. Education is now seen as the entrance to a fuller and improved way of life and the village families are eager to give their children all they can. I have been able to give up the land-labouring and (thanks be to God) the taking in of washing. Lucilla is no longer a bird-scarer, often chilled nigh unto death at seed-sowing time, but is helping me with the little pupils that congregate in my front room. Richard joins us in the lessons, too, and both of them can now read, write and do a bit of figuring. Soon, of course, they will both have to go to work properly and I am thinking of putting Richard to be apprenticed to our blacksmith as he is a sturdy boy and practical. That is, if I can find the money for his Indentures.

I am hoping Lucilla will be taken into the house of the Reverend Downes, whose wife is not strong after child-bearing and who needs a quick and biddable girl to help with the babies and the stillroom. I have taught the child much that is house-wifely and I think she would do well in such a position.

For myself, I am content with the teaching. I have to be.

Based on:

The Stuart Age by Barry Coward. Longman, 1980.

Society and Puritanism in Pre-Revolutionary England" by Christopher Hill. Penguin, 1964.

The World Turned Upside Down by Christopher Hill. Penguin, 1972.

The Civil War in Hampshire by G N Godwin. Reprinted by Laurance Oxley, Alresford, 1973.

Cheriton 1644 The Campaign and the Battle by John Adair. Roundwood Press, 1973.

Death, Burial and the Individual in Early Modern England by Chase Gittings. Croom and Helm, 1984.

A History of East Meon by F G Standfield. Phillimore, 1984.

Handbook of English Costume in the 17th Century by C Willett - Cunnington and Phyliss Cunnington. Faber, 1972.

M.S.
CATHERINE SHARROCK
wife of
ROBERT SHARROCK
of GATELEY in NORFOLK ESQ.
and younger Daughter of ASGₐ Dickins
after a long and painful illness
which she bore with true
Christian patience and Resignation
departed this life May 18ᵗʰ 1781
Aged 56

Chapter Fourteen

The Shepherd, 1782

CHARLES Sharrock stood in the Lady Chapel of East Meon church and studied the tablets commemorating his relatives.

On the South Wall he found the memorial to his cousin, Catherine Sharrock. She had died quite recently at her home in Gateley, Norfolk, after a long illness. He knew her maiden name had been Dickins, the family who had previously lived at Riplington, and he was not surprised to find many monuments to them on the walls. Distinguished, they seemed to have been. Francis Dickins, who had died in 1755, was remembered by a long text which, if his own Latin sufficed, meant that he had been Regius Professor of Civil Law at Cambridge and a Fellow of Trinity Hall. His brother, Ambrose, had been a medical man: Principal Sergeant-Surgeon to Queen Anne and Kings George the First and George the Second. Clearly the family had moved in elevated social circles.

He turned to look for memorials to his other cousins, the Buckles, but could find none. Perhaps their family plaques were all in Surrey, where they lived at Burgh House, Banstead. The only possible reason for tablets to have been in this church was because Cousin Lewis Buckle, who was now an old man, had inherited all the extensive Bordean and Langrish estates from another Lewis Buckle, who had died childless in the later 1720's. Charles knew that an even earlier Lewis Buckle had married Mary Lewis, granddaughter of Sir William Lewis, Bart., who had owned Bordean in the seventeenth century and was buried in the chancel of Froxfield Chapel. It was through her that the estates had come to the Buckle family. To complete the circle, the present Lewis Buckle had married Eleanor Dickins, granddaughter of George Dickins of Riplington and so niece of the eminent Francis and Ambrose. Thus the Dickins, the Buckles and the Sharrocks were all related. How pleasant to realize his family was so long established in this region – and seemingly important! What a good and convenient practice it was to record such family members in churches, even though their only connection with a parish might be by birth or marriage, rather than by continual residence. It was genealogy made easy, he thought.

Satisfied with what he had seen Charles left the church, and in the welcome heat of the sun, sat on a grassy bank nearby. After a moment or two he was aware of renewed restlessness. He had been restless for some weeks now and unable to settle to anything. Perhaps twenty-three was a bad age to be. What was certain was that he did not know what to do with his life. He had considered joining the Army, like so many of his contemporaries, but truth to tell, he did not wish to fight in America against the struggle of the Colonists for independence. Rather was he a follower of John Wilkes and his call for liberty and freedom. Two of his friends from Harrow School had been killed in that war, and one of his many Buckle cousins in the Navy had died when his ship came under fire from a rebel shore-battery. He did not wish to go into the Church, either, although no doubt he could have gained preferential treatment through his uncle, the Reverend George Dickins, vicar of Rayne in Essex. There must be something he could do that was more enterprising than these professions? It was a pity that younger sons were no longer encouraged to go into Trade, as had been the case a generation or so ago. He would have liked to have been a merchant, perhaps with the East India Company, trading in tea, spices, silks and delicate porcelain from China. Or a traveller, exploring in Turkey for the remains of ancient Greek cities, or Roman temples such as that at Palmyra, in Syria. He would have liked to have helped rediscover the buried towns of Pompeii and Herculaneum, but that had all taken place thirty years ago. He was too late.

Walking down Church Street towards his rooms at The George Inn, he realized full well that he was deliberately avoiding all consideration of a life in Law. His degree at Cambridge had been of a sufficient standard and his family connections were more than adequate. Yet he recoiled from such a step. He did not wish to be a lawyer, despite the pressure from his father.

Deciding not to enter The George after all, he wandered without aim along the river bank, watching the ducks besport themselves. Perhaps he should go home. He had come to this little out of the way village to find his family roots and, now that he had done so, surely he should go back to Norfolk?

Further along the High Street there was much building going on. He supposed that smaller farmers had grown richer and the bigger farmers wealthy, and that all were renovating the exteriors of their houses accordingly, even if the interiors were much older and probably still showed ancient timbering. He crossed the river by the carriage bridge so he could look back at the handsome brick house, built in the time of William and Mary. As he stood there, appreciating the building, he heard himself addressed

"Good day to you, sir."

The man who spoke did not wear the smock-frock of a labourer, but a craftsman's jacket of fustian and a pair of grey corduroy trousers. "A fine day, to be sure," the man went on. "Are you visiting, sir, or travelling through?"

Charles hesitated. Coming from the town of Swaffham, he was not accustomed to being spoken to by people of the lower sort. Not unless he spoke to them first. "I'm visiting," he replied shortly.

"Well then, welcome, sir. I am John Habin, cordwainer, and should it be that you find yourself in need of a pair of shoes, I would be pleased to make them for you. Here in the country our footwear has to be strong and waterproof, and I can see from the elegant fineness of yours, with their silver buckles, that you're more accustomed to carriage-riding than tramping in dusty lanes. My prices are very reasonable, sir. I have the highest references. I have served all the gentry hereabouts – the Eyles of Court Farm; Mr Edward Sheldon and his family who were up at Bereleigh Farm until he mortgaged it all to Nicholas Baconneau. I also serve Mr Richard Eames, who leases Langrish Farm from the new owner, Mr William Joliffe. But as that gentleman resides in Petersfield, being Member of Parliament, I don't have his business." He put his head on one side and looked cockily at Charles. "If you want me, sir, just ask around. I'm the Parish Clerk, so everyone knows me."

"Thank you." Charles nodded briefly. Not wishing to be accosted by other villagers he walked on, soon finding himself beyond the houses. As the lane towards the downs became increasingly dusty from its chalk surface, and mindful of the recent comments of the shoe-maker, he turned left at the first junction. Gradually the exercise eased the restlessness of his mind and the pace of his walking increased. Striding out, he took the first turning left and a later one to the right, intending to make a wide circle and so return to The George. Eventually he came to a small hamlet, where he hesitated, for there was more than one track. As he debated which to take, a single cow appeared, driven by a man, of whom Charles asked the name of the place.

"Ramsdean, sir," he was told. "This beast be that of Mr Stephen Steele, a yeoman farmer hereabouts, and I be taking her to another pasture. Mistress Olive says she can't sleep o'nights for the bellowing after the calf, now we're weaning it." He grinned and went on, "Cow, she makes a fair old racket, I do allow. But then I don't mind 'cos I'm up at first light, anyways. In olden days a farmer's wife'd be up, too. Up early, down late. That were the old way, sir. Not lie abed. And," he added, "that new pasture be a deal further off for the maid to walk for milking. And for coming back. Even with yokes, those pails weigh heavy and besides which, she has her little stool to carry."

Charles delivered a mild reprimand to the man for the seeming criticism of his mistress, and continued on his way. He was amazed at the free speech of the country people. So little subservience or docility and so much independence of mind! This was not what he had expected, for he had become accustomed to the idealised picture of the countryside, described by the poets, with its rural innocence, obedience and happy simplicity. The reality was very different.

The next day was again fine and he set off for the downs. Tramping up the coombe that led to the higher hills he heard distant sheep bells and made his way towards them. He did not doubt that there he would find the standard classic scene of the shepherd boy and his flock. He reached the sheep in a hollow of the hills, drawn there by the bleating of lambs and the different tones of the bells. Not a boy, but a young man of about his own age was their guardian, a dog at his feet. With his crook laid on the springy turf, the shepherd was engaged in knitting what appeared to be a stocking. When they had greeted each other and commented on the beauty of the day, Charles asked whose sheep they were and what was the size of the flock. He was told they belonged to Farmer Clarke of South Farm and numbered four hundred and thirty-five.

"That's a lot for one man to look after, isn't it? What happens if they stray?"

"They doesn't stray much," he was told. "And if they do, Rosie here'll gather them in again. Once they be up on the hill, they only doddle along – going not as much as half a mile in the whole day. They're no trouble." He went on with his knitting, the needles clacking softly. "Normally we have three shepherds – not just me. But one is ill and the other broke his leg. But I can manage. They're no trouble, like I said."

"The breed?" Charles asked. "Are they Southdowns?"

"No, sir. They be mostly Hampshire Downs and Wiltshires – but all crossbred and mixed up. But I'm surprised you know of Southdowns, sir, for I guess you're not from these parts, and Southdowns is a new breed, got up recent in East Sussex. There aren't many about yet, and a terrible price, I dare say."

"I'm from Norfolk. I have a cousin there who's a sheep farmer and goes in for specialist breeding. He told me about Southdowns and the way they are good for both meat and wool."

"My, sir! You be sounding like a proper sheepman! And your cousin? Follows that Coke of Holkham with his new breed improvements, does he?"

Charles was amazed at the man's knowledge. Here was no simple rustic, such as a sophisticated townsman like himself had been led to expect. Clearly the poets, so fond of Classicism and high education, had never stepped outside university or cathedral close. He became interested and alert. He liked the shepherd's direct speech and open ways and he was, in any case, tired of hearing about this being the "Age of Reason" and time of "Enlightenment", with yokels being of no account at all. All this century there had been too much emphasis on learning, balance, objectivity, restraint and adherence to form. He realized now that part of his restlessness had been due to discontent on this score – his attitudes and thinking had been too formal and unemotional. Life, surely, should be based more on the individual, the power of feeling, free imagination and creativity? Impulsively, he turned to the shepherd.

"I'm Charles Sharrock, related to the Dickins family who until lately were at Riplington."

"Ay, I've heard o' them. An' my name's Robert Silvester – there's plenty of us in these parts!"

"So what do you do all day?" Charles asked. "Just watch the sheep?"

The shepherd laughed. "Watching them nibble's only part of the job! I had to fetch 'em up here, first along. Later, when the sun begins to sink, I fetch 'em all down to the ploughlands to fold, 'Feed and fold!,' sir. That's the way of things for a shepherd. That's when he's not lambing or washing or marking or dagging or shearing or doctoring or taking them to market!"

"And the fold," Charles asked. "Where's that?"

"Down on the ploughland, like I've said. I sets up the hurdles first thing each morning on a new spot. That way the sheep'll manure the whole field. That's heavy work, that is, pitching hurdles. It wouldn't do for a gentleman like yourself, sir. You need strength. Not just for the pitching, but the hurdle carrying – that's three at a time on a pole."

Rather piqued at this estimate of his physique, Charles offered to assist the shepherd on the following morning. Robert looked at him sideways and said, "Well, I'll have to get you a smock-frock. And a cap. Can't carry hurdles or pitch 'em with a tall hat on – hurdles, they keep knocking the brim over the eyes and you can't see nothing. My hat's made of dog's hair and so strong I can stand on it. But it's hot, see, when working in the sun. Then I needs the cap."

"Well, thank you," Charles replied cautiously. "This smock-frock. Have you one my size?"

The shepherd laughed again, making the dog lift her ears. "Bless you, sir! They're mainly one size with not even back nor front. That's why the sleeves is loose fitting. I could give you a loan of my Dad's, if you like. He died a year or two back but it's still good for use. Linen it is, you see. My mother makes all our wear, smock-frocks, canvas leggings, shirts and all." He glanced down at Charles' feet. "Aye, you'd best have a pair of tacketty boots. Don't want to scratch that fine leather of your'n." Then he laughed again. "D'you really want to try at shepherding? I must admit, being short-handed, as I've said, I'd be glad of your help."

"Where do I meet you tomorrow – and when?" Charles asked stubbornly.

"The fold's on the flat lands by the farm, if you really means it. I'll see you at half past four, or thereabouts. Daybreak."

Charles blinked. That was early indeed but he did not demur. He did not want to be seen as a weakling. As he left the shepherd to continue his way to the summit of the hill, he wondered at this new turn of events. Why did he wish to waste time with sheep? Then, unexpectedly, he knew. He wanted to own land and be an "Improver." His Gately cousin could advise him – after all, Norfolk was the foremost county for new developments in animal breeding. It was there, too, that many of the new crops were first tried and new methods of agriculture introduced. He was already aware of Thomas Coke, Earl of Leicester, at Holkham, with his insistence on enclosure of the common fields to improve breeding stock. And he had heard of Sir Robert Walpole and Viscount Townshend who, earlier in the century, had advocated growing turnips as winter fodder for sheep and cattle. In so doing they had destroyed the old belief that over wintering a quantity of animals was virtually impossible. Those men were only three of the many aristocrats and landed gentlemen who were doing so much for English agriculture. What was needed now were new tools – something as useful as Jethro Tull's horse-drawn seed drill, which made the later weeding between lines of growing crops so easy. How wonderful if he could do something similar! Something really worthwhile! After all, his Sharrock cousin was already well into Improvements and now he burned to do something similar himself. He would persuade his father to buy him an estate on which he could carry out experiments and, if all went well, he would be able to contribute something to the well-being and prosperity of his fellow men. Perhaps food production would become easier and cheaper, to the great benefit of the common people. It would be an agricultural revolution!

Striding along the hill-top, he was filled with excitement. From now on, he thought, salted meat would be replaced by fresh beef and mutton all the year round. Health would improve. With better yields from wheat and barley due to the enclosed fields, their price would come down, making bread cheaper for townsfolk and country-dwellers alike. This is what he wanted to do! This would give a purpose to his previously aimless life!

He slept little that night, partly out of eagerness to begin what he saw as his life's work, and partly from fear of oversleeping and not reaching South Farm sheepfold in time. However, as the sky began to lighten, he left The George and strode out to the rendezvous, astounded to see how many others were already about and beginning their day's work. When he joined Robert Silvester he removed his smart billycock hat and put on the smock-frock, this one blue instead of the shepherd's grey. Then he tried on the big boots with flaps of leather like additional tongues above the laces. "To keep out the dew," he was told. The woollen cap which he pulled on his head was red, and although he did not need the yorkers that would have tied below his knees to keep his stockings in place beneath his breeches, he felt a real labourer. Only a shepherd's crook was missing. His own clothes he left in the big barn, out of the way.

The first task was the pitching of the new fold, to which the sheep would be brought back at sundown. The shepherd chose an area of ground on which young vetches were growing, and handing Charles a sturdy pole, he pushed his own through the central holes of three in a stack of wattle hurdles. Expertly, these were lifted and, with the pole over his shoulder, he set off for where they were to be erected. Glad he was not watched, Charles managed to do the same, only to find that in his amateur hands, the hurdles caught the early morning breeze and spun round like the sails of a windmill. Abashed and struggling, he managed to reach the shepherd and lower them to the ground. Many more trips were required before there were sufficient hurdles to make a fold large enough for four hundred sheep, with ground for them to feed from. It meant fencing a surprisingly large area.

Charles was next given a pitching iron with which to make holes in the earth for the hurdle stakes. Driving in the iron with a heavy mallet was hard work and he could feel his hands beginning to blister. He was also aware that the holes he made were seldom in the correct places, making it difficult to set the hurdles upright. Finding himself a failure at this simple task somewhat damaged his pride, but at last the fold was complete and the two men returned to the penned flock. The dog, a rough-haired crossbreed, was whistled up, the fold gate opened and the sheep urged out, their bells tinkling gently and the young lambs bleating by their mothers' sides.

"I see only a few have bells," Charles remarked as they began the slow plod up the hill to the feeding grounds.

"Aye, no point in having more. They be of several different notes, see, and I can tell from that which sheep is strayed or in difficulties. Today's all right, but you do this job in a hill-mist and you need to know where the stragglers are. All the bells come off at shearing time, of course, and I don't always put them back on the same ewes." He paused and put his head on one side. "Pretty, in'it? All our lambs is born to the sound of bells. Some of them know their own mother mainly by the note of her bell. I loves 'em – I loves the sound of sheep bells."

The quiet satisfaction in the shepherd's voice humbled Charles. Here was a man who seemingly gained full satisfaction from a job well done and from the well-being of his flock. He could see from the condition of the man's clothing that the wage was low, and he vowed when he was himself a landowner, to pay his shepherds well. He was sure a farmer could afford to do so, for much of his wealth must be tied up in the flocks. Thinking of this, he asked, "Does a farmer look for a big return on his sheep? In wool? Meat?"

"That he does" Robert replied. "But he doesn't look to sheep for his main livelihood, like they did in years gone by. Now much of his money-gains come from corn, so he keeps sheep for their dung – their overnight droppings on the ploughland. Without that, the crops would be real poor and get poorer as the years went by. No, the purpose of sheep is to keep arable land fertile and well fatted. Corn for bread is the main thing now, with towns so big with hungry mouths. Wool and the sale of animals is extras, like."

Charles thought about this and then asked, "And you sell the wool to a dealer and take the animals to market?"

The shepherd explained about the fleeces, rolled and packed in the barn after shearing, and the way the shorn sheep were driven to Alresford Sheep Fair. "Takes us two days to get there, it does, for a sheep can only do twelve miles a day, them not walking fast, like. Have to eat as they walk, too, for they have to end up in good condition, not exhausted nor scared, else no one'll bid. We goes by the green lanes. Drove roads, they be, for bringing the black cattle off the Welsh hills for the fattening pastures in the South. The drovers is a regular sight hereabouts, coming down Sir William's Hill alongside Bordean and Langrish and then on to Sussex and Kent. Mayhap you've noticed the smithy at Pidham, where the track come off the hill? Cellar Lane, we calls that track. If any of the oxen have lost their shoes they get them put on again there. As do ox-teams when they're hauling timber from Alice Holt Forest, near Farnham, down to Portsmouth for the ship-building. Have to keep on the higher ground, see, else oxen, timber and men'll be stuck in the mire. That's why they come our way. That, and to avoid paying tolls on the highways."

He paused and then laughed softly. "Sheep Fairs is fine things! Us shepherds get some days off and have a grand time in Alresford. We goes from here up the lanes to Bramdean or Apple Down, then into Alresford. New Alresford, that is, last Thursday in July. Howsoever, the people there don't like the Fair – too much in the streets, they say. All the smells and noise and dust and mess and every one of their own dogs barking! I can't say as I blames them – there's many a thousand sheep, as you can guess, and all being driven to the one place, blocking up the ways. But we shepherds enjoys it! All the inns is full of drovers and never a place for those as live there!"

By this time the sheep had reached their grazing ground on the hill-top, so Robert sat down on the sweet-smelling, springy turf. "A bit of breakfas'," he announced. "I can see as you ain't brought nothing, so you'd best have a share of mine."

Charles demurred politely but was glad nevertheless to be handed a hunk of bread from the shepherd's frail, the woven straw basket he had been carrying slung over one shoulder. This was followed by a drink of cold tea, straight from the small wooden costrel, hung by a piece of cord from his trouser belt. "I've bin thinking about they drove roads – it's not only drovers what use them. Smugglers do, too. All along our coast is their landing places – inlets and that. We're real close to France, see, and Havant's a terrible spot for smuggling. They come up to Petersfield by all the little lanes and secret routes and, as I've said, the drovers' tracks. I've heard they have a secret place near Petersfield where the gangs meet the traders and exchange their goods for coin. Risky it is, but pleasurable. Sometimes, of course, the weather be too bad for the smuggling boats to come across, so the gangs give up waiting and take to stealing sheep. A lot is lost from Thorney Isle like that. Seems that what they do is skin a sheep, load the skin with big stones and sink it in the sea. Then they makes off with the carcase." He took another draught of tea and added thoughtfully, "Ropley's a known place for hiding contraband – plenty of cottages and outlying farms with room for storage. They say even the Squire's in on it, and him a magistrate, an' all! Some of the goods they keep, of course, but some they sell on, when the way's clear for the London dealers to come down."

He wiped his mouth and took another bite of bread. "And there's Medstead. Seems like that's a big centre for the lace and silk and brandy. Said they keeps the stuff in an old cave or some'at. But there's Cheriton, too. A proper haven for Holland Gin, seemingly, but I don't know for sure."

"And does it all come in by way of harbours – Southampton, Portsmouth and so on?"

Robert laughed. "It comes in, dead o'night, to the beaches all along the coast. Then it's carried away inland, as quick as a pack-horse will go, for the Preventy Men only watches the shoreline. 'Tis said Soberton Church has a vault smugglers use to keep goods in, pending the traders coming."

"But aren't they ever caught? Those Revenue Men are armed and on horses, aren't they?"

"Course some are caught. Stands to reason. I remember hearing a case of years back when they finally was. A Fordingbridge man, named Chater, had turned King's evidence after a raid on the Custom House at Poole in Dorset. He was being taken by an officer called Galley to Sussex, as witness against one of the Hawkhurst gang, about whom he'd laid information and who was held by the Revenue. Now, it seems when this pair reached Rowlands Castle, they put up at the White Hart. It so happened that the landlady had two smuggler sons who did not want Chater to give his evidence. So they overpowered the travellers, and Chater and Galley was tied up together and put across the one horse. While they were trotting on towards where the Hawkhurst gang had their centre, the girth broke and the two men slipped right round and under the horse's belly. The animal got terrified bad, so the smugglers took up their whips and beat the horse. They beat Chater and Galley, too, aiming at their private parts. At last the party arrived at Rake, not far from Petersfield, as you may know, and undid Galley, who fell down unconscious. So the gang buried him in a shallow grave, although he was still living. Chater, the informer, they took on to Trotton (which is on the way to Midhurst) and there decided to kill him. First off, though, they took out their knives and mutilated him. Then he was dropped down a well with stones hurled on top of him 'till he was covered."

"But how do you know all this?" Charles cried. "Are you a smuggler, too?"

"Not me!" Robert laughed. "Besides, this gang were from Hawkhurst, away off in Kent, and it all happened over thirty years since. No, the tale's well known, for the Law caught up with them finally and all of 'em was hanged. One corpse was hung in chains near where poor Galley had been buried alive at Rake. To warn off others, I guess." He shrugged. "I don't suppose it did, though. But you can't keep secrets in the country – we all knows something about Ropley and Cheriton and Petersfield, but not the details. The gangs don't let those slip."

"Have you ever smuggled?" Charles enquired curiously. "Or run up against the Law? Poaching, perhaps?"

"Oh, poaching! Round here we don't reckon that's a crime – not wicked crime, leastways. Most of us do a bit from time to time." He grinned. "Rabbits mostly, with snares. It's easy to do, once you've found their run, and we cottagers depend on them for food. There isn't much other meat, see. We have to sell everything else to live. Even eggs. And hares, now – we shepherds is good at catching them, especially if we have a good dog who'll stare out a hare while we creep up behind and hit it with our crook. Pheasants are easy, too, down in the woods. A cock bird will cackle away at roosting time, telling us where he's hiding, and then we knock 'em off with a stick. But there's one thing I don't hold with, and that's trapping wild songbirds for the cage. Finches and thrushes mostly. Blackbirds, starlings, sparrows and larks are for the pot. They're all caught with sticky bird-lime or nets, but I do dislike the idea of birds caged up, just for their song."

"I've seen those cages for sale in Swaffham market. I didn't like it, either."

"Tell you what, though," Robert smiled. "Getting rid of evidence of a poach is hard! Ever woke in the night to the smell of pheasants' feathers burning in the embers of a fire? Or a rabbit paunch, for that matter? Or gone to draw a pail of water from a well and found it fairly blocked with deer antlers? No, 'course you ain't! But should you ever see someone going next door to beg water from a neighbour's well, you'll know the

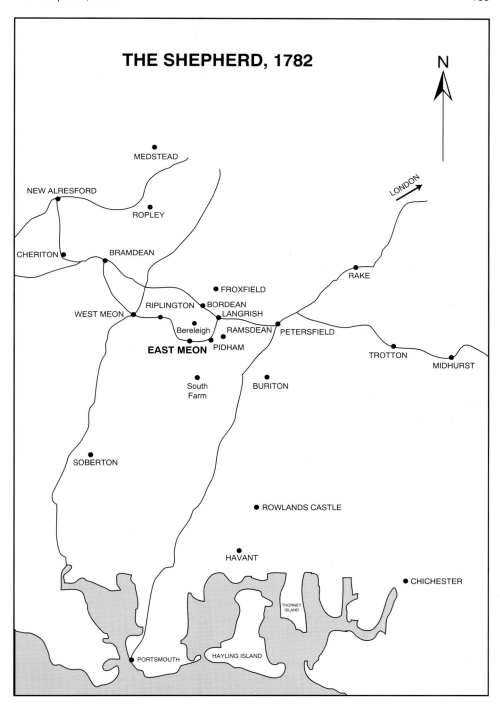

THE SHEPHERD, 1782

N

LONDON

MEDSTEAD

NEW ALRESFORD

ROPLEY

CHERITON

BRAMDEAN

FROXFIELD

RAKE

RIPLINGTON   BORDEAN

WEST MEON   LANGRISH

Bereleigh

RAMSDEAN

EAST MEON   PIDHAM

PETERSFIELD

TROTTON

MIDHURST

South
Farm

BURITON

SOBERTON

ROWLANDS CASTLE

HAVANT

CHICHESTER

THORNEY
ISLAND

PORTSMOUTH   HAYLING ISLAND

reason why! Payment's often made with a lump of black mutton. That's what we call 'deer meat!' He grinned again. "Oh, you're learning things, aint you, sir? Learning what the country's all about." Then he paused and added sombrely, "But I aint told you nothing of the way we live. Hand to mouth, and nothing spare for the morrow. But I won't distress you with all of that."

Charles though guiltily of the hunk of bread and cold tea he had consumed so casually and wondered how he could repay the debt without causing offence. When rain began to fall the shepherd urged him to go home. "There's no call for you to get wetted through, you not being used to it," he said.

"No, no, I'm fine," Charles replied, disliking the implication of weakness. The other looked at him doubtfully. "Tell you what — we'll make a shepherd's cave and we'll both shelter for a while. See those furze bushes over there? Run for 'em."

Charles did as he was told and then copied Robert in pushing his way backwards into the gorse from the lee side, until he was more or less in the dry. After a while the shower ceased and the two emerged. "What do we do now?" he asked. "Watch the sheep?"

"Aye, and I'll go on with the knitting. Don't like wasting time."

Another breakfast was eaten after an hour or so but by this time Charles was becoming bored. He had studied the view, examined the wild flowers, learnt the names of the birds. Restlessness overtook him again. Then he remembered the snuffbox in his waistcoat pocket. Lifting up his smock, he brought it out and offered some of the contents to Robert.

"Do you take snuff? You're welcome to some of mine, especially as this isn't just a hard lump of old tobacco, grated down. It's spiced and scented and very finely powdered. Comes from the Americas. Here, take some. Like this — between your finger and thumb. Some people have a little silver spoon for it, but I lost mine. Now, put it to your nostrils, as I'm doing, and sniff." He broke off then because he could feel the onset of an horrendous sneeze. When that was over (having startled the sheep) he looked to see how Robert was faring. The shepherd was sniffing gingerly at his pinch from a distance, with a look of alarm on his face. "Go on," Charles encouraged him. "Its all the rage in Society. King George and Queen Charlotte both take it. Mine's scented with cedar wood, but you can have jasmine, orange or violets. I get it from specialists called Fribourg and Treyer. Fairly expensive. But it is better than smoking a pipe. As Dr. Johnson says, smoking has quite gone out. Now it's all snuff."

"Don't think I fancy it," Robert said, not knowing what to do with his pinch. Finally, he bent down and wiped it on the wet grass.

"Here," Charles said. "You take the box and practice at home. I don't want it back — its a present. It's made of papier-maché but you must remember to keep the lid tightly closed. It's worth quite a bit."

After much protestation, Robert was persuaded to keep it, Charles feeling his debt now repaid. The shepherd slipped the box into his trouser pocket and grinned. "Seems like you be the shepherd and I be the gentleman!"

Charles felt this was the moment to leave. Half a day was enough and he had, after all, learnt a great deal. Now he was impatient to return to Norfolk to begin his new career. He felt sure his father would consent to the purchase of a farm, but if not, he could ask his cousin whether he could work for him as a learner. Perhaps he should do that, anyway. There was a very great deal he did not know.

"I must be away, now," he said . "Thank you for your company and loan of the clothes. Shall I put them in the barn for you to collect this evening?"

The two men shook hands and Charles hurried down the hill. Before he had gone far, he turned to wave and saw the shepherd was watching him with a smile on his face and was shaking his head as if amused. Charles realized he was being laughed at. Disconcerted, he reached the barn and left the clothes in a tidy pile. Once more in his own shoes and hat, he set off for The George Inn.

By the time he reached there the feeling of foolishness had increased. He saw himself as perhaps Robert had seen him – a young gentleman playing at being a peasant, even to the wearing of borrowed clothes. Had he not heard that Marie Antoinette, Queen of France, frequently played at being a milkmaid in the company of her ladies at the Palace of Versailles? Despising himself for a pretentious and patronising fool, he sought the landlord of the inn, arranged to leave the following morning and inquired at what time the carrier left for Petersfield. The next day he saw his baggage put in the cart and then strode out along the lanes in an attempt to walk off his depressed humour. What, after all, did it matter if a country shepherd saw him as a joke? It was more important that he had come to East Meon to acquaint himself with his relatives and was leaving with a new life to lead. That was worth even the small humilation he had suffered.

From now on he would be a different man. Liberated. No more would he turn for guidance to the dry, academic world of Adam Smith and his "Wealth of Nations". Nor, in philosophy, to Locke or Hume. He was finished with Latin and Greek, with the writings of Alexander Pope and Jonathan Swift, even with Gibbon and his history of the "Decline and Fall of the Roman Empire" (despite nearby Buriton being his family home). Out with the Classics! When he built his own home he would not copy the style of architecture of Lord Burlington or William Kent, nor would he fill it with pictures by such as Claude Lorrain, all classical ruins with pastoral figures in Roman dress. He thought he would still attend the concerts of music by Haydn and Mozart, but he would also turn to these new composers on the Continent with their free, more emotional and spontaneous way of writing. Oh, yes! He would forget Classicism with its Augustan pomposity and look for the new, in what he had heard called the 'Romantic'.

As he approached Petersfield he began to study the surrounding countryside and the animals it held. He supposed he was testing his seriousness about farming, and the desire to enter the new world of selective breeding, whether of animals or crops. He looked with interest at the smallness of the sheep and the insufficiency of the cows' udders. And the grasses – he thought something new should be tried in the Norfolk Brecklands. More and improved clovers, perhaps? Or sainfoin? He could not wait to begin. But first, he must see about enclosures. Without those nothing could improve. The days of open fields and strip-farming were past. He would have an enclosed and hedged farm where he could experiment, and conveniently placed near the centre of the land, he would build a house for his manager. No more having farm buildings or farmhouse in the village centre, with long distances to be walked by both animals and men to outlying fields. Everything should be modern, inventive and progressive. He would be an Improver in all things.

Feeling ridiculously light-hearted, he entered the Red Lion in Petersfield to enjoy a substantial dinner. Now he had nothing to do but await the arrival of his baggage and the Portsmouth to London coach. He should be all the way back in Norfolk by tomorrow evening, and could then seek a long conversation with his father.

Based on:

A History of East Meon by F.G. Standfield. Phillimore, 1984.

Some Aspects of Langrish Life through the Ages by Evelyn Hickox. 1986

Life and Labour in Rural England, 1760 – 1850 by Pamela Horn. Macmillan Educational, 1987.

The Downland Shepherds by Barclay Wills. Reprinted, Alan Sutton, 1989.

Shepherding Tools and Customs by Arthur Ingram. Shire Publications, 1977.

The Drovers by Shirley Toulson. Shire Publications, 1980.

Smuggling in Hampshire and Dorset, 1700 – 1850 by Geoffrey Morley. Countryside Books, 1994.

Trapping and Poaching by Arthur Ingram. Shire Publications, 1994.

Taking Snuff. Article published by The Norfolk Museum Service.

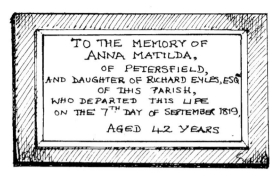

TO THE MEMORY OF
ANNA MATILDA,
OF PETERSFIELD,
AND DAUGHTER OF RICHARD EYLES, ESQ
OF THIS PARISH,
WHO DEPARTED THIS LIFE
ON THE 7TH DAY OF SEPTEMBER 1819,

AGED 42 YEARS

Chapter Fifteen

The Eyles of East Meon, 1819

WRITTEN on this last day of August in the year 1819 at my home, Stodham Park, near Petersfield, in the County of Southampton. I write for my children, that they may know something of their mother's family and the manner in which we lived in East Meon during my childhood and youth.

My name is Anna Matilda Hector but I was born an Eyles and was brought up in the Court House of East Meon, along with my brother and sisters, and then at Bereleigh House in the same parish. I am dying now, and because I am the last of this branch of the family, I have decided to write something of our recent history.

My grandfather was called Richard Eyles and he was born in 1729 – his family, I believe, had been yeoman farmers in Hambledon. My grandmother was called Mary, born in 1727. Although she was two years older than he, she died long after he did and at the age of 87.

Grandfather Eyles continued in the family's farming tradition, becoming well-to-do and respected in the area, running Court Farm in East Meon to a goodly profit. When he was only 26 or 27 he became one of the two churchwardens of the parish church of All Saints, so you can see how well thought of he was.

Clearly he did very well in farming for he also took over land at Duncombe, which is just south the village, and by 1765 he had Bereleigh Farm in his care. Within another ten years he also held the land that had previously been farmed by Mrs Marriott, which she herself had taken over from the Seals and the Poats. So he was a big man for East Meon (which mostly had only small farmers) and in the Court House we Eyles counted almost as gentry. Proud of that, my grandfather was, and rightly so. He was a bit rough, as I remember, and never lost his local way of talking, but the villagers doffed their hats to him and the women-folk curtsied. He counted as gentry, anyway, and that is what mattered.

By this time my father was born – another Richard – coming into this life in 1754. I suppose there is nothing that drives a man to succeed so much as having a son to inherit his wealth and property, although there is always a gamble on whether the boy will turn out well. So, with an heir to follow him, my grandfather worked, not just in planning and buying and marketing, but in the fields alongside the labourers. He was not of yeoman stock for nothing.

As it turned out, my father was no gamble. He grew into a fine man with the same flair for farming as my grandfather had. The village thought well of him, too, as did the vicar, Mr Boisdaune, for eventually my father was also elected churchwarden.

In the year 1780 my grandfather passed the running of Bereleigh Farm and that of Tigwell (which is adjacent to Bereleigh) to my father, the younger Richard, which shows how proud the older man was of him. My father really was in charge, too, not just playing at farming under my grandfather's watchful eye, for my father was rated to himself for all those lands in the church rate book, and had to pay out his own money for them.

My mother was called Anna Maria, born in 1753, and so just one year older than my father, Richard the Younger. I was born in 1777, my sister Jane in 1780, the next sister, Henrietta, in 1783 and our brother, Joseph, in 1785. How pleased my parents must have been to have a son and heir at last – girls were delightful but expensive to marry off, and sons were naturally more important. I was very pleased to have a brother, and we girls doted on him, but I do not believe we spoiled him. He was a lively fellow, full of mischief and when he was old enough to ride, loved his pony above all else.

Grandfather Richard was beginning to fail by this time and no longer had the strength or the will to carry on with the farming. Perhaps it was because nothing in the agricultural world was as it had been when he was young, and he felt too tired to modernise or to invest in all the new methods of production. He could not bring himself to use mechanical drills or to replace the teams of ploughing oxen with horses. In addition, the workers were again agitating for higher wages, and this saddened the old man for he had tried to be generous to his workforce and now it seemed his generosity was overlooked.

Whatever the reason for his decline, Grandfather Richard died in May of 1788, having handed over the running of Court Farm to my father a few years earlier, although he and my grandmother continued to live in the Court House.

I was eleven years old at the time of the death and can remember how solemn we all had to be. Solemn and quiet. We all paid our respects to the old man as he lay in the open coffin in the front parlour, his face so peaceful against the white of the grave clothes, but I remember, too, the sadness and loss I felt when I kissed his forehead and found it cold.

Being a girl, I did not attend the funeral and as Joseph was only three and would not come out of petticoats for another two years or so, he did not do so either, but we listened to the church bell ringing the knell and afterwards watched villagers, friends and relatives enter the Court Hall for the funeral feast. All wore black ribbons on their hats and as many black clothes as they could find, for the old habit of the bereaved family providing black cloaks and gloves for the mourners had then died out.

I marvelled that so many had come. It was the first time I appreciated that the Eyles were important people and looked up to in the locality. I felt quite important and pleased with myself.

My father, who was no longer 'Young Mr.Richard' but now 'The Squire,' moved his family into the Tudor wing of the Court House and we lived there with my grandmother in a rather more Society manner than before. We children had a tutor to teach us now, and a music master rode over from Petersfield once a week to give us lessons in music, singing and dancing. My mother taught us embroidery but Joseph was given fencing lessons. We all studied Latin but Joseph had also to learn Greek.

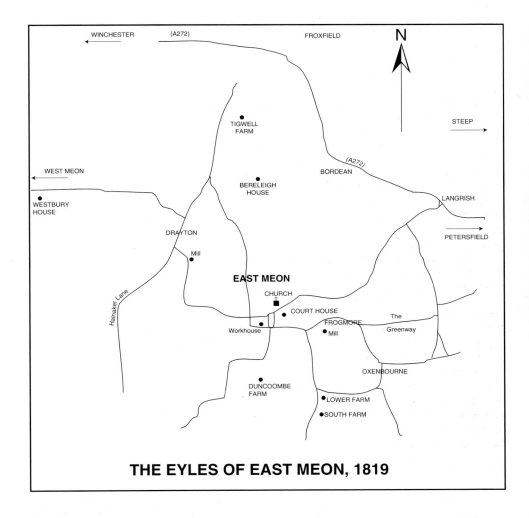

THE EYLES OF EAST MEON, 1819

I think I must have been a rather serious child for I worried about what went on around me. Perhaps this was because our nurse, to whom I was devoted, was a local girl and had explained to me how it was to be poor. Her father worked at Lower Farm and had a cottage close by (I passed it once in our carriage and it did not seem much – just a mud hovel with a bit of thatch as roof). She said he was in constant dread of being thrown out of work through his illness and of being sent to the Workhouse in the village. She told me also that there was a new Act of Parliament (called the Gilbert Act, I think) which meant that even if he remained well enough to work, but yet could find none, then he would have to take charity, being kept in sufficient funds by the parish Overseers, at the expense of the Rate Payers. Outside relief, this was called, and he dreaded being reduced to such a low estate.

In hard times it was difficult to find work, and the unemployed who were on the Rates would be sent by the Overseers from house to house to seek employ. Such men were called Roundsmen, from going round from house to house, and they never knew what work they might be given or for how long the job would last. If a man was lucky enough to be taken on for work, the housekeeper or housewife at the property was legally obliged to give him his victuals and perhaps 6 pence a day, to which the Parish might add another 4 pence for the support of his family. If there was no work to be had, the Parish supported the whole family out of the Poor Rate. This told heavily on the Rate Payers, particularly in a harsh winter with snow on the ground or a deep frost for months at a time, and sometimes came near to beggaring the Rate Payers themselves.

I can remember my father grumbling about the Roundsmen. He complained that some of them presented themselves at a farmhouse door and gave as bad an impression as they could, for if no one would give them employ they had to be supported wholly by the Parish in a week of idleness.

"Encouraging laziness!" my father declared "I don't think they want to work!" And it was not only the able-bodied adults who went on the rounds, but children also who, if not given work, could claim anything between 1s.6d and 3s. a week from the Parish for doing nothing. "Never turn that sort into real workers", he said. "If they start lazy, they end lazy".

But after our nurse told me about the Roundsmen, I looked each winter Sunday for the notice on our church door, put up by the Vestry, which gave that week's agreed rate of wages to be paid to the labourers. Two-thirds of that sum was to be paid by the employer in cash and one-third by the Parish Officers from the Rates. This arrangement was to run from 30 November until 28 February each year. I often wondered what happened to the men if snow fell in March and lay for weeks – as it can do. However, being young I did not worry very much, for even ten pence a day seemed a lot of money to me then. A kind uncle sometimes gave me three or four pennies when he came to visit and that usually bought a fair amount. Once, when I had saved up a little, I was even able to buy several ounces of lace (but admittedly not of the best quality) to give to my grandmother at Christmas, so ten pence a day seemed riches.

One thing I remember about my parents' new wealth was that we no longer had to eat from plates of tin, wood or pewter, but had beautiful china ones instead. It was said that our health was better for this as pottery and china were easier to clean. It looked prettier, too, and I often sat with my mother while she turned the pages of a manufacturer's catalogue with all its delicate pieces so well illustrated.

By now we had that other important innovation – cotton clothing – and this was something very new. I remember Nurse rejoicing at the ease of their washing, and the way she would proudly set out clean under-garments for us at much more frequent intervals than before. And how pleasant they were in summer! Flannel next to the skin was welcome in the winter but almost unbearable in the heat. (Some children, I heard though, were kept in cotton all the year round and nearly froze.)

There was one wonderful thing about my childhood that I did not recognize at the time because I had no idea that things had once been different, and that was that in our generation, and really for the first time, children were not expected to be little adults from infancy, but were allowed to be purely childish. So we spent much more time playing with our parents, which was a great joy to me. I can remember accompanying my mother on walks through the village and being allowed to drop twigs in the river which ran beside the High Street, and of chasing after them along the banks; of accompanying my father up the hill-road to Bereleigh to watch the sheep being sheared or, on my fat little pony, out towards Oxenbourne at harvest time.

And then we had expeditions for the whole family to the annual Taro Fair in Petersfield. We children were driven in a farm cart, sitting on loose straw with my mother and nurse, while my father rode beside us until he tired of the slow pace and went on ahead. Of the Fairs themselves I remember very little, for I tended to be nervous in crowds and, in any case, had to hold the hands of Henrietta and Jane which was a great responsibility as they, though younger than I, were more full of adventure.

I was happy enough in my childhood and I think was actively encouraged to be happy. This was another of the great changes that took place in our late eighteenth century – happiness was now allowed to be found on earth as well as in Heaven. Not that we were to indulge in happiness in a selfish way but to look for a moral purpose within our actions. Happiness, I suppose, was becoming less an inward-looking concern for one's own immortal soul and more an outgoing wish to benefit others. Perhaps this was because the moneyed classes had more leisure, and with the cultural changes that had taken place (although well before I was born) people felt able to indulge in pleasurable – but purposeful – activities, in the belief that the works of the bountiful Creator should be enjoyed, rather than shunned in the old, puritanical way.

So we had books as well. And I loved reading the new children's literature which was now being produced. I read for pleasure and not just for instruction or moral education, and felt that I was becoming quite socially accomplished as well as intellectually advanced. This self-conceit was especially true at Christmas time when Father threw parties in the great Court Hall. He hired a small band (mostly of two or three violins with a tabor or French horn) and everyone danced and sang and we young ones were allowed to join in. I felt especially proud and grown up when I found that not all the country folk in our part of Hampshire knew the exact steps of the minuet or the gavotte (being more used to plain country dances) and that they often cast sideways glances at my feet to see what step I was doing.

Another thing that happened when I was young was that Father took to having "The Hampshire Telegraph" delivered once a week, and to us that meant the Advertisements. When he had finished with the political news (and I understood that to be very grave) and the farming items, Mother and we girls scanned the pages for information on forthcoming concerts, theatres, assemblies, balls and lectures. (Race meetings we ignored, for we knew we would never go to those.)

'Travel' was certainly the rage in my youth, for with the great improvements to the roads and the betterment of the coaches, everyone seemed on the move. If you had money, that was. And as our family was becoming increasingly affluent we could see the world of culture opening before us. It was a wonderfully exciting period in which to be young, even in behind-the-times rural Hampshire.

By 1793 most of Europe seemed to be in an alliance against the French revolutionaries, and war had begun. As a consequence farming was becoming increasingly prosperous. Sheep and corn were what the land produced hereabouts, and sheep and corn were what sold best. The towns were all expanding and needed to be fed; the Army was overseas and needed woollen uniforms to wear. So prices rose, and the farmers reaped the benefit.

But Father did not rely solely on his agricultural profits, for he saw that one day the War would end and the profits drop again. So he invested in property and concerned himself with politics and local affairs in Petersfield. With his newly-established position in society, he contemplated entering my brother Joseph for Winchester College. However, he came to hear such disturbing reports of riots, drunkenness and unruly behaviour that he chose Eton instead.

Later we heard of these goings on at Winchester College from a cousin who was there during the Great Rebellion of 1793. Disgraceful things happened, apparently, with boys refusing to attend School and arming themselves with clubs. When the Warden sent for the Prefects they refused to go, and instead took the keys from the Porter, broke into one of the Masters' rooms, blocked several doorways with benches, entered the Warden's lodgings and kept him, the Usher and another Fellow prisoner in the Warden's dining-room all night. When the Warden was finally let out he had to seek the aid of the Magistrates and the Sheriff to free the other prisoners, but by then the boys had barricaded one of the gates and had taken paving stones from a courtyard to the top of the Tower for use as ammunition. As I remember the story, they had also loosened some of the tower parapet so they could hurl down the stones. They had also fetched their swords and more bludgeons. Worst of all, they had hoisted the Red Flag of Liberty as if they were part of the French Revolution and avid readers of the "Rights of Man" by that traitorous renegade, Tom Paine.

How horrible it must have been – and shameful, too. Apparently there had been several mutinies in the College in earlier years, with quite serious affrays between the boys and the townsfolk, with pistols fired, fights in the Cathedral churchyard, broken windows and damaged property. On one occasion, I understand, the Riot Act had to be read and the Military arrived with fixed bayonets.

Such a rough, ill-disciplined and unruly place. I can see why Father turned against it. I believe much cruelty went on under the fagging system as well as drunkenness, gambling and general bullying. At least (and this is no real comfort) Winchester was not alone in its bad behaviour, for Rugby School was at least as rebellious, with the Headmaster's door being blown open by gunpowder, while at Harrow the boys set up a roadblock and blew up one of the Governor's carriages. And I have since heard that last year (1818, that was) even Eton had rioted. I really do fear for this nation if these are the boys who are to be our future leaders. Clearly the young are not what they were in my early days. They have become degenerate, I am afraid. I cannot tell why.

Apart from Joseph going to school, there were others excitements for we three girls, and especially for me as the eldest. By this time I was nineteen years of age and my parents were beginning to think of marriage for me. Father continued to encourage the sons of his Petersfield friends to ride over to East Meon for what he liked to call "the shooting". In reality it was an attempt to launch me into Society, for we had no Assembly Rooms nearby where I could be paraded, nor a spa resort, such as Bath or Tunbridge Wells, where I could have sauntered up and down the especially wide pavements on my father's arm after taking the waters.

But somehow I was never spoken for. We were still too provincial, perhaps, or the Court House not grand enough in the modern style to impress the young men. Perhaps a coincidence, but I think it was about then that Father decided to build a larger house on the Bereleigh estate to replace the old Tudor manor house which was, in any case, in considerable disrepair. He could see, I think, that with three daughters to marry off such a change was necessary. Besides which, he now had aspirations to grandeur on his own account for he was wealthy, successful and mixing with the upper sort of people.

So plans were drawn, builders consulted and the latest London designs studied. As you can imagine, my mother was delighted at the thought of having a modern house with everything so convenient, with even a back wing for the additional servants who would now be necessary. No longer would she have to supervise the kitchen and the stillroom, for we were to have a housekeeper to do all that. Indeed, I think my mother saw herself as sitting in her new drawing-room entertaining the County ladies, while my father plied their distinguished husbands with his best port. (I do not think she quite achieved this for my father never obtained a title and did not become a Justice of the Peace, but we did very well for all that.)

A great deal of my father's time was now taken up with the new buildings at Bereleigh but he continued to keep a close eye on his farming interests, for it was from them that our main financial support came.

The old problem of wages for day labourers was constantly to the fore, especially since a few years previously (in 1795, I believe) a new arrangement of payment had come in called the 'Speenhamland Act' of which my father did not approve. He said it caught the poor in a trap of poverty from which they could not escape – especially as some farmers and landowners abused the system. Despite this, it was recognised that the intention of the Act had been to benefit the poor, not to penalize them.

Many were the hours spent in trying to find a means by which to subsidize the destitute from the Poor Rates while yet enabling them to better themselves by saving. The landlords have been criticized – even in my hearing – for their greed in keeping their wealth to themselves while others starved but, truly, not many did. Bad reports on people always circulate faster than those that are good, and it does not seem equitable that the work deliberately invented by the landowners to keep the poor employed in winter and other hard times should be ignored. Much of the great tree-planting of our day, the wall-building around the estates, the creation of new roadways and the improvements of the old – these were all done in the winter when day-labourers had no work and would otherwise have starved. The landlords benefitted also, of course, but these schemes did at least prevent some of the workers drifting despairingly to towns to seek work there. And they and their families were kept alive. Look at how many people even our own modest estate supported – by living somewhat grandly we gave employment to much of the village and surrounding area.

At last Bereleigh was finished – or, at least, enough of it to enable us to move in. It was wonderful! A portico for us to drive under in the coach, a big entrance hall, a fine staircase, a multitude of large and gracious reception rooms and bedroom after bedroom upstairs. Now we really were gentry, and I felt that perhaps my chances of a good marriage had markedly improved.

Father was elected Mayor of Petersfield at this time – about the year 1800, I think – and was now increasingly concerned with business and finance in that town. He became friends with Mr Edward and Mrs Sarah Patrick, who were prominent Petersfield people, interested in the new banks which were springing up throughout the country. The Patricks introduced us to a family called Hector, who were also in banking.

With Father being Mayor we three girls were included in the invitations to many a 'rout' in the neighbourhood and were able to mix with all the polite society, enjoying official banquets, assemblies and balls as well as private entertainments. I think we were becoming more acceptable to people of rank now that Father was increasingly prominent in the locality. Especially since he had just built a grand new house of his own at Bereleigh. We became 'their sort', for we had all now learnt the necessary etiquette and behaviour to enable us to mix with ease in those elegant surroundings.

And so it was that I came to meet young Mr Cornthwaite Hector of the banking family. Their home was in Portsea, where they had many other interests, but he was often in Petersfield and I came to like him very well and – to my amazed delight – it seemed the feeling was returned. It so happens that he was not the first young man to whom I had given my affections, for when I was much younger I had formed a deep (if undeclared) attachment to a cousin of Lady Gage of Westbury House, and I had hoped that this would be returned. He and I met quite often, for Miss Susanna Skinner (who had finally inherited Westbury) had married Henry Gage, the third Viscount of that name, and they entertained quite lavishly at their splendid house and were in the habit of kindly inviting us. I had been truly enamoured of this young cousin of Lady Gage and it was to my deep and private distress that he married elsewhere. The attentions of Mr Hector were therefore all the more welcome, and his obvious liking for me was balm to my soul.

My age was now twenty-three years, while my younger sister Jane's was 20 and Henrietta's 17. Joseph, now near to finishing his time at Eton, was 15. With all three daughters still unmarried (and Mr Hector not having yet declared his affections for me) I think both Mother and Father worried a good deal, for periodically we were taken off to Bath or up to London for the Season in order to find ourselves husbands. My two sisters were delighted of course, but it was all to no avail.

We were still at war with the French now led by that brute Napoleon, and most of the eligible young men were in the Army and serving overseas, or else were in the Navy. And of those, many were killed and did not return, or were cruelly maimed and not fit to be anyone's husband. Others died by their hundreds of disease. A terrible time it was and, all over the country, people scanned the lists of the dead and wounded in the newspapers.

Finally, to my delight, Mr Hector asked Father for my hand and, as I was very agreeable to such an arrangement, we were married in East Meon Church by licence (the banns not having been called) on the fifteenth day of August in the year 1800. Our vicar, Mr John Docker, officiated, and I was glad to have present so many of my friends and family, including various relatives from Petersfield although Sir Joseph Eyles, Knight, being a Captain in the Royal Navy, was not free to attend.

After the repast at Bereleigh I travelled with my husband to Petersfield where we took up residence in a house already prepared for us, my baggage and belongings having gone on ahead and been unpacked by my own maid. (I had never had a lady's maid to myself before, having had to share our old nurse with Jane and Henrietta.)

Being but five miles from East Meon I was able to see my family with very pleasurable frequency, and often Cornthwaite and I travelled out to Bereleigh for a short stay. Occasionally, if he had to leave us to attend to business in London or Portsmouth, I would remain with my loved ones in the new house on top of the hill.

When my brother, Joseph, finally left Eton he was unable to go on a Grand Tour of the continent because of the War and so, as he was disinclined to further his education at University, we were able to enjoy his lively and boisterous company at home. We all deemed him exceptionally handsome and now that the fashion for wigs was outmoded he was able to wear his beautiful hair to shoulder length or neatly tied back in a queue. As can be imagined, when young ladies came visiting he was always the centre of attention.

Still a country lover, he now rode to hounds with the Hampshire Hunt, often staying overnight with friends in Ropley, for it was the Alresford, Kilmeston and Ropley country that the 'H.H.' mostly covered. A wild time they had of it, I believe, and succeeded in killing many of the wicked, predatory and obnoxious foxes that abounded in those parts, as well as enjoying the chase. He did complain, though, that with so much of the land now enclosed into neat fields, with the new brick farmhouses at their heart, the old freedom to gallop for miles over open land had largely gone.

He went out shooting, too, often with my father. Although big 'bags' were deplored, he was a fair shot (despite his flintlock which weighed quite seven or eight pounds, I think) and brought home many a pheasant or partridge from the estate, or a mallard off the river. I think Joseph really enjoyed walking his beautiful English Pointer up the hedgerows, and I know that she enjoyed herself, too. Such exercise for man and dog was so much healthier than this new way of 'beating' the woods with labourers, who are required to shout and bang sticks to drive the game into the open, while the shooting party stands immobile in selected places, waiting to indulge in the 'battue' with their new-style guns.

Changes are not always for the better – and that goes for cricket, too. When I was young the bat was curved and there were only two stumps. They worked perfectly well like that. Another change is that the famous Hambledon Cricket Club nearby, which did so much to raise the game from a sport to an art, is no more – by 1796 too many of the Gentlemen Players were entered on the Club notices as "Gone to Sea" or "In the Army" and the Club had to close down.

The only good thing that can be said of the closure of the Club is that the thousands of people who drove to Broadhalfpenny Down could no longer gamble on the outcome of the game, often wagering huge sums of money. Why is it that menfolk, whether gentlemen or labourers, feel the constant need to place bets? And on such ridiculous things. Once I was present when 20 guineas was gambled on a dog catching a certain number of flies within the half-hour. At the gaming tables in the London Clubs I believe whole fortunes, family estates and, in the end, happiness, can be wagered and lost. The men lose their money and do not seem to care, so long as they appear to be proper Macaronis with plenty of 'bottom'. It is the wives and families who suffer.

Suffering began for us, too, in those early years of the nineteenth century, for in November, 1809, my sister Jane became ill and just faded away from us. She died aged 29 and still unmarried. We were all heartbroken and Father ordered a handsome tablet from Mr Brewer, which was later put up in the Lady Chapel of our church at East Meon. It was all he could do.

I do not think he ever really recovered from the loss, for Jane was his favourite daughter, and it was in that same year that he leased out Bereleigh Farm to Mr Jacob Fitt who, from then on, had the running of it. Father did debate whether to give up his pack of harriers (which he kept at Bereleigh for hare-hunting on the estate) but he decided to continue with them, for the riding on horseback was good exercise and kept him fit, for he was becoming increasingly corpulent. I did notice, though, that after Jane's death he took them out less often.

He kept up his business interests, however, and particularly those concerned with banking. In 1807 he had joined with his friend in Petersfield, Mr Edward Patrick, (who, with his family, has since removed to Heath House in Petersfield) and together they founded the bank known as 'Patrick, Eyles & Co'. This organization helped to finance many of the new projects taking place in the locality as well as funding many of the loans to farmers for fencing, hedging, cultivating and irrigating their newly, enclosed farms – and, in those years of high wartime prices and great profits, offered a safe place to deposit their monetary gains.

Small businesses were also springing up in Petersfield itself. The little town was developing rapidly from a small rural market centre to a major halt on the great turnpike from London to the Naval dockyards of Portsmouth. It was not surprising, therefore, that the other bank in Petersfield, 'Hector, Lacy & Co' had been founded in the same year of 1807. This, of course, was managed by my husband, Cornthwaite Hector, and it, too, prospered. Perhaps this was because he was not only a banker but a lawyer, having many clients, and was well-known in the town. Eventually he became a prominent and successful man in Petersfield, serving as Recorder for the town in addition to being Clerk to three Turnpike Trusts and to the Weston Charity.

I was very proud of my husband, for his interests lay far and wide, including investment in another bank (called 'Hector, Jackson & Co' of Portsmouth), in several breweries and inns in the Portsmouth area and in Petersfield itself. He also owned land in Steep and Froxfield, and later on he bought Stodham Park, to the north east of Petersfield, to where we eventually removed with our children. He was a powerful and influential personage and many envied me my marriage to him.

Then sorrow arrived again for in the year of 1812 our mother, Anna Maria Eyles, died aged 59 years and also my second sister, Henrietta. Like Jane before her, she was unmarried and also aged 29 years. What dread we had then for Joseph, for he would be 29 in 1815 – a bare three years away. That age seemed to be truly fateful for my family, although I am long past it myself. We never spoke of Joseph's age, and as he continued healthy and full of life, we dared to hope that he would reach full maturity.

He was now hunting, not with the Hampshire Hunt (the 'H.H'), but with the Hambledon, for this had been formed as a Club in about 1800 by Mr Thomas Butler of Bury Lodge, Hambledon, with over twenty couple of foxhounds. This gentleman kept the pack at his own expense as well as covering the cost of their kennels, maintenance and the Hunt servants. (These, Joseph told us, wore a livery of green coats of such an inferior quality cloth that they were known as the 'Green Baize Hunt', much to their chagrin!)

Joseph used to attend the Hunt dinners, which were held once a month for Subscribers of the annual 10 guineas fee, at either The George Inn, Hambledon, or The Red Lion, Fareham. Because England was still at war with France, no French wines could be ordered (except on forfeiture of £5) and so port from our allies in the Iberian Peninsular was much drunk. The bill was always called for at 8pm and the members would then disperse to their coaches, most being too inebriated to risk the ride home on horseback.

When Mr Delmé of Fareham, Master of the Hunt, died while dressing for a day's sport, the meeting was called off and later his pack of hounds was sold at Tattersalls in London. It then fell to our Richard to become the Master of Foxhounds of the Hambledon Hunt and very proud of him we were. His huntsman was Old Will James and his hounds were kept in East Meon village (to the annoyance of many who disliked their baying at feeding time).

In that same year of 1814 our grandmother Mary, relict of Grandfather Richard Eyles, died aged 87 in the dreary month of February. Then, in the month of May, our father died also, aged 60. Richard Eyles the Second was now no more, and with his passing Joseph and I were orphans. We put up a monument to him in the Lady Chapel and added our mother's name to the same tablet, for we knew this would have been the wish of them both. Their tablet is directly above that to our grandparents.

It was in the next year, 1815, on the fourth day of March that Joseph died. A fever had struck him following a day on horseback in a downpour of rain and he never recovered from its effects. Joseph died – and his age, like that of both his sisters, was 29. There is a seeming inevitability about such things that is beyond our comprehension.

In deep mourning, Hector and I buried him. His friend, the Reverend John Dampier of Haslemere, officiated. In despair, I ordered yet another plaque to be erected in the Lady Chapel, and in despair I left East Meon for good, never returning there.

There was talk of amalgamating 'The Patrick, Eyles & Co Bank' with that of my husband's, 'The Bank of Hector, Lacy & Company', for with both my father and my brother dead there was no Eyles to continue the business. There is talk, too, that the new name will be 'The Petersfield and Hampshire Bank' and now that our friends, the Whickers, have moved out of Number Four in the High Street, this will become the Bank's new address.

After all the sadness that had engulfed us we did have the wonderful victory at Waterloo in the summer of 1815. This, at long last, brought to an end the Napoleonic Wars. How glad we all were and how we rejoiced! I believe that in Petersfield the celebration continued for many days. My own joy is marred only by the death in 1817 of Miss Jane Austen, late of Chawton near Alton, who was perhaps the greatest of our authors, for she wrote of life as we have known it and, in her 'Pride and Prejudice' especially, I have recognized characters very similar to some I have known. She was but two years my senior and died in Winchester, being buried in the Cathedral there.

And now, in my turn, I am about to die. I am in great pain and shall be glad to go, for I am beyond all further medical aid and am but a hinderance and a worry to my husband and children. It is now early September of the year 1819 and I am 42 years of age and very tired.

What I now ask of my dear Cornthwaite is that I be buried in the church of All Saints in East Meon, and that our good friend, Mr John Whicker, curate of St Peter's church in Petersfield, should take the service as he did at my father's burial in 1814. I would also ask that a plaque be erected in the Lady Chapel there that I might be remembered in the company of those I have loved.

May God bless my soul and allow me Eternal Peace. Amen.

Based on:

The Georgian Gentleman by Michael Brendon. Saxon House, 1973.

England in the Eighteenth Century by J. H. Plumb. Pelican History of England, 1985.

Georgian Delights by J.H. Plumb. Weidenfeld and Nicholson, 1980.

Growing up in the Eighteenth Century by Nancy L. Fyson. Batsford, 1977.

The Village Labourer: 1769-1832 by J. L. Hammond & Barbara Hammond. Alan Sutton, 1987.

The Rural World, 1790-1850 by Pamela Horn. Hutchinson, 1980.

A History of East Meon by F. G. Standfield. Phillimore, 1984.

High Street of Petersfield. (Petersfield Area Historical Society, 1984 Monograph)

Baptisms, Marriages and Burials in East Meon. (Hampshire Record Office M,64)

A History of Hunting in Hampshire by Brig.-Gen. J. F. R. Hope. Wykeham Press, 1950.

A History of Winchester College by A. F. Leach. Duckworth, 1899.

Chapter Sixteen

The Agricultural Riots, 1830

ROBERT Combe sat on the edge of the bed and wearily pulled on his boots. The morning was still dark – dawn came late in November – but he had the cattle to feed and delaying here at home did not help to get the work done. Nothing helped any more, he thought. Life was very grim.

He shrugged himself into his old top coat, still wet from the rain of yesterday, and left the house. As he tugged the door closed behind him he heard his wife, Ellen, rattling the ashes in the grate and knew there would be at least a cup of hot tea when he returned. Breakfast would not consist of much – it never did. A crust of bread, perhaps, soaked in a little hot water was all they ever had nowadays. A starvation diet, really.

She was getting so thin, Ellen was, and the children were little more than skin and bone. He thought that with winter coming on it was doubtful whether the baby would survive but she, at least, could be spared. As long as William and the bigger girl kept well – that's what mattered. At ten and eight they were beginning to bring in regular pennies from the odd jobs they did (bird-scaring, stone-picking or the like) and without their labour and their pennies the family would be desperate.

Carrying his lantern he walked through the village to the farmyard and then across to the cattle shelters. He envied the cattle: they were warm and well-fed and they had no worries – no rent to pay, no tithes to the vicar, no debts to clear with the village shops, no fear of unemployment and no dread of the workhouse.

As he hung the lantern on its hook he was grateful for the steamy heat coming from the animals. Grasping the pitching-fork he began to toss hay into the mangers and waited for the circulation to come back to his numb fingers. He felt almost warm by the time he began to chop turnips, using the new and much sharper chopper that Mr. Sutton had bought in Petersfield market after the old one had broken. The men had hoped that he would buy a machine they could turn by hand but he had pleaded hard times. "Anyway," he had said, "it'd still do only one turnip at a time – like with your hand chopper. So I think I'll wait until they invent a cleverer one that'll take a lot of turnips all at once. No point in having to change machines again. Not with the price they are."

As Robert raised the chopper and brought it down on the turnips he thought about prices and his own wages. Wages weren't high enough, and that's all there was to it. A man had to live as well as work, and he felt dying was nearer to his family than was living. Ellen was a real worry to him.

When he had chopped and re-chopped the turnip pieces until they were small enough for the cattle, he took the shovel and threw them over the wooden partition and onto the shelter floor. The animals came for them greedily, liking them more than hay.

With the cattle fed and the pigs seen to, he returned to his own cottage and found that breakfast was indeed a hunk of bread with hot water poured over it. But today he was in luck — there was a scrap of pork fat added and this, melting a little, added flavour to the dish. The children had the same as he did but he noticed that Ellen had left none of the fat for herself. No wonder she was thin. The children warmed their hands round their mugs of weak black tea (there being no milk) but pulled faces when they drank it — the taste was terrible. Nobody knew what was in tea nowadays, adulturation being so bad, but at least it was hot.

As he felt the heat passing down him he was thankful, as always, that there were still enough sticks in the outshed to make a fire. Jonathan Grimble, down the lane, had no firing at all as his allowance from the Overseers of the Poor went on medicines for his sick wife. He had no time for scratching along the copse edge looking for twigs, for he was a shepherd and out on the downs all day. Now that much of the Common Lands had been taken away from poor people and made into farms with enclosed fields, wooding was very difficult. And the penalties for breaking down the hedges or fences for firing were cruelly fierce. Without children to go wooding it could not be long before Jonathan's wife died of the cold. They were still only twenty years old, or thereabouts.

Newly-marrieds were in the worst state of all before the children came – or when the babes were still at the breast or were toddlers and could not earn money. The best thing, Robert knew, was to marry a girl who already had three or four bastard children of working age, for a young woman with all her children aged over five was a great help to a man. Such a one was much sought-after in marriage.

When Robert left the house again the sky was lighter and as he trudged into the farmyard he was surprised to see a group of men beside the corn rick. Who two of them were he did not know – he only recognised John Sutton, the farmer, and his fellow labourers. It seemed they were arguing, but doing so politely and without shouting.

"It makes sense, Mr. Sutton," one stranger was saying. "Raise the wages and with more food in their bellies your men'll work better. Look at these three here! Scarecrows, they are! And tired out before the day begins. Give them a chance, Mr. Sutton. Give them a chance – and do yourself some good, too. You'd make money if the men were fit."

"I see your point, that I do," the farmer replied. "But raise wages? I'm too hard pressed for that. Since the Bonaparte Wars were ended prices have dropped something terrible. We used to be paid well for wheat – and for fat lambs – while the war was on but not now. Not now. Wheat's down to half-price. They call it a depression. A 'farming depression'. Most of us farmers is hard pushed, and that's the truth. What with these bad harvests, and all."

The other stranger spoke angrily. "While the wars were on you were raking it in. Don't tell me you haven't got a little nest-egg tucked away in the Bank. 'Course you have! So let your men have some of it now. Why should they starve? Tell me that, eh? Tell me that."

Robert and his two fellow-workers stood silent, amazed that anyone should speak to their employer in such a manner. It was as well these strangers were not working for him or they would be out of a job at a moment's notice! No working man dared to cross an employer, even if he did have the right of it. With so many out of work since the Wars were over and the soldiers came home there were very few jobs in the countryside. Work was clung to, however bad.

Mr. Sutton shook his head. "It's not my fault the prices are low. I pay the going rate for my men and I can't afford to pay more. And that's the truth of it." Then his tone changed and he said more strongly, "Now, I don't know who you are or where you've come from but I'd be glad if you'd leave and let us get on with the day. I'm not against you, you understand. I'd like to pay more but what with the low prices, the rent and taxes, and the Poor Rate as well as the tithes I'm hard pressed. Hard pressed."

"Tithes!" exclaimed the second stranger angrily. "Tithes is the work of the Devil."

The man who Robert had heard speak first looked about the farmyard. "Mr. Sutton, sir, I see no machinery here. Do you have none? Threshing machines? Winnowing machines?"

"That I don't! If you think the likes of me is a big enough farmer in the way of corn to put myself in debt for the sake of a machine, you be wrong! I couldn't afford a great thing like a thresher."

"I'm glad to hear it, sir. For we're against those, taking away men's livelihoods as they do, and leaving nothing to be done in the winter. Threshing with flails is hard work but it does keep a man in bread. As you know, one threshing machine in the autumn can do the winter work of ten men. So that's ten men and their families made to starve in the winter, when they're turned off."

He held out his hand to Mr. Sutton. "I'm very glad to hear you have no machines, Mr. Sutton, sir. Very glad. So we'll be off."

And off they were. The farmer immediately rounded on his workforce and for the first time raised his voice. "What do you think you're doing, standing idle? Isn't there enough to be done without you listening to seditious rubbish such as that? Get on with things. Get on with things." Then he stumped angrily back into the farmhouse and slammed the door.

Robert and his two companions hastened out of sight of the farmhouse windows and stood muttering together in the cart-shed.

"What was that about? Who were they?" None of them knew but Robert said he had heard that in Kent that August there had been trouble between labourers and farmers. "Wanting more wages, like as not," he said. "And the machinery – threshers and that – I heard they smashed some. How they dared, I don't know."

"Take some doing – smashing a thresher. Great iron things they are. You'd need a crowbar or sledge-hammer or some'at."

There was a moment's pause and then Robert spoke slowly. "But they was right you know, those two men. We shouldn't be poor like this. It's not right. Without us labourers there'd be no cattle nor sheep nor wheat for the farmers to sell. We do the work and they make the money. And they're no better than us, really, the landowners and farmers. Some of them are only jumped-up working men, making out they're gentry. Only they get fat and we gets thin." He paused, and then added, "And if they do take to threshing-machines we'll be out of work all winter, with no flailing to do. Like that man said."

"And then we gets thinner still and the children die. Something should be done, before it's too late."

The three of them stood silent, taking in this momentous thought. Never before had they heard anyone challenge the existing situation – there had always been the poor and the comfortably off, the labourers and the landowners. It seemed strange to question that now.

Later that morning when Robert returned home for his midday meal he told Ellen what had happened. "And I do see the sense in it," he said. "Look at this dinner, now. Two small potatoes and those spoiled where the frost's got at them. No bacon, no pork, no meat, no cheese, no nothing. Just potatoes with a little fatty water over them, and turnips from the back yard. Where's the goodness in that? I wanted to give you a decent living, Ellen. And I haven't." Then his voice changed. "Now I think about it, I'm getting proper angry." He banged his fists on the table and stood up from his three-legged stool. "Even our tea has no milk – and the maids took gallons off the cows this morning. Mr Sutton could have let me have a ha'pence worth, even if only for the children. But no – it's all for marketing now. All wholesale and none retail. Nothing in small amounts now, he says."

He stared angrily round him, seeing the shabbiness of his house – the thin fire, barely warming them, the broken window-frame patched with straw, the damp and mildewed walls, the bare, uneven earth floor, the home-made table, the two elder children with tattered clothing. Both had to stand up to eat because there were no stools or even a bench for them to sit on. Everything he saw spoke of poverty. More than that – of destitution. "I'm angry, Ellen. Right angry." Suddenly he pushed his plate across to her. "Here, you eat my potatoes. I've gone off them."

His wife looked at him with fright in her face. Before speaking she quickly cut the cooling potatoes into pieces, giving some to each of the older children and sharing the last with the toddler on her knee. "We'll get by," she said, anxious that his anger should not pose yet another problem to their lives. "Don't you go fretting, now. Our pig's getting fat and you're to kill him next week. We'll eat well then. The children found a patch of sow-thistles for him and filled a bucket full of snails and piggy ate them all up, loved them he did, and he's getting real...."

"I know, I know," Robert interrupted. "But how things are now is not right. Not right at all. Being poor is one thing, but we're not poor – we're starving. Starving paupers. And our house is worse'n the pigsty. At least that roof doesn't leak."

In his bitterness he left the house and strode angrily down the lane, away from the village. If there was to be trouble with the employers he was one to join in. He was ready for a fight. He had been poor too long. He might be thin, hungry and destitute but he still had spirit. All he asked for was a living wage.

Several days passed. Nothing more was heard of the Kent machine-smashing or unrest until the second week in November, in that year of 1830. Then word went round the village that gangs of men, armed with what they could find, had confronted several farmers in the Portsmouth and Gosport areas. Word had it that the leader, Captain Swing, always wrote a letter to the farmers first, giving them warning that if they did not raise wages from the miserable 6s a week to at least 10s and dismantle their threshing machines, they would be punished. Nobody in the East Meon beer-houses

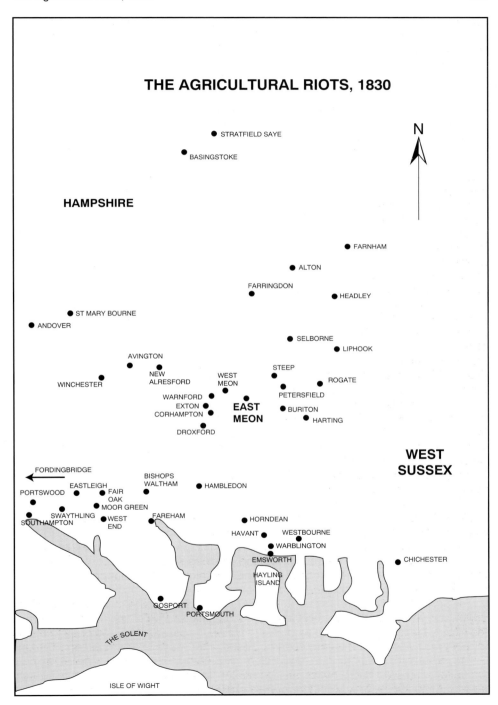

THE AGRICULTURAL RIOTS, 1830

N

● STRATFIELD SAYE

● BASINGSTOKE

HAMPSHIRE

● FARNHAM

● ALTON

FARRINGDON
●

● HEADLEY

● ST MARY BOURNE

● ANDOVER

● SELBORNE

● LIPHOOK

AVINGTON
●

NEW
ALRESFORD

WEST
MEON
●

STEEP
●

● WINCHESTER

WARNFORD ●
EXTON ●
CORHAMPTON ●

**EAST
MEON**
●

PETERSFIELD
●

● ROGATE

● BURITON

DROXFORD
●

● HARTING

**WEST
SUSSEX**

◄ FORDINGBRIDGE

● PORTSWOOD

EASTLEIGH
●

BISHOPS
WALTHAM

● FAIR
OAK
● MOOR GREEN

● HAMBLEDON

SWAYTHLING
●
SOUTHAMPTON ●

● WEST
END

FAREHAM
●

● HORNDEAN

HAVANT ●

● WESTBOURNE

● WARBLINGTON

EMSWORTH

● CHICHESTER

HAYLING
ISLAND

● GOSPORT
● PORTSMOUTH

THE SOLENT

ISLE OF WIGHT

knew what the punishment would be but it was soon shown that arson was a common and speedy choice. The burning of unthreshed corn-ricks took place in the dark of night, leaving the farmer bewildered, frightened and with no future profit from his year's crop of wheat.

'That Captain Swing' became of obsessive interest to the villagers and Robert thought back to the two strangers talking to Mr. Sutton in his farmyard. Nobody spoke of Swing when the farmers were within earshot but he was a subject of immense and constant curiosity. 'Captain' was a familiar title to them all as it denoted a foreman or leader and there was always a Harvest Captain to oversee the work at the reaping, just as the bell-ringers in the church tower had a Tower Captain. But why this Captain was called Swing nobody knew, unless it was in imitation of the moveable blades of the thresher, swinging down on the corn where a good man's flail ought to be. When 'Swing' letters were found in different parts of the county, delivered to farmers or pinned to barn doors, to field gates or to door-frames of houses, it was even supposed that there might be more than one 'Captain Swing'.

Another leader of whom they heard was a 'Captain Hunt' but he came from Wiltshire and stirred up trouble in the Fordingbridge area, riding round the countryside on a white horse at the head of a mob of three hundred men. But Hunt's men did not come near East Meon. This was Swing's land.

Robert Combe listened and brooded. If other men could rise up and confront the employers, why then, so could he. But not alone. Not alone. Only in a mob, because there was safety in numbers and he was too unsure of himself and too scared for Ellen and the children to fight alone. Then word spread round Petersfield market that labourers at Harting and Rogate, just over the border in Sussex, had joined forces on the night of the 17th November. They had visited farms to demand higher wages and had succeeded in extorting money and provisions from their terrified employers.

After that rumours spread daily, brought by the village carriers or by the drivers of mailcoaches on the Portsmouth to London road who stopped at Petersfield to bait their horses. It seemed that the Duke of Wellington's estate at Stratfield Saye had been attacked; that on the 18th, corn-ricks had been fired at St. Mary Bourne, north-east of Andover; that a mob a thousand strong had passed through Chichester and Emsworth destroying all the machinery they could find and then had turned north to Fareham and on to Horndean, doing the same there. In daylight, on that same day, riots had broken out in Havant, Westbourne and Warblington, with nine threshing-machines being broken up and demands for beer and food being made.

East Meon was amazed – amazed and excited, with the younger men being filled with a previously unknown aggression against not only the farmers but the bigger landowners. They also condemned the parsons who took the tithes and the Overseers who administered the Poor Relief. Talk was now all of 'Them' and 'Us' and the unfairness of starvation wages and pauperization. Tempers were up and with them hope. Perhaps if enough men rioted something could be achieved.

Then word came through that threatening letters had been delivered to farms at Exton, just down the Meon valley, and that threshing and other machines had been destroyed at Warnford, as well as at West Meon. Wages meetings were also being held at West Meon with the local farmers, just as they were at Hambledon.

It did seem, though, that the rioters had some sort of central organizing committee. Based in Westbourne, it was thought, for the labourers at Steep had been ordered by 'delegates from the general committee' to meet on the 23rd. They were then to present their letter of protest to the farmers and gentry of that area, asking for higher wages. But before that meeting took place there were tales of an uprising at Farringdon and yet another at Buriton, with others at Corhampton, Liphook, New Alresford and Avington, mostly asking, it seemed, for food and cash in hand as well as higher wages. (Alresford was the only place where there was much machine-smashing.)

Robert and the other East Meon men waited for Captain Swing and the General Committee to call them, too, as they had the Steep men. But no word came, and the swaggering bravado of the youngest of them began to look a little premature – and worrying, too, for if the local farmers heard of their bold threats (uttered though they were in the safety of the beer-houses) reprisals, job losses and evictions could take place. In 1830 the employer was king.

At dinner-time on the 23rd November an amazing story was brought to the village. The night before there had been a riot in Selborne and the hated workhouse had been largely pulled down. The anger there was aimed at the vicar, the Reverend Mr. Cobbold, whose tithe receipts of £608.12s.6d a year crippled the labourers and small farmers of the village. Gradually word percolated through to East Meon that the rioters had demanded the tithes be reduced by half: "We think £300 a year quite enough for you". Even that amount would be nearly £6 a week – a sum beyond all reach of a farming labourer. And amazing as it was, Mr. Cobbold signed a written undertaking to do this. It seemed that men only had to show spirit and determination to achieve their aims. (It was only discovered much later that the vicar had gone back on his word and continued to exact tithes of £608, as of old.)

After Selborne and the apparent success there, a jubilant mob went to Headley, near Farnham, to challenge that vicar, whose tithes were also seen as exhorbitant. When he, too, gave his written consent, the rioters next harassed the Overseers of the Poor and threatened to pull down the Workhouse as had been done at Selborne. The leaders of the mob gave adequate and courteous notice of their intentions to the Headley Workhouse Master and his family, with whom they had no quarrel. This gave him time to move the children who were ill out into the yard on two beds, for the separate sick ward had no room for them, being full of infirm old paupers. The rioters then set about demolishing the building. It was later reported that 'of all the rest of the place not a room was left entire', excepting the sick ward which was not touched.

The excitement and apprehension in East Meon was intense for the village had a Workhouse, and many were the debates about whether anything could be achieved by making it a ruin also. Many of the village families had relations or erstwhile neighbours there, and the puzzle was what would be done with the inmates if it, too, was made uninhabitable. Besides which, the village was tolerably content with the efforts made by their own Overseers on their behalf. If there was no quarrel to be picked with them, if the Vicar's tithes were not totally unreasonable and nor were those paid to private landlords now holding lands once belonging to the church, if there was no threshing machine on a local farm, then there seemed little reason to rebel so violently, especially if what jobs there were would be at risk. So the East Meon men did nothing.

For a short while, more news came of machine-smashing, rick-burning, wage-meetings and tithe revolts. At Droxford on the day after the Selborne riot there was trouble, largely aimed at the farmers, and again on the next day £1 in cash was demanded – and paid – and some machines were smashed. In Liss, on the 25th, a house was pulled down, the constables assaulted and some of their prisoners set free. On the same day there were workers' riots at Eastleigh, Fair Oak, Moor Green, West End, Swaythling and Portswood. Then the troubles spread further westwards to Dorset and Wiltshire but these were too far away to affect East Meon. The last local gesture was the posting up of threatening letters in Bishops Waltham.

And then nothing more happened. In this part of Hampshire the Swing Riots of 1830 came to an end after barely sixteen days of disturbances.

What did then begin was the retribution. Word began to reach the village of troops and Special Constables arresting troublemakers and imprisoning them in Winchester gaol; of violent suppression, even executions, and of transportation to Australia or New Zealand.

Robert Combe was both ashamed that he had not had the courage to march with the West Meon or Steep men and yet deeply and humbly grateful that neither his life nor his employment had been at risk. Never before had his small and tumble-down cottage seemed so precious or to offer so much security and never before had Mr. James Sutton been so gruffly conciliatory. No threshing-machine or winnowing-machine was ever employed on his farm and, after a few face-saving months had passed, he did increase his men's wages by at least a little.

The tithes had never really become onerous in East Meon and because so much of the farmland was tithe-free, having once belonged to the Knights Templar and then the Church, complaints on this score were few. This applied particularly to the extensive lands of Park Farm which were also tithe-free. This meant that not many properties were due for tithes. Those that were, such as Robert's, were just unlucky. With so many tithe-free holdings, it had meant that Captain Swing, the riots and the mobs had passed the village by.

After their brief period of militancy had faded, Robert and his fellow labourers lost most of their new-found hope and sank yet again into despair and apathy. Any showing of independence was now seen to be not only useless but harmful – too many men from the rioting villages had been cruelly punished. Near starvation still dominated the lives of those in East Meon, of course. It was not unknown for a labourer to be seen swaying from weakness as he walked to work, or apathetic and listless children just sitting in the roadway, too debilitated to move.

Despite the passing of the new Poor Law in 1834 it was not until Joseph Arch initiated the first Agricultural Labourers Union in 1872 that the farmworkers' self-respect returned. And by that time young William Combe, son of Robert, had grown to full manhood, had married and become a small shopkeeper in Winchester, not having wished to follow in his father's footsteps and work on the land.

Based on:

Hampshire Machine Breakers by Jill Chamber. Published by J. Chambers, 1990.

Captain Swing by E.J. Hobsbaum & George Rudé. Penguin, 1973.

Agricultural Riots of 1830 by Eastleigh & District Local History Society, 1980.

Plenty & Want: A Social History of Diet in England from 1815 to Present Day by John Burnett. Routledge, 1989.

Conflict in Hampshire by Donald Featherstone. Hampshire County Magazine, 1975.

Agricultural Workers Revolt by T.G.W.U., Region 2, 1982.

'A Want of Good Feeling': A Reassessment of the Economic and Political Causes of the Rural Unrest in Hampshire by Bethanie Afton. Hampshire Field Club & Archaeological Society, Volume 43, for 1987.

The Motive Which Has Operated on the Minds of my People: 1830, Propensity of Hampshire Parishes to Riot by Bethanie Afton. Hampshire Field Club and Archaeological Society, Volume 44, for 1988.

The Farmworkers' Revolt by Tony Brode. Article in "Facets of Crime". Bosiney Books, 1975.

Chapter Seventeen

The Golden Jubilee, 1887

SARAH Mullins, youngest assistant to the schoolmaster, William Tregear, sighed in disappointment. Something was missing from the account of Jubilee Day that she was writing and she did not know what it was. As her intention had been to record all the activities that had taken place last Saturday, the twenty-fifth of June, she had begun with the walk by the children from school to the church. This had been followed by the Service of Thanksgiving for the fifty years of Queen Victoria's reign and the march behind the band from the church to the big tent set up in the meadow opposite Glenthorne. Her account of all of this was faithful – but uninspired.

Frowning, she pulled the stoneware bottle of Stephenson's ink towards her and refilled her fountain pen. Perhaps she should liven things up a little? With a lighter touch, she now wrote of the dinner given to all the inhabitants of East Meon, of the speeches that followed, of the races for the children, of how she had been required to blow the whistle at the start of each one. She told of the tea provided by the ladies of the village, including her mother, and of the later bonfire and torchlight procession through the streets, led by the band. It was an accurate account – but she still found it somewhat unexciting.

It was the next day before she knew what was needed. She must give an account, not just of the celebration itself, but of what these last fifty years had meant to those who had lived through them. In this way, the Jubilee would be seen as celebrating local achievements and changes, as well as the Queen's long reign. Cheerfully, she completed her household tasks for her mother and, the school having a special holiday all week, left the house with notepad and pen. Setting off down Coombe Road to the village, she turned into Church Street and was delighted to see old Mrs. Tother shaking her rag mat outside the door of her almshouse. Having asked if she might call in for a minute or two, she joined the even older husband in the small living-room and explained why she had come.

"Oh, aye," Mr. Tother said. "There's been plenty of changes in my day – not all for the best, mind, but mostly so." He pondered for a while and then ventured, "These here almshouses, for a start. Blessing, they be. If it hadn'a been for Mrs. Forbes, up at Bereleigh House, and the seven and sixpence what she gives us each week, the wife an' me would be in a very poor way of things. Built these houses, she did, in memory of her husband. Died young, see, at fifty-seven. Leastways, that's young to me, for I'm in my seventy-eighth year."

When Sarah had responded to his age with suitable admiration, she turned to Mrs. Tother.

"Well," the old lady agreed, "We're more comfortable now than what we've ever been, for Joseph began as a labouring man and didn't earn much. Up on the Langrish road, we lived then, for he worked for Mr. Waddington at Langrish House. That was when that village was still in East Meon parish and afore the new church was built. In 1871, that were. Separated off it was, with its own vicar and all. All changed Langrish is. Even has its own coach service, now. Two years back, that began. Coach an' horses comes out of Petersfield, up Langrish Hill, then Bordean, and onto I don't know wheres, afore it gets to Winchester. They say it waits a bit at station, if steamtrain's late. And there'll be no stopping at tollgates by next year. Them'll be done away with. Aye, it's a different life, I tells you."

Mr. Tother sucked noisily at his clay pipe before saying, "I worked as a roadman, one time. Breaking flints for the Turnpike on our length. Our Bordean road's as much used now to get to Winchester as the old one that went up Stoner Hill an' on to Ropley an' Alresford. I did hear Turnpike Trust had straightened that road out a bit – made it shorter, like. But a new lot of folks is to look after the roads soon. And do away with the Trusts. From next year, like the wife says. County Council, or summat. That'd be an improvement, I tells you! Flint breaking's hard." He rubbed the bowl of his pipe before adding, "I've heard they have great big steam-rollers now. Puffing and panting away. Flatten a road o'flints in no time. Do a day's work in half an hour, they would. An' put many a poor flint-breaker out of work – machines don't always help the poor."

Silence returned, so Sarah looked about her. Several coloured prints hung on the walls, depicting Biblical subjects. One was of Abraham carrying wood for the sacrifice of Isaac. Another seemed to be of Moses with the tablets of stone.

"That Ab'ram," Mrs. Tother remarked. "Not enough wood in his faggot-bundle to make more'n a little flame or two, let alone burn up a great big lad like Isaac. Painter never tried to burn nothing, I guess. But I likes them pictures. Had them off a pedlar many a year back. Here!" she said. "I'll show you something! Got this off a travelling man, too."

Creaking a little at the knees, she pulled a heavy wooden box from beneath the dresser. "I keeps all my best bits in boxes," she said by way of explanation. "This one was made special for when I went into service. Had all my clothes in it. But I've plenty of other boxes too."

Mr. Tother gave a throaty chuckle. "That she has! Under bed, and all! No room for nothing else – which comes awkward of a night, if you sees what I mean, and begging your pardon, miss!"

"There!" The old woman held up a baby's muslin jacket. "That were for our Harry's baby at the christening, but she died a few hours old. And her mother. Fever, that were. Tooked 'em both. An' our Harry, he got fatal ill a'working on the railway. A navvy, he were, and dead by forty. He went with them 'cos pay was better building railways than for farming. We didna' see much of him, for they navvy gangs, they had to go wherever work was. Or'nary workers did the labouring – come off nearby farms, most of they did, for the wages, see. But if farmer found out what they was doing, like as

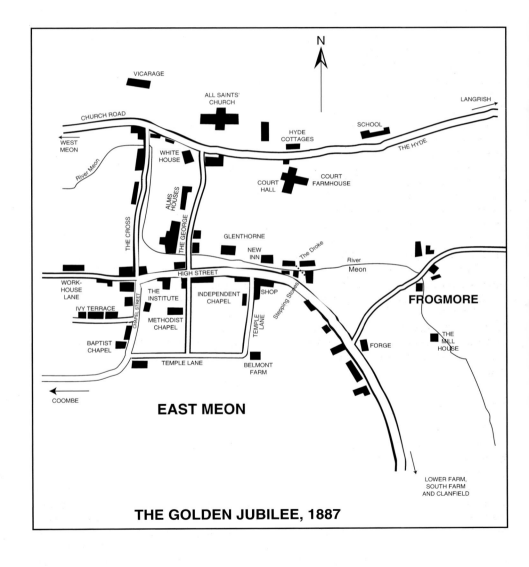

THE GOLDEN JUBILEE, 1887

not the parents'd be turned off work and put out of their cottage. Farmers and landlords was scared there'd be strikes if their workers heard what pay other men was getting. But Harry said they navvys were tough. A lot of them over from Ireland or the Lincolnshire fens. Or Scotland, or Yorkshire. Could out-drink, out-work an' out-fight most men. Only thing what kept our Harry straight was his wife being with him. And the Navvy Mission, run by the Church."

"Seems a terrible lot of men died as navvys," Mr Tother added. "Dysentery, consumption of the lungs, cholera, dyptheria, sunstroke. And from injuries they had, of course. There was a rare old battle down Havant way, thirty years back. Seems two of they railway companies wanted the same bit of track, so the gangs went at each other – pickaxes and crowbars, so it's said. Two hours, that fight was, and a whole lot o'men wounded. But men died even without fights. Terrible lot of deaths. Living in them rough shanties along the line's what done it. The cold and damp an' that. Aye, and drink as well, I must admit, for men get careless when not proper sober. An' now there's talk of a new line to be built – Alton to Fareham, seemingly. With a station or halt or summat at West Meon. And a tunnel through hill near Privett, 'tis said."

His wife sighed, still gazing at the little jacket. "So with our Harry gone, I never had no grandchilder. The little jacket's stayed along of me these years since. Off a pedlar, it was." She folded up the small garment and replaced it in the box, taking out an unused linen pillowcase in its place. "Look at that!" she exclaimed proudly. "When I was a girl we did drawn-thread work. Pretty edging, i'nit? Crochet work we did, too. A girl wasn't nothing unless she'd many a piece of linen and garments set aside for her wedding. Nowadays you girls don't know nothing. Buy everything in they big shops in towns. We made all ours. Even the sheets – from our own flax, handspun and woven. Mind you, those sheets, they was real stiff and didn't need no starch like an apron or table cloth. But wear! They went on for ever!"

Mr. Tother broke in to echo his wife. "You young ones don't know how easy you got it! We never had nothing, save what we made." He pointed the stub end of his pipe at a sacking bag hanging from a nail in the wall. "Know what's in that? Sheep's wool. Picked off the hedgerows. Whenever I goes up lanes, I pick bits off and brings them home. Fills all our pillows and cushions. Even now I goes on doing it."

"Not for our mattress, though," his wife declared proudly. "That's a feather bed – from hens an' ducks an' geese what I collected when I went a'plucking for farmers come Christmas-time. If farmer's wife didn't want them all, I took a sack or two home. Saved them up, see, for my marriage bed, whenever that was to be."

Shortly after this Sarah left, going slowly to the river bridge, wondering who to visit next. The decision was made for her, for Mr. Begbie, the curate came round the corner of the shop.

"Ah, my dear Sarah! I congratulate you on the behaviour of the children on Saturday. Exemplary! Exemplary! Mr. Tregear must be very pleased."

"Yes, sir. And thank you. He did say he was gratified."

"So what are you up to today, notebook in hand?"

When Sarah explained, the curate declared her plan to be excellent and suggested she return with him to the Vicarage, where they could talk in peace. When they were seated in the drawing room of the big brick and flint house to the west of the churchyard, Mr. Begbie said, "I've been thinking of changes during these last years. On one level, I suppose the restoration of our church in Mr Brodie's time has made the biggest difference. That was finished, I understand, by 1870, the year after this house was completed. The church is now very splendid – and the spire and roof are safe. A great achievement. Great achievement. And we have Mr. Brodie's lime trees in the churchyard, which he planted the same year. They'll be a great asset. But we've lost Langrish – a separate parish since 1871. Mr. George Waddington paying for the church, as I'm sure you know."

He paused for a moment to allow Sarah to complete her notes. "But I think Charles Darwin is making the biggest change – and one I deplore. All this about being descended from monkeys. His researches – even if they are indeed scientific – are quite incompatible with Genesis and, indeed, with the whole of the Church's teaching. His thought is quite alien to our existing beliefs on Creation – as it is on the central place of Man in the universe. It seems to me, child, that such intellectuals are becoming increasingly anti-clerical, anti-religious and distressingly materialistic. There is now a deplorable battle between Faith and Science, causing great distress to many good people. I am truly thankful that Darwin is now old and can do little more damage."

Somewhat defensively he went on, "I do accept freedom of thought, but he has gone too far. Religious freedom is quite another thing and I am happy about the presence in the village of Methodists. They have had their chapel here just twenty years, I understand. And the Baptists have their chapel in Halley Street – which, I gather, is often called Chapel Street – and the Independents in Temple Lane. Mr. Thomas is an excellent Minister, I believe. So you see, child, I am not against other denominations, and I do have to admit that chapel-folk are among our most respectable residents – sober, industrious and self-disciplined." He broke off and smiled at her. "And I'm not against scientists or intellectuals, either, for both are essential to the progress of this country. Even within this village we are to have our Working Man's Reading Room and Library – that excellent building the villagers are already calling The Institute."

"And then there are the Mothers' Meetings, taken by your wife, sir, as well as the Sunday School. We do keep education to the forefront of our lives and have, I believe, associated it very firmly with religion."

At her earnestness, the curate smiled a little and nodded. "Quite right, child! Quite right! And I'm glad to note that Bible reading and family prayers still continue. We're a Christian nation, even now, but I am concerned for the young. Some from the village are running wild and I deplore the way they misbehave in the churchyard, playing over the graves and headstones. Something will have to be done to stop them. But what? But what? They take no notice of me." He paused and gazed out of the window. "And the graveyard itself is another problem – the bereaved have recently taken to placing artificial flowers on the graves, under glass domes. I shall have to take a stand over that, otherwise we'll soon have all manner of marble angels and weeping cherubs. Quite out of place, I'm afraid." Then he stood up and held out his hand. "Now, if you'll excuse me, I have letters to write."

When she had left the Vicarage, Sarah walked down The Cross and turned left, meeting nobody. As she passed through The Square, she remembered having heard that the land against the river and part of Pound Meadow had been bought by Mr. Aburrow of Drayton Mill. It seemed he was to set up a wheelwright's and blacksmith's shop, now that corn-milling was not as profitable as it had been. Flour and animal foodstuffs was still milled, of course, at Drayton, South Farm and Frogmore mills, but it was said the wheat coming in from Canada and the United States was cheaper for bread. Also it was a hard wheat, more suitable for the new commercial roller-mills than was the English soft wheat. In addition, there had been some terrible harvests of late, with crops rotting in the fields and livestock suffering all manner of diseases. This meant English wheat had been in short supply and so very expensive. Because of this extra cost, imported foodstuffs were more than welcome to the cottagers, even though their wages had risen markedly over the years. This last was largely because there were now fewer labourers, so many families having moved to the towns, where wages were said to be even higher. The agricultural poor no longer had to subsist on bread and potatoes, with 'tea' made from burnt crusts soaked in hot water. Real butcher's meat was beginning to replace stewed sheep's heads or chitterlings, especially since coal-fired and refrigerated ships were now bringing in cheap beef from the Argentine, and mutton and lamb from Australia or New Zealand through the new Suez Canal. Even those with lower wages could now afford at least some butter, cheese, sugar, milk, fruit, margarine and cheap tinned jam. Food was becoming cheaper in relation to earnings.

Today it was the farmers who were suffering, owing to the Government's policy of Free Trade and unrestricted imports. They were suffering as were the manufacturers, who could no longer compete profitably with the new industrial expansion of France, Germany and the United States. Those countries had adopted British inventions and then improved on them, using new techniques and new machinery. In addition, they were erecting harmful tariff barriers against Great Britain. Although the villagers of East Meon were undergoing a period of comparative prosperity, Sarah had heard Mr. Tregear say that industrialists were suffering a real depression, with many factories and businesses having to close. Her thoughts returned to the Aburrows and their new acquisition in the village. It would be strange to have their Drayton business one of mainly timber-sawing instead of milling. With a steam-engine, it was said. At least sawn wood was still needed. With so many labourers having left the village, many of their ramshackle and tumbledown houses were being bought up by middle-class incomers, knocked down and rebuilt. Sarah knew that many older people resented this incursion, but at least it kept the shopkeepers and tradesmen busy and provided work for young girls as domestic servants, as well as for their mothers as charwomen and their brothers as garden-boys or stable-lads.

She wandered along the High Street until she reached the Stores, opposite the New Inn. On entering a little nervously, she saw Mr. Adams was putting up an order, ticking off each item as he placed it in the big woven basket, which would later be taken by one of the delivery boys to the house in question. Two other customers were in the shop and Sarah would have retreated if Mrs. Adams had not caught sight of her. Instead, she pretended to study a packet of Spratts Patent Dog Biscuits, although there was no dog at home.

As she waited patiently for attention, Mr. Adams asked, "Was there something I forgot on your mother's order? It went up earlier."

"No, no. As it happens, I don't want to buy anything – just ask some questions, if I may."

At that, not only did Mrs. Adams look round but so did the other two ladies. Abashed, Sarah went on, "I thought I'd write an article. On the Jubilee. But also how things have changed over the years – that is, within living memory."

One of the ladies then spoke up. "What an interesting project! And I can certainly help you, for I was only commenting on the subject to my dear sister but yesterday. Of what I am thinking is packet tea. When our mother was a new bride in the 1820s, tea was all loose. And very adulterated – she never knew what she would find in her half-pound. But since the government stepped in, we have received clean tea in packets – from Typhoo, P.G., Mazawatee, Lipton's, Lyons, and I don't know from what firm else. A great boon, and much less detrimental to our health."

Mr. Adams added, "It was the Excise Department that did it, ma'am, and the Food Acts. I understand a very large number of dealers and merchants, as well as shop-keepers, have been convicted of selling food unfit for human consumption. Such food was cheap, I grant you, but since those days the country has become much richer, and more prosperous all round. Prices have certainly risen a little of late but wages have, too. Why, even the ordinary labourer can now afford a few little luxuries."

"And I beg you not to forget the convenience of canned foods. Look at Mr. Adam's delicious corned beef, sold by the slice. Such an easy way to serve meat. And excellent for a labourer's packed dinner."

"Yes, and condensed milk in tins," her sister added. "And canned rabbits or boiled mutton or beef from Australia! If you'll excuse me saying so, Mr. Adams, we've seen such things in the bigger stores."

"Of course, ma'am, of course!" the shopkeeper agreed. "And I understand they're putting more fish into tins nowadays – not just sardines, but salmon and such like. I'll be getting some in myself before long."

At that point, the brother of Mr. Adams entered the shop. Nowadays he was the publican of The George, although he had begun as a baker. As his reputation was a little unsavoury, the two ladies hastily completed their purchases and left, followed by Sarah who did not like to remain. Continuing up the High Street she met Mrs. Sarah Beagley, wife of Noah – Young Noah, that is, for his father had borne the same name. He was a tailor, but Sarah hardly knew him, being more acquainted with his brother, Henry, who had married Elizabeth Pearson, a friend of her mother's. Further on, she saw Billy Rush sitting on the riverbank. Being in the class for nine-year olds, he was still taught by her in the village school.

"You did well in the Jubilee races," she said. "I hope you liked your prizes?"

"I did that, miss. Bull's eyes is my favourite sweets – them an' acid drops. They did give me liquorice bootlaces, but I swapped 'em. My mum gives us liquorice powder on a Sat'day night, after our baths in the tin tub. An' that's horrible – green, it is, and gritty. So I swopped mine for lemonade crystals."

"I hope you don't cause trouble over the Saturday dosing?"

"I does sometimes – but if I'm too bad or mitch off school, my mum beats me with the copper-stick. She was real angry with me once, though, so I ran away."

"Oh? Where did you go?"

"Bereleigh main gate. That hill were too steep an' I didn't have no puff left. If I was going to run away, then I had to run, see. So when I couldn't run no more, I went back home."

Sarah laughed. "Are you often naughty?"

"Not like some," he replied. "When I was very little, an' my mum had to work in the fields along of Dad, she'd shut me up in the cupboard to keep me out of mischief. But when I was bigger, she'd lock me out of the house till she came back."

"I thought you worked in the fields, too? You always seem to have time off school to help the farmers."

"Course I works in the fields! Specially harvest time. An' potato planting an' hop-picking. Don't like picking stones, though. But my mum says she needs the money. Buys all our boots with harvest money, see. From Mr. Atwood. An' our coats for winter, she buys. Can't do without harvest money." Billy climbed to his feet. "Better be off," he said. "Meant to be picking dandelions for me mum's wine. She gives me a gobstopper if I brings in a lot. I got two at cowslip time."

Swinging the rush bag in circles round his head, he left her, wandering over the bridge and through the narrow droke between the cottages, towards the meadow where it was said allotments would be made. If they were not prevented, that is. Farmers thought that having a bit of land made the workers too independent. Also they feared thefts of seed and fertilizers from the farms and, of course, disliked the idea of men expending energy on their own plots rather than on those of the employer. Mr. Gladstone, the Liberal Prime Minister, had promised an Allotments Act but, when his Government was defeated over Home Rule for Ireland and Lord Salisbury and the Conservatives came in, this Act was postponed. Still, the feeling was that in a year or two it would be passed, and then cottagers would be able to grow an increased amount of vegetables. Meanwhile, the field was full of dandelions for Billy to pick.

As Sarah reached the forge at the end of the village, she saw Mrs. Dodds coming towards her, pushing a wheelbarrow. Loaded into it was a blanket and a big hessian bag, with a small infant lying precariously on top. When they came closer, Sarah offered to take the baby, fearing he would roll off. "You've got a big load to push," she remarked.

"Aye. Am taking my maternity bag back to Vicarage. Don't need it no more, him being so big now. An' the loan blanket. Should've took that back in mid-May, but forgot. Weather's too warm for it now but my old dad was real glad of it in the winter. For his rheumatics, see. He don't ever seem able to keep warm, despite sitting near enough on top of the fire."

Sarah agreed to retrace her steps to the Vicarage, so the child was handed to her. She was glad to be given a torn length of cloth to wrap him in, for he seemed very wet and she was concerned for her dress. As they walked, Mrs. Dodds continued to chatter and Sarah tried to gain something of use for her notebook, Mr. Dodds being a carter at Lower Farm. Occasionally she was able to insert a question and sometimes receive an answer.

"No, I don't work on farm as much as my mum did. 'Cept at hay-making and harvest, o'course. Not worth the money, see. Only a few coppers, an' I got enough to do at home without traipsing out in all weathers to do a farmer's bidding. Proper sick of field-work, I used to be. Didn't matter how much hessian or old potato sacks I put on to keep me dry, they never did. And mud – Lord love you! It'd be near enough up to my knees in gateways, an' my leg-rags always sopping cold. Must a'looked a real gallibagger, fit to scare the crows. I'd grease my boots with melted fat to keep wet out, but it did na'. Big boots, they are, an' I puts them on different feet each day to keep the wear even. Have to put a two-three stocking-feet on as well, to keep me toes warm come winter. My mum, she used to wear pattens in the cowyard to keep dry, but I never. Too clumsy, they be."

Sarah enquired about her family, and when the eldest child was due to begin school. "School!", came the reply. "Now, that's a thing I don't hold with. Book-learning's no use to likes of us. Girls'd be better helping at home. This here Education Act takes a mother's helpers away from her. 'Tisn't natural. And having to pay for schooling –

that's wicked! When they gets round to giving us learning for free, why, then we might think otherwise. And as for my hubby joining a Union – he'd be a proper dummle to do that. What farmer's going to take on a Union man? Laying up trouble for himself, he'd be." Then she paused. "Though I have heard tell of a worker up Oxenbourne way what's joined – he has a warrant or summat, saying as how he's a member, an' it's bin framed and hung up in his cottage. Stupid, I calls that! No landlord'd like to see it, 'cos they can't arguefy with a Union man. Just laying up trouble, ready to get the sack."

"But the Union has funds to help in sickness – and to assist with emigration," Sarah put in. "Plenty of families are going overseas. That must be a good thing?"

"Ah!" Mrs. Dodds said darkly. "But can't be sure of that, can I?" She nodded several times and Sarah realised the woman did not know what emigration was, but did not enlighten her. Instead she asked another question.

"With wages being up a bit these days, is your cottage improved? A few years back it was rather tumbledown, I remember. Your landlord didn't seem keen on doing repairs."

"Well, I can't say I know about improved," Mrs. Dodds answered doubtfully. "I still have to whitewash walls an' ceilings reg'lar to keep down them black beetles an' bed bugs. An' in wet weather the mud floor's terrible messy. Heaves, it does, an' goes all into bumps." Then she brightened. "But I do have a bit of range. For cooking on, like. Takes me a proper old time to blacklead it – but it do shine up pretty. An' I've all sorts of knick-knacks on the mantelshelf. Bits of china – fairings an' that, from the Taro. Looks real nice. Takes the candle-box, too, now we don't have rush-lights so much. Oh, yes! I thinks I can say we're improved. All us wants now is a bit more thatch on the roof so it don't leak so much. That, an' new window-frames. In winter, bedroom's so cold our breaths freeze on the sheet. Don't do to linger over dressing come morning, I can tell you! We just shoves our feet into boots an' our arms into jackets, an' downstairs we go. No use trying to wash overmuch, either. Just get chapped skins, chilblains an' that. Glad to see summer, we are."

By the time the pair had reached the Vicarage drive Mrs. Dodds had tired of pushing the wheelbarrow, so she removed the articles it carried and left it inside the gate. They walked up the steep drive to the house with Sarah still clasping the now sleeping infant. They found their way to the back door, pulled the bell-chain, and waited.

"Why, if it isn't Florence!" Mrs. Dodds exclaimed when the door was opened. "Forgot you was here. Parlourmaid, is it?"

The girl replied rather primly in the affirmative and Sarah was struck by the veneer of gentility she showed, belying her rough upbringing in Frogmore. "I'll tell Madam you've brought them back," she said, gingerly taking the maternity bag and loan blanket. "Thank you, and good day."

Without more ado the door was closed, and Sarah and Mrs. Dodds retraced their steps to the road. The baby was then wrapped in his mother's hessian apron and laid in the barrow, continuing to sleep peacefully. Sarah left them at the corner of Church Street and turned towards Court Farm. Mrs. Darvill had always seemed friendly enough and her more imposing husband would surely be engaged in his office or out on the land. Bravely, she rang the bell and, when the door was opened, asked to speak to Mrs. Darvill. She was escorted to the comfortable living-room of the farmhouse, which lay at right-angles to the old Court Hall, and waited there while the lady she sought was fetched.

Mrs. Darvill was a big woman, wearing a plain black skirt and high-necked white blouse, fastened with a cameo brooch. True to fashion, she had abandoned the bustle and wore her sleeves in the newest leg-of-mutton shape.

"Sarah, my dear! How very pleasant to see you! So, now – what can I do for you?" When the project was explained, Mrs. Darvill bade her sit down, seating herself in a chair richly covered in red plush. "What sort of thing do you want?" she asked. Again Sarah explained, and the older woman gazed meditatively out of the window. "I suppose one of the biggest changes in my life is the ease of travel and the increase of leisure time for the likes of us – the bigger farmers and their wives. Mind you, we don't have people down by train to make up weekend parties like those at Westbury and Bereleigh, with games of tennis, or croquet on the lawn, and cards in the evening – that sort of thing. Young ladies are so free nowadays! Hunting, attending University, agitating for women's suffrage. One can't tell where it'll stop." She laughed. "You should hear Mr. Darvill on the subject! Doesn't hold with it at all! Our daughters are brought up to become proper housewives."

Sarah then pressed for details of domestic changes.

"Oh, without a doubt the treadle sewing-machine from Singer! I can't describe to you the difference that one item has made to ladies with a house to keep. Curtains go up in no time, dresses can be made without eye-strain, children's clothes altered to fit the younger ones. A great boon, I assure you. And after that – well, perhaps the upright mangle. No more hand-wringing, and clothes and sheets drying so much quicker." Mrs. Darvill sighed wistfully. "But I do wish we could have gas-lighting down here, like they do in towns. So clean and bright. But still, the new paraffin lamps are very good, and with their glass chimneys and glowing mantles they're a great improvement. Much less cleaning now, and certainly less smell." She smiled and went on, "Life really is easier. And on the farm, too. But you really need Mr. Darvill to talk to you on that subject. Although I suppose I could help you a little."

At Sarah's prompting, she described the beneficial use of the new chemical fertilizers, of steam-ploughing, land drainage in the fields, of modern farm implements such as drills, cultivators, hoes, tedders and corn reapers – all horse-drawn. "Factory-made they are, and cheaper than those from the blacksmith," she explained. "Agriculture is becoming very technical. What is called capital-intensive, I believe. As Mr. Darvill says, Science is now the handmaid of Agriculture. And the farm does benefit, I assure you. The yields per acre are very much higher. Milk-cattle produce more milk. Beef-cattle fatten up quicker and heavier. Even the chickens are bred for more eggs."

"And are you troubled by foreign goods coming into the country by sea? I understood that English farming – from the farmers' point of view – was undergoing a difficult period."

For a moment her hostess did not reply. Then she sighed and admitted that the financial aspect was becoming increasingly difficult. "Yes, my dear Sarah, we are indeed greatly troubled by these things, but we do not like to consider them too closely. In some ways, as I've said, life is so much easier now. But prices for our produce are too low. The rents from our cottages are down, too, while working hours are shorter – but all for the same pay. You see, with increasing militancy among the men now they have a Union and the vote, and with so many having drifted to the towns in search of better living conditions or having emigrated to the colonies, wages have to be higher to keep those that remain. With food prices lower, the agricultural worker is better off now than ever before – he's better fed and better housed. But I fear farming is in for a deep depression unless profits for farmers increase. Mr. Darvill fears that hard, hard times are coming."

She sighed again, and then murmured half to herself "I should not be surprised if many of our present farmers go under. Sell their animals to pay their bank debts. If that happens, all they'll have left are the corn crops, and with prices so low they'll lose out on those. Then there'll be nothing for it but to sell their land or, as tenants, to fail on the rent. Strange, isn't it? At the turn of this century, in the Napoleonic Wars, agriculture was very prosperous. Then there was a slump when the war was over, then a long period when we built up again, became financially stable and increased the workers' wages. The 1870s were the golden age of farming. But now, back again to slump." Mrs. Darvill smiled sadly. "I can't tell you what a worry it all is. I don't want this farm to go downhill, to turn men off, to let the buildings fall down from lack of repair. Which they would, in no time at all. And I would not wish to see farms empty, up for sale at ludicrously low prices per acre. That would mean prosperous city-dwellers buying them up, for reasons mostly of status, I guess. Such people wouldn't know the country as we do. Nor will they tend it as we do. They'll be flash and alien and inconsiderate to the villagers. Let us hope that if the worst does come to pass, we will acquire some real farmers, for if agriculture declines so will the number of workers needed. Then where will the villagers be?"

Sarah remained silent and eventually Mrs. Darvill continued, "We're lucky here with those already in the big houses. They do what they can for the village. Look at Mrs. Forbes at Bereleigh House. Her almshouses, for instance. She supports so much – the coal club, the nurses's fund, the soup kitchen, cricket club. She gives good donations every year to those. Also she pays for the washing of the choir surplices, I gather, which would no doubt be very ill-washed otherwise. Subscribes to the bell-ringers, too, as well as the clothing club. A very, very charitable lady – and the best of the old sort. Then there is Mr. Le Roy Lewis, over at Westbury House, he's as generous. As is Mr. William Nicholson of Basing Park. It is he, as you'll know, who is paying for the building of the new Privett church. Then there's Mr. John Bonham-Carter who has so much land hereabouts. He gives generously, too, as did our last vicar, Mr. Brodie. And there's Mr. Talbot-Ponsonby of Langrish House, a stalwart funder of the cricket club. And before him, the Waddington family – George Waddington paying for the new church there. But we must not forget their wives, who do so much behind the scenes – teas and outings and treats for the children. Yes, we are very lucky. And they do try to support our village shops and craftsmen, although much of the expensive goods they naturally purchase elsewhere. Let us hope it can all continue."

After a moment's silence Sarah asked tentatively, "Is there anything else farmers could do? To keep going? Branch out into something else, perhaps? Then we wouldn't need to have the incomers."

Mrs. Darvill did not answer at once and looked down at her hands. Hesitantly, she said finally, "Well, there is, actually. But whether we'll ever do it, I don't know."

When she said no more, Sarah waited in the hope she would continue. At last Mrs. Darvill murmured, "I should not tell you, really, but Mr. Darvill has it in mind to go in for cheese-making. On a commercial basis, that is. But not yet. We can still keep our heads above financial water. Just. We would have to put the arable land down to grass and just have cows. For milk for the cheeses. With just cows, we'd need fewer men. The wages bill would be lower and we could sell off much of the farm machinery – save the Bank interest on that, too. But we'll have to see how things go. It is all very uncertain." Then, in an artificially brighter tone, she said, "So there we are, Sarah! We all have our problems! And I hope your article goes well and that I have been of some help to you?"

Sensing her dismissal, the girl rose to leave. Before she reached the door, Mrs. Darvill added urgently, "And Sarah, what I have just said about the – the cheeses, and so on – you'll keep to yourself, won't you? I would not wish Mr. Darvill to hear I had been telling folk about his private problems. So, please, my dear, silence."

Sarah assured her that she would keep the conversation to herself and make no mention of it in her writing. "Just the helpful bits," she smiled. "The sewing-machine, and the other things."

Somewhat depressed by this new view of farming, she turned towards home. She had no heart now to seek an interview with Dr. Batten, although he would be in his surgery in the White House at this time. In any case, she knew what he would say about health: "Sanitation, sanitation and sanitation." This was his constant theme, railing against the insanitary and dangerous condition of the school privies, and badgering officials over the filthy open gutters that ran along the village street. He had pointed out most forcibly that many of the house-wells were polluted, being far too near those same drains or the garden privies. The villagers had been lectured time without number about their use of river water, not only for washing and cooking, but for drinking. He had pointed out that Washers Cottages, among others, did not even have privies (or dummocks, as some called them) but emptied everything straight into the river. And it was in that same river that dip-holes were made in its bed, so that buckets could be lowered on a rope to give water to a household. Which they then drank. Oh, yes! She knew what the doctor would say. "Few changes for the better, girl. Folk won't learn. Just die of diphtheria, typhus and the rest. Few improvements. Few changes." Yes, she knew what he would say. And he would keep on bullying the village until they heeded him – or tapwater was put in. Or drainage. Or inside lavatories. But the villagers loved him. They knew him as a fine man, ever solicitous to those in distress and seldom asking a fee from those too poor to pay. A wonderfully good man, and the village was blessed by his presence.

Thoughtfully, she entered her own house and was greeted by her mother, asking how the note-taking had gone.

"Not very well, I fear," she replied. "But I've learnt a great deal."

"I'm sure you have. And the village is so pretty on a day like this, with the sun shining and everybody happy because of the dear Queen. We are so favoured to be here, living in these advanced times."

Sarah nodded. "Yes, we are. And I wouldn't want to live anywhere else." She dropped her notebook and pen onto the table. "But I don't think I'll write my article, after all. It seems rather pointless, somehow." She paused for a moment and then declared, "No, I'll not write any of it."

And nor did she.

Based on:

A History of East Meon by F. G. Standfield. Phillimore, 1984.

Rural Life in Victorian England by G. E. Mingay. Futura Publications, 1979.

Conflict in Hampshire by Donald Featherstone. Paul Cave Publications; 1975.

The English Countrywoman by G. E. And K. R. Fussell. Bloomsbury Books, 1985.

A Remembered Land. Recollections of Life in the Countryside, 1880 – 1914.
Edited by Sean Street. BCA/Michael Joseph 1994.

England in the Nineteenth Century by David Thomson. Penguin Books, 1978.

Some Aspects of Langrish Life through the Ages by Evelyn Hickox.1986.

Late Victorian Britain, 1875 – 1901 by J. F. C. Harrison. Fontana Press, 1990.

Britain Since 1800: Towards the Welfare state by Howard Martin. Macmillan Educational, 1988.

Index